G000066028

BS 7671:2008
17TH Edition Learning Guide

A practical guide to understanding the IEE Wiring Regulations 17th Edition

The NICEIC

'NICEIC' is a trading name of NICEIC Group Limited, a wholly owned subsidiary of The Electrical Safety Council. Under licence from The Electrical Safety Council, NICEIC acts as the electrical contracting industry's independent voluntary regulatory body for electrical installation safety matters throughout the UK, and maintains and publishes registers of electrical contractors that it has assessed against particular scheme requirements (including the technical standard of electrical work).

The registers include the national Roll of Approved Contractors (established in 1956), and the register of NICEIC Domestic Installers that, since January 2005, have been authorised to self-certify their domestic electrical installation work as compliant with the Building Regulations for England and Wales.

The NICEIC Approved Contractor scheme is accredited by the United Kingdom Accreditation Service (UKAS) to EN 45011 *General requirements for bodies operating product certification systems.*

The Electrical Safety Council

The Electrical Safety Council (formerly the National Inspection Council for Electrical Installation Contracting) is a charitable non-profit making organization set up in 1956 to protect users of electricity against the hazards of unsafe and unsound electrical installations.

The Electrical Safety Council is supported by all sectors of the electrical industry, approvals and research bodies, consumer interest organizations, the electricity distribution industry, professional institutes and institutions, regulatory bodies, trade and industry associations and federations, trade unions and local and central government.

Published by:

NICEIC Group Limited
Warwick House, Houghton Hall Park, Houghton Regis, Dunstable, Bedfordshire LU5 5ZX

Tel: 01582 531000   Fax: 01582 556024

Email: customerservice@niceic.com Website: www.niceic.com

ISBN 978-19060910-4-0

INDEX OF MODULES

Page

Introduction

How to use the Learning Guide *and*

The structure of *BS 7671*

1. THE LEARNING GUIDE AND CITY & GUILDS 2382-10

This Learning Guide has been produced by NICEIC and endorsed by City & Guilds as part of a packaged learning resource based on *BS 7671: 2008* (IEE Wiring Regulations 17th Edition). The IEE Wiring Regulations are the definitive standard for the safety of electrical installations in buildings within the UK. The packaged learning resource includes this Learning Guide, lecturer's Lesson Plans, PowerPoint Presentations and a DVD.

This packaged learning resource has been produced to support electricians, electrical managers, designers and others requiring a knowledge of *BS 7671: 2008* (IEE Wiring Regulations 17th Edition) and in particular students undergoing the:

- **City & Guilds Level 3 Certificate in the requirements for Electrical Installations (*BS 7671* June 2008) (2382-10)** (full course) and/or the
- **City & Guilds Level 3 Certificate in the requirements for Electrical Installations (16th to 17th update BS 7671 June 2008) (2382-20)** (update course).

The 2382-10 and 2382-20 Schemes are aimed at practising electricians, designers and specifiers with relevant experience and is intended to ensure that they are conversant with the format, content and the application of the Requirements for Electrical Installations *BS 7671: 2008* (IEE Wiring Regulations 17th edition).

All future references in this document to Requirements for Electrical Installations *BS 7671: 2008* (IEE Wiring Regulations 17th edition) will simply state *BS 7671* to simplify the text.

Attendance on the above courses will require students to have a prior knowledge of basic electrical theory and science as well as some knowledge of electrical systems. Although the courses cover all Parts, Chapters and Appendices of *BS 7671*, specialised subjects are not covered in depth, and in these cases specialised knowledge should be sought.

Although the courses cover inspection and testing (Part 6), this subject is not covered in depth and students requiring a more in-depth knowledge of inspection, testing, verification and certification should consider attendance on the:

- **City & Guilds Level 2 Certificate in Fundamental Inspection, Testing and Initial Verification (2392-10) - (for the initial verification of new work, alterations or additions)** and/or the
- **City & Guilds Level 3 Certificate in Inspection, Testing and Certification of Electrical Installations – 2391-10 (for the inspection, testing and reporting procedures for existing properties (often referred to as Periodic Reporting).**

It should be noted that the City & Guilds 2382-10 and 2382-20 Requirements for Electrical Installations *BS 7671: 2008* (IEE Wiring Regulations 17th Edition) full and update courses are open-book exams. This means *BS 7671* can be taken into the exam by students. Whilst this could appear to make the exams easier it also means the exams can cover a very wide range of subjects within *BS 7671*. Familiarity with the layout and contents of *BS 7671* is, therefore, essential.

2. HOW TO USE THIS LEARNING GUIDE

a. Introduction

This Learning Guide contains information and related diagrams, written in modules. Each module relates to a respective Part, Chapter or Section in *BS 7671* and includes:

INTRODUCTION TO THE LEARNING GUIDE

- Essential text and pictures covering the requirements of the City & Guilds 2382-10 and 2382-20 syllabus.
- Revision exercises to confirm understanding.
- References to *BS 7671* to ensure Learners interact with *BS 7671*.

It should be noted that because it is very important that students understand the structure of *BS 7671* it is recommended that the module covering the structure of *BS 7671* (which follows this introductory section) should be completed prior to moving on to the more detailed modules.

b. Margins

A wide note margin is provided for students to make notes

c. Tables used in the Learning Guide

Within the Learning Guide the tables are either reproduced from *BS 7671* (in which case the same table number is used) or they are specific to the Learning Guide. In each case the title of the table will indicate whether it is from *BS 7671* or not as shown below:

Table 42.1 (Reproduced from *BS 7671*) Temperature limit under normal load conditions for an accessible part of equipment within arm's reach.

Accessible part	Material of accessible surfaces	Maximum temperature (°C)
A hand-held part	Metallic	55
	Non-metallic	65

Table 52.2 (Learning Guide Table) Summary of cables concealed in walls or partitions and not requiring RCD protection

Type of insulation	Temperature limit
Thermoplastic	70 °C at the conductor
Thermosetting	90 °C at the conductor

d. Interim exercises

Within each module there are interim exercises. These exercises either require the learner to answer a question directly from the text in the Learning Guide or will require the student to review a particular section of *BS 7671* before answering the question (remember familiarity with *BS 7671* is an essential part of the learning process). The exercise number relates to the module in the Learning Guide. Answers to interim questions can be found at the back of the Learning Guide. The text boxes below illustrate typical interim exercises.

The interim exercises are in a text box as shown below and highlighted by the symbol set in the note margin.

Exercise 56.1

You should now refer to Chapters 35 & 56 to answer the following: (1) Name three sources that are recognized for use in safety service circuits. (2) What are the minimum and maximum change-over times for short break and medium break automatic supply systems?

Exercise 43.1

Provide examples of each of the following: - Overload current, overcurrent, short-circuit current and earth fault current. (See Part 2 Definitions)

e. Final Revision exercises

Final revision exercises can be found at the end of each module. They consist of **multi-choice questions** and *'Things to do and find'*

Multi-choice questions and 'Things to do and find' are in the following format with an accompanying icon in the note margin.

Multi-choice questions

FINAL REVISION EXERCISE

1.1 The interior of the basin of a swimming pool would be described as which of the following?
- ☐ a. Zone 0
- ☐ b. Zone 1
- ☐ c. Zone 2
- ☐ d. Outside the zones

1.2 An automatic supply that is available between 5 s and 15 s would be classified as which of the following?
- ☐ a. Short break
- ☐ b. Lighting break
- ☐ c. Medium break
- ☐ d. Long break

Things to do and find

1. Where would you find the full list of external influences in *BS7671*?

2. List four different examples of warning notices.

3. In which Section of *BS 7671* would you find the requirements relating to caravans?

notes

f. Further information

At the end of each module a further information text box provides further reading/reference documents. This is indicated by the following text box with accompanying icon in the note margin.

> Further information relating to Protection, isolation, switching, control and monitoring can be found in:
> * *BS 7671* Chapter 53
> * Electrical Safety Council Technical Manual articles F133-17, I17-4, I17-15, M141-1, M141-5 and R101-19
> * IEE Guidance Note 4

g. Sparky Tony

Sparky Tony appears in each module of the Learning Guide providing a key piece of advice relating to each module. The character Sparky Tony appears in the note margin with a speech bubble with the heading 'Key Facts.'

Glossary of terms used in the Learning Guide

The following abbreviations are used within the Learning Guide. Many defined terms are also used but these are explained in Part 2 (Definitions) or within the section of the Learning Guide where they are used. It should be noted that all BS, BS EN and IEC references throughout the Learning Guide are in italics.

Key Facts
Designers and installers must be aware of the types of installations that are included in *BS 7671* and those that are excluded'

BS 7671	British Standards *BS 7671:2008* Requirements for electrical Installations IEE Wiring Regulations 17th edition.
BS	British Standard
BS EN	Harmonised European Standard (EN stands for Euronorm)
CPC	Circuit protective conductor (Defined within *BS 7671*)
csa	Cross-sectional area
DCL	Device for connecting a luminaire
DNO	Distribution Network Operator (Defined in *BS 7671* as Distributor)
ELV	Extra-low voltage
EMC	Electromagnetic compatibility
EMI	Electromagnetic interference
ESQR	Electricity Safety, Quality and Continuity Regulations 2002
HV	High voltage
IEC	International Electrotechnical Commission
IEE	Institution of Electrical Engineers (now known as Institution of Engineering and Technology (IET))
LSC	Luminaire support coupler
LV	Low voltage
MET	Main earthing terminal
PE	Protective earth
PEN	Protective earth and neutral (conductor)
PME	Protective multiple earthing
PNB	Protective neutral bonding
PV	Solar photovoltaic (Defined in *BS 7671*)
RCBO	Combined residual current circuit breaker with overcurrent protection
RCD	Residual current device
UPS	Uninterruptible power supply

For abbreviated terms that are defined such as TN-C-S, TN-S, TT, IT SELV, PELV, FELV, see Part 2 Definitions of *BS 7671* and/or this Learning Guide.

1. Introduction

This Learning Guide has been written to provide guidance in relation to *BS 7671: 2008* Requirements for Electrical Installations (IEE Wiring Regulations 17th Edition) issued on 1st January 2008. *BS 7671: 2008* came into effect on 1st July 2008; installations designed after 30th June 2008 must comply with the 2008 version.

The changes to *BS 7671* incorporated into the 17th Edition are part of an ongoing process to maintain alignment with CENELEC Harmonization Documents in the 60364 series. CENELEC (Comité Européen de Normalisation Electrotechnique) is the European Committee for Electrotechnical Standardization. CENELEC is composed of the National Electrotechnical Committees of 30 European countries. The British Standards Institution is the National Standards Body of the UK, responsible for facilitating, drafting, publishing and marketing British Standards and other guidelines and represents the UK on CENELEC.

In addition to CENELEC, consideration must also be given to the International Electrotechnical Commission (IEC). This organization is a world-wide body that produces international standards. In recent years many documents have been produced under the IEC/CENELEC cooperation agreement with parallel voting. European Harmonization Documents (HD) in the 60364 series, mentioned above, are basically the same as the equivalent parts of the IEC 60364 standard (Electrical installations of buildings) with some common modifications to suit individual European countries

As *BS 7671: 2008* is being aligned with the IEC and HD 60364 series of standards the numbering system throughout *BS 7671:2008* has been aligned with these standards (see item '4' below).

Key Facts
'The first edition of the Wiring Regulations was issued in 1882 and included requirements for shock protection, overcurrent protection, protection against the risks of fire and frequent testing'

The UK National Standard for electrical installation work, *BS 7671: 2008* Requirements for Electrical Installations, also called the IEE Wiring Regulations - 17th Edition is published under the direction of the British Electrotechnical Committee (BEC) and The Institute of Engineering and Technology (IET).

The structure of BS 7671
(IEE Wiring Regulations 17th edition)

Fig Str1. First edition of the Wiring Regulations

2. Statutory documents and their relationship with *BS 7671*

BS 7671 is non-statutory. It may, however, be used in a court of law in evidence to claim compliance with a statutory requirement. The relevant statutory provisions are listed in Appendix 2 of *BS 7671*.

It should also be noted that *BS 7671* is referred to in the Electricity Safety, Quality and Continuity Regulations 2002 as being an acceptable standard which will satisfy those statutory Regulations. Additionally, the Health and Safety Executive considers compliance with *BS 7671* is likely to achieve conformity with the relevant parts of the Electricity at Work Regulations 1989.

3. The structure of *BS 7671* 17th Edition

Getting to know where topics are in *BS 7671* is very important. Although students aren't expected to know where all the individual Regulations are, by understanding how the Parts, Chapters and Sections relate to specific topics you should be able to get close to finding the correct location for a given subject. In some cases it is important to know where, for example, a specific Table or Appendix is to be found.

Before we start to identify individual Regulation numbers it is important to understand the format of *BS 7671*.

BS 7671 contains seven main **Parts** and 15 **Appendices**.

The seven main **Parts** each contain **Chapters** and each Chapter contains **Sections**. The sections contain the individual **Regulations**.

Key Facts
'Remembering what the Parts of BS 7671 relate to will help you get a lot closer to finding the Regulation you want'

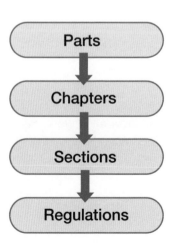

Parts

↓

Chapters

↓

Sections

↓

Regulations

The seven Parts of *BS 7671* are:

- Part 1 **Scope, object and fundamental principles**

- Part 2 **Definitions**

- Part 3 **Assessment of general characteristics**

- Part 4 **Protection for Safety**

- Part 5 **Selection and erection of equipment**

- Part 6 **Inspection and testing**

- Part 7 **Special installations or locations**

Exercise STR1

(1) How many Parts are there within *BS 7671*? (2). What does Part 7 relate to? (3) What is the number of the Part relating to Selection and erection of equipment?

It is important to note that the first three Parts of *BS 7671* lay down the foundations for compliance whilst Parts 4 & 5 provide more specific requirements. Part 6 covers inspection and testing and Part 7 is intended to supplement or modify the general requirements contained in other parts of the Regulations.

4. Regulation numbering system

a. Introduction

The following guidelines explain the regulation numbering system used within *BS 7671*. Whilst the numbering system is consistent throughout Parts 1 to 6 it should be noted that there is a different numbering system for Part 7 (see below).

b. Numbering system for Parts 1 to 6

Each Regulation number can be broken down into its constituent Part, Chapter and Section.

In the numbering system used, the first digit signifies a Part, the second digit a Chapter, the third digit a Section, and the subsequent digits the specific Regulation number.

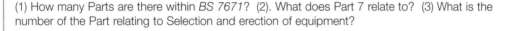

Parts	Chapters	Sections	Regulations
5	52	524	524.1

Example 1   Regulation 524-1

PART   **5**   - Selection and erection of equipment

CHAPTER   **52**   - Selection and erection of wiring systems

SECTION   **524** - Cross-sectional area of conductors of cables

REGULATION   **524.1** - Cross-sectional area of conductors in AC and DC circuits

Exercise STR2

(1) Consider the Regulation 610.1. What subject does this Regulation relate to? (2). What are the numbers of the Part, Chapter and Section contained within this Regulation? (3) In this Regulation who should the verification be made by?

As well as Parts, Chapters and Sections some parts of the Regulations also have Regulation Groups. Regulation Groups are a number of Regulations that are grouped together because they relate to a common subject or set of requirements.

When quoting a Regulation the . between numbers should be quoted as 'dot'. For example Regulation 543.2.6 would be quoted as 'five four three **dot** two **dot** six'.

Example 2: Regulation 521.9.3. A flexible cable or flexible cord shall be used for fixed wiring only where the relevant provisions of these Regulations are met

Part	Chapter	Section	Reg Group	Regulation
5	52	521	521.9	521.9.3

Exercise STR3

(1) What is the Regulation number that includes the text 'types of earth electrodes that are recognised for the purposes of the Regulations'? (2) What is the number of the Part, Chapter, Section and Regulation Group relating to this Regulation?

Numbering of figures and tables in *BS 7671* take the number of the Section they are in followed by a sequential number.

c. Numbering system for Part 7 Special installations or locations

In Part 7 the numbers appearing after a Section number refers to the corresponding Chapter, Section or Regulation within Parts 1 to 6 or another Chapter, Section or Regulation within Part 7. The numbering system, therefore, does not always follow sequentially.

Example 3: Regulation 701.415.2 – Relating to Supplementary equipotential bonding in a location containing a bath or shower.

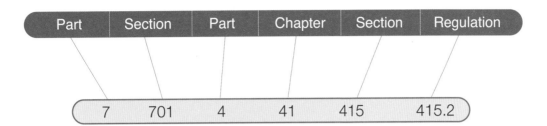

In the above example the first numbers in the Regulation (701) tell us that this Regulation is in Section 701 – Locations containing a bath or shower (which is in Part 7 Special installations or locations). The following numbers in the Regulation (415.2) tell us this Regulation relates to Regulation 415.2 which is located in Part 4 (Additional protection: Supplementary equipotential bonding). Therefore, Regulation 701.415.2 relates to supplementary equipotential bonding within a location containing a bath or shower.

Example 4: Regulation 701.753 – Relating to electric floor heating systems in a location containing a bath or shower.

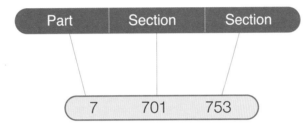

In the above example the first numbers in the Regulation (701) tell us that this Regulation is in Section 701 – Locations containing a bath or shower. The following numbers in the Regulation (753) tell us this relates to Section 753. This section having a '7' prefix tells us this is another Special Installation or location, in this case electric floor heating systems. Regulation 701.753, therefore, relates to electric floor heating systems in a location containing a bath or shower.

Further information relating to Harmonized Standards can be found at:
• http://www.cenelec.org/ *or*
• http://www.iec.ch/

THE STRUCTURE OF *BS 7671* FINAL REVISION EXERCISE

Str1 **Which of the following is correct? The Regulations are split into seven:**
- ☐ a. Parts
- ☐ b. Chapters
- ☐ c. Sections
- ☐ d. Regulations

Str2 **In the Regulation 536.1, the '536' relates to which of the following?**
- ☐ a. Part
- ☐ b. Chapter
- ☐ c. Section
- ☐ d. Regulation

The structure of BS 7671
(IEE Wiring Regulations 17th edition)

Str3 Regulation 512.1.1 relates to which of the following?
- ☐ a. Compliance with Standards.
- ☐ b. Fire propagating structures
- ☐ c. Suitability of equipment in relation to the nominal voltage
- ☐ d. Main protective bonding conductors

Str4 The regulations relating to insulation resistance testing can be found in which of the following Regulation Groups?
- ☐ a. 537-1
- ☐ b. 442.1
- ☐ c. 612.3
- ☐ d. 331.1

Str5 Part 4 of *BS 7671* relates to which of the following?
- ☐ a. Inspection & Testing
- ☐ b. Protection for Safety
- ☐ c. Definitions
- ☐ d. Assessment of general characteristics

Str6 Information relating to Selection and erection of equipment can be found in which of the following?
- ☐ a. Part 1
- ☐ b. Part 3
- ☐ c. Part 5
- ☐ d. Part 7

Things to do and find

1. In Regulation 410.3.6 what is the related Chapter number?

2. What does the Regulation in Q1 above relate to?

3. In the Regulation 527.2.1 what is the Regulation Group number and what is its title?

4. In which two Chapters of *BS 7671* are the main requirements relating to Safety services?

5. Which Regulation Group contains the requirements relating to: (i) Earthing requirements for the installation of equipment having high protective conductor currents (ii) Additional protection: Residual current devices (RCDs) (iii) Other mechanical stresses (AJ).

Part 1
Scope, object and fundamental principles

Chapter 11 Scope and Chapter 12 Objects and effects

Chapter 13 Fundamental principles

1. Introduction

As the title of Part 1 of *BS 7671* suggests there are three distinct topic areas covered in Part 1, **Scope, Object** and **Fundamental principles,** each topic being allocated a separate chapter. This section of the Learning Guide covers Chapter 11 Scope and Chapter 12 Object; Chapter 13 is covered in the section immediately following this one.

In many ways Part 1 is the most important part of *BS 7671* as it outlines the areas covered, the intentions of the Regulations and the **fundamental principles** that should be followed to ensure safety of persons, livestock and property against dangers and damage which may arise in the reasonable use of electrical installations.

Part 1, and particularly Chapter 13, lays down the general requirements of *BS 7671*; Parts 3 to 7 provide more detailed information as to how compliance can be achieved.

2. Chapter 11 Scope

a. Introduction

Chapter 11 provides the details relating to the types of installations that are included or excluded from *BS 7671*. Chapter 11 also clarifies the voltage range, the relationship between *BS 7671* and Statutory Regulations and contains information in relation to premises subject to licensing.

b. General (Installations included within the scope of *BS 7671*)

BS 7671 applies to the design, erection and verification of electrical installations such as those listed in Regulation 110.1. As well as the more common types of installations such as residential, commercial, industrial and public premises, numerous special installations and locations are referred to in this regulation. The majority of the electrical installations that require special requirements are to be found in *BS 7671* in Part 7 or Chapter 55.

Further clarification is provided in Regulation 110.1 in relation to the maximum nominal voltages that are applicable as well as preferred frequencies for alternating current supplies. Additions and alterations including the parts of the existing installation affected by the addition or alteration are also within the scope of *BS 7671*.

In addition to the requirements of *BS 7671*, designers and installers need to be aware of the requirements or recommendations of other related British Standards. These documents may be needed to supplement the requirements of *BS 7671*, particularly where more specialised installations are being designed and/or constructed such as emergency lighting or fire detection and alarm systems (for further British Standards that may be relevant see Regulation 110.1).

c. Exclusions from scope

Designers and installers need to be aware of the exclusions from the scope of *BS 7671* as well as the areas that are covered. Typical installations that are excluded from *BS 7671* are public distribution systems, railway traction equipment and equipment on board ships.

notes

Exercise 11.1

You should now refer to Regulations 110.1 & 110.2. In relation to the following types of installation, put them into one of the following categories: 'included', 'excluded' or 'supplementary document may be required', in line with Chapter 11. (1) Marinas, (2) Equipment on board ships (covered by *BS 8450*), (3) Fire detection and alarm systems, (4) Public premises, (5) Lightning protection system, (6) Electric surface heating systems.

d. Equipment

BS 7671 does not deal with the requirements for the construction of electrical equipment, which are required to comply with appropriate standards. However, the regulations do apply to items of electrical equipment so far as selection and application in the installation are concerned.

e. Relationship with Statutory Regulations

BS 7671 is non-statutory. They may, however, be used in a court of law in evidence to claim compliance with a statutory requirement. The relevant statutory provisions are listed in Appendix 2 of *BS 7671*.

Key Facts
Designers and installers must be aware of the types of installations that are included in *BS 7671* and those that are excluded'

It should also be noted that *BS 7671* is referred to in the Electricity Safety, Quality and Continuity Regulations 2002 as being an acceptable standard which will satisfy those statutory Regulations. Additionally, the Health and Safety Executive considers compliance with *BS 7671* is likely to achieve conformity with the relevant parts of the Electricity at Work Regulations 1989.

f. Installations subject to licensing

Where licensing or other authorities exercise a statutory control, their requirements should be ascertained and complied with when design and/or installation work is being carried out. Examples of

Fig 11.1 Statutory documents

installations where this would apply are premises under the Licensing Act 2003 (for supply of alcohol entertainment etc), premises licensed under the Petroleum (Consolidation) Act 1928, caravan sites and houses of multiple occupancy.

Fig 11.2 Typical premises requiring licensing

3. Chapter 12 Objects and effects

BS 7671 contains the rules for the design and erection of electrical installations so as to provide for safety and proper functioning for the intended use. Regulation 120.2 clarifies the point that Chapter 13 states the fundamental principles of *BS 7671*.

As mentioned previously, Parts 3 to 7 of *BS 7671* set out the technical requirements intended to ensure that electrical installations conform to the fundamental principles of Chapter 13 as follows:

• Part 3 Assessment of general characteristics

• Part 4 Protection for safety

• Part 5 Selection and erection of equipment

• Part 6 Inspection and testing

• Part 7 Special installations and locations.

(Part 2 covers Definitions).

Any intended departure from these Parts requires special consideration by the designer of the installation and must be noted on the Electrical Installation Certificate specified in Part 6 and shown in Appendix 6 of *BS 7671*. The resulting degree of safety of the installation must not be less than that obtained by compliance with the Regulations.

4. New materials and inventions

Departures to *BS 7671* may be acceptable when new materials and inventions are being used provided the resulting degree of safety is not less than that required by compliance with the Regulations. Where this occurs it should be noted on the Electrical Installation Certificate.

Exercise 12.1

Where, on the Electrical Installation Certificate, would the note, as required by Regulation 120.3 & 120.4, be inserted?

notes

> Further information relating to Chapter 11 & 12 Scope and Object can be found in:
> • *BS 7671* Chapters 11 & 12
> • Electrical Safety Council Technical Manual articles I93-19, V29-1,
> • IEE Guidance Note 1
> • Electricity Safety, Quality and Continuity Regulations 2002
> • Electricity at Work Regulations 1989

CHAPTERS 11 & 12 FINAL REVISION EXERCISE

11.1 **Which of the following Regulations are non-statutory?**
☐ a. *BS 7671 Requirements for Electrical Installations (IEE Regulations)*
☐ b. *Electricity Safety, Quality and Continuity Regulations 2002*
☐ c. *Electricity at Work Regulations 1989*
☐ d. *Health and Safety at Work etc Act 1974*

11.2 **Which of the following is excluded from the scope of *BS 7671*?**
☐ a. Equipment of aircraft
☐ b. Caravans
☐ c. Commercial premises
☐ d. Agricultural and horticultural premises

11.3 **Which of the following is included in the scope of *BS 7671*?**
☐ a. Lightning protection systems
☐ b. Equipment of motor vehicles
☐ c. Those aspects of mines and quarries covered by Statutory Regulations
☐ d. Photovoltaic systems

11.4 **Which of the following is not a preferred frequency as outlined in *BS 7671*?**
☐ a. 40 Hz
☐ b. 50 Hz
☐ c. 60 Hz
☐ d. 400 Hz

Things to do and find

1. What are the maximum a.c. and d.c. voltages as specified in Chapter 11?

2. Does *BS 7671* apply to the design, erection and verification of an electrical installation in a fairground?

3. Does *BS 7671* apply to the design, erection and verification of electrical equipment of aircraft?

4. Name two statutory documents that have a relationship with *BS 7671*.

5. Name three types of premises that may need special consideration due to them being covered by licensing.

6. Where on an Electrical Installation Certificate would you insert a design departure (in accordance with Regulation 120.3 or 120.4)?

1. Introduction

Chapter 13 provides the fundamental principles for safety on which the detailed technical requirements of Parts 2 to 7 are based. There are many sections in Chapter 13 covering the principle safety aspects of electrical design and installation. Because many of these sections are covered in detail later in this Learning Guide they are only outlined in this section.

Chapter 13 is split into five sections:

- Protection for safety (Section 131)
- Design (Section 132)
- Selection of electrical equipment (Section 133)
- Erection and initial verification of electrical installations (Section 134)
- Periodic Inspection and testing (Section 135)

2. Protection for Safety (Section 131)

a. General

The requirements of this chapter are intended to provide safety for the following against dangers and damage which may arise in the reasonable use of electrical installations:

- Persons
- Livestock
- Property

Risk of injury in electrical installations may result from a range of dangerous occurrences including shock currents, excessive temperatures likely to burn and fires.

> **Exercise 13.1**
>
> (1) Apart from shock, burns and fire list 4 other items that risk of injury may result from.

b. Protection against electric shock (Regulation Group 131.2)

Regulation Group 131.2 introduces the two important terms **Basic Protection** (formerly known as direct contact) **and Fault protection** (formerly known as indirect contact).

In line with *BS EN 61140 (Protection against electric shock. Common aspects for installation and equipment), BS 7671* outlines the methods for protection under fault-free (or normal) conditions this being by basic protective provisions **(basic protection)**, and protection under single fault conditions which is provided by fault protective provisions **(fault protection)**. Alternatively, protection against electric shock is provided by an enhanced protective provision which provides both basic and fault protection.

The protective measures that can be applied to ensure the requirements for basic and fault protection have been met are detailed in Chapter 41. Most of the measures are for general use. Part 4 of *BS 7671* and this Learning Guide provide further details in relation to protection against electric shock.

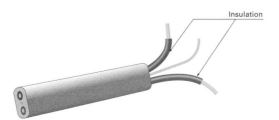

Insulation

Regulation 131.2.1 relates to basic protection and requires persons and livestock to be protected against dangers that may arise from contact with live parts of the installation. This can be achieved by one of the following methods:

• Preventing a current from passing through the body of a person or livestock.

• Limiting the current which can pass through a body to a non-hazardous value.

Fault protection (Regulation 131.2.2) is intended to provide protection against dangers that may arise from contact with exposed-conductive-parts during a fault by preventing the passage of current, limiting the magnitude of current or limiting the duration of current flow.

Exercise 13.2

Refer to Regulation 131.2.2 and review in full the three methods for achieving fault protection.

Regulation 131.2.2 clarifies the point that the application of protective equipotential bonding is one of the most important safety requirements in an electrical installation.

c. Protection against thermal effects (Regulation Group 131.3.1)

The risks of ignition of flammable materials due to high temperature or electric arcs must be minimized when designing or constructing electrical installations and there should be minimum risk of burns to persons or livestock. Equipment must be protected against harmful effects of heat in order to avoid the following:

• Risk of burns
• Combustion or ignition of material
• Dangerous functioning of equipment

In addition, electrical equipment must not present a fire hazard to adjacent materials

Chapter 42 of BS 7671 and this Learning Guide provide further details

Exercise 13.3

(1) List four items that risk of injury might result from in an electrical installation. (2). What are the two general terms used to describe the provisions required to protect against electric shock?

d. Protection against overcurrent (131.4)

Protection should be provided against damage due to excessive temperature or electromechanical stresses caused by any overcurrents likely to arise in live conductors to ensure persons or livestock do not suffer injury and property is not damaged.

Chapter 43 of BS 7671 and this Learning Guide provide further details.

e. Protection against fault current (131.5)

Conductors and other parts intended to carry a fault current (such as live conductors which are covered by Regulation 131.4) must be capable of carrying that current without attaining excessive temperature. Electrical equipment, including conductors, must be provided with mechanical protection against electromechanical stresses of fault currents in order to prevent danger or injury to people or livestock.

Chapters 43, 52 and 54 of BS 7671 and this Learning Guide provide further details.

f. Protection against voltage disturbances and measures against electromagnetic influences (Regulation Group 131.6)

This group of regulations requires protection for the electrical installation due to a range of harmful effects both internal and external to the installation. People and livestock must be protected against injury and property from harmful effects resulting from faults between systems of different voltages, overvoltages from atmospheric conditions (such as lightning) and undervoltages

Chapter 44 of BS 7671 and this Learning Guide provide further details.

g. Protection against power supply interruption (131.7)

When danger or damage is expected due to the interruption of an electrical supply, suitable provisions should be made in the installation or equipment.

h. Additions and Alterations (131.8)

Before any additions and alterations can be made to an existing electrical installation it must be verified that the rating and condition of any existing equipment, including that of the distributor will be adequate, for any increase in electrical load. In addition, the earthing and bonding arrangements must be assessed for the safety of the addition or alteration to the electrical system.

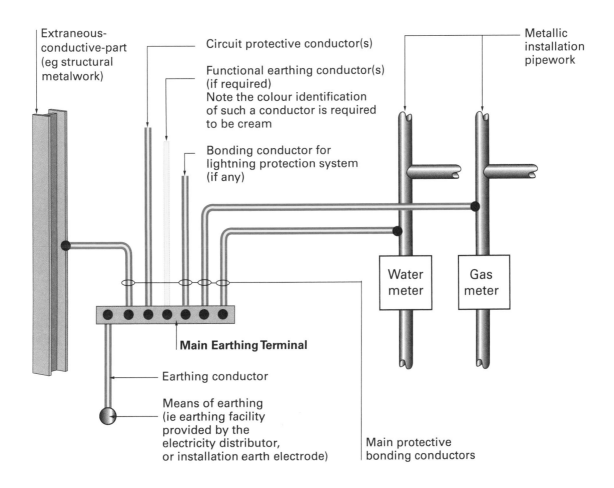

Extraneous-conductive-part (eg structural metalwork)

Circuit protective conductor(s)

Functional earthing conductor(s) (if required)
Note the colour identification of such a conductor is required to be cream

Bonding conductor for lightning protection system (if any)

Metallic installation pipework

Water meter

Gas meter

Main Earthing Terminal

Earthing conductor

Means of earthing (ie earthing facility provided by the electricity distributor, or installation earth electrode)

Main protective bonding conductors

notes

3. Design (Section 132)

a. General (132.1)

An electrical installation must be designed to provide for:

• Protection of persons, livestock and property in accordance with Section 131.

• The proper functioning of the electrical installation for the intended use.

b. Characteristics of the available supply or supplies (132.2)

The characteristics of the supply must be determined by measurement, calculation, inspection or enquiry. The characteristics to be considered include the nature of the current, the purpose of conductors, values and tolerances of voltage and protective measures in the supply (for example earthed neutral)

Exercise 13.4

(1) Refer to Section 132 of *BS 7671* and list the type of conductors that may be required by Regulation 132.2 for an a.c. circuit (2) List four items under the heading values and tolerances in Regulation 132.2.

c. Nature of demand (132.3)

Key Facts

'It is essential that you check the incoming earthing system and main protective bonding when you intend to alter or add to an existing electrical installation'

The number and type of circuits (for example lighting, power, control etc) should be determined by considering all the relevant factors such as; location of points of power demand, expected loads, load variations, anticipated future demands and any special conditions or requirements.

Part 3 of *BS 7671* and this Learning Guide provide further details in relation to maximum demand, supplies and division of installation.

d. Electrical supply systems for safety services or standby electrical supply systems (132.4)

Where a supply for safety services or standby electrical supply systems is required the characteristics of the supply and the circuits to be supplied by the safety source should be determined.

Chapter 35 and Chapter 56 of BS 7671 and this Learning Guide (located at Chapter 56) provide further details in relation to Safety Services.

e. Environmental conditions (132.5)

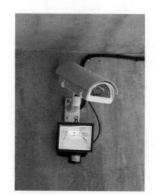

Equipment likely to be exposed to adverse conditions (such as weather, corrosion etc) must be constructed or protected as necessary to prevent danger from the adverse exposure'

Chapter 51, Chapter 52 and Appendix 5 of BS 7671 provide further details in relation to environmental conditions. This subject is covered generally in Part 2 (Definitions) of this Learning Guide.

f. Cross sectional area of conductors (132.6)

The cross-sectional area (csa) of conductors should be determined for both normal operating and where appropriate fault conditions. Many aspects need to be considered when determining conductor csa, such as the method of installation, voltage drop limit and admissible maximum temperature.

Sections 523, 524 and 525 and Appendix 4 of BS 7671 provide further details in relation to the determination of conductor csa and this subject is covered in Section 523 (with Section 525) and Section 524 of this Learning Guide.

g. Type of wiring and method of installation (132.7)

Consideration needs to be given to the choice of the type of wiring system and the method of installation. Many aspects may need consideration including the nature of the location and supporting structure, building use, and accessibility of wiring.

Sections 521 & 522 of BS 7671 and this Learning Guide provide further details in relation to types of wiring and installation methods.

> **Exercise 13.5**
>
> Refer to Regulation 132.7 (1) List four considerations that need to be considered when choosing the type of wiring system and method of installation.

h. Protective equipment (132.8)

Protective equipment must be selected to include for the following:

- Overcurrent (overload, short-circuit)

- Earth fault current

- Overvoltage

- Undervoltage and no-voltage

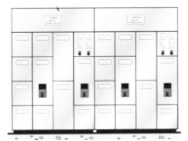

Chapter 41, 43 and 44 of BS 7671 and this Learning Guide provide further details in relation to earth faults, overcurrent, overvoltage and undervoltage/no-voltage.

i. Emergency Control (132.9)

A means of emergency switching must be provided where there is a risk of danger. This device must be easily recognized and interrupt the supply quickly and effectively.

Section 537 of BS 7671 and this Learning Guide provide further details in relation to emergency switching.

j. Disconnecting devices (132.10)

A means of disconnecting the electrical installation, circuits or individual items of equipment must be provided to permit switching and/or isolation to enable maintenance, testing, fault detection and repair to be carried out.

notes

Chapter 53 and in particular Section 537 of BS 7671 and this Learning Guide provide further details in relation to isolation and switching.

k. Prevention of mutual detrimental influence (132.11)

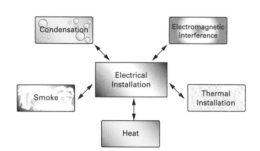

'The effects of mutual detrimental influence between electrical and non-electrical installations should be avoided by effective arrangement of the electrical installation'

Sections 515 and 528 of BS 7671 and this Learning Guide provide further details in relation to prevention of mutual detrimental influence.

l. Accessibility of electrical equipment (132.12)

Electrical equipment should be arranged so that there is sufficient space for the initial installation and replacement of items of equipment at a later date. Access should also be available for the operation, inspection, testing, repair, and maintenance.

Sections 513, 526 and 529 of BS 7671 provide further details in relation to accessibility and this subject is covered in Chapter 51and Section 528/529 of this Learning Guide.

m. Documentation for the electrical installation (132.13)

Appropriate documentation, including that required by Regulation 514.9 (Diagrams, charts and schedules relating to the distribution boards) and Part 6 (Inspection and Testing) should be provided for every installation.

Chapter 51, Part 6 and Appendix 6 of BS 7671 provide further details in relation to documentation for the electrical installation and this subject is covered in Chapter 51 Part 6 and Appendix 6 of this Learning Guide

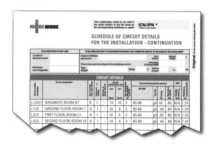

n. Protective devices and switches (132.14)

Regulation Group 132.14 contains the requirements relating to the locations of switches and protective devices including the restrictions relating to the location of single-pole devices only in the line conductor and restrictions relating to earthed neutral conductors'

Related topics can be found in Chapter 43 and Chapter 53 of BS 7671 and this Learning Guide.

Exercise 13.6

(1) Refer to Regulation Group 132.14 and review the requirements relating to protective devices and switches.

o. Isolation and switching (132.15)

As may be necessary to prevent or remove danger effective means of isolation, suitably placed, must be provided so that all voltage is cut off from every installation, from every circuit and from all equipment.

An efficient means of switching off, readily accessible, easily operated and placed to prevent danger should be provided for every fixed electric motor.

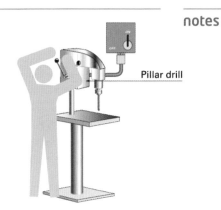

Pillar drill

Chapter 53 (and in particular Section 537) of BS 7671 and this Learning Guide provide further details in relation to isolation and switching.

4. Selection of electrical equipment (Section 133)

a. General

Every item of equipment should comply with the appropriate British Standard, *IEC* standard or national standard of another country.

Exercise 13.7
(1) List four items that must be considered when selecting protective equipment (Regulation 132.8) (2) What type of switch or circuit-breaker must be used if inserted in an earthed neutral conductor?

Where there are no applicable standards, the item of equipment concerned should be selected by special agreement between the person specifying the installation and the installer. In this case the designer or person responsible for specifying the installation must ensure the equipment provides at least the same degree of safety as that afforded by compliance with the Regulations.

Chapter 51 of BS 7671 and this Learning Guide provide further details in relation to compliance with standards.

b. Characteristics

Every item of electrical equipment must have suitable characteristics appropriate to the values and conditions on which the design of the electrical installation is based and in particular in relation to voltage, current, frequency and power.

c. Conditions of installation

The stresses, environmental conditions and characteristics of the location should be taken into account when equipment is being selected. Where an item of equipment does not have the required properties for its location adequate further protection should be provided.

notes

5. Erection and initial verification of electrical installations (Section 134)

a. Erection

Regulation 134.1.1 is repeated below:

'Good workmanship by competent persons and proper materials shall be used in the erection of the electrical installation. Electrical equipment shall be installed in accordance with the instructions provided by the manufacturer of the equipment.'

This regulation is very important as it sums up all the aspects that are required to ensure an installation is installed properly.

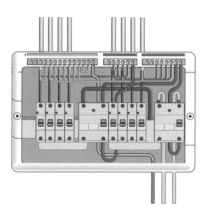

Further to the above, Section 134 requires electrical equipment to be erected without impairing the characteristics (as outlined in Section 133 above) and installed in such a manner that the design temperatures are not exceeded. Electrical equipment likely to cause high temperatures or electric arcs should be placed or guarded to minimize the risk of ignition of flammable materials.

Conductors and where necessary terminals should be identified in accordance with Section 514 and electrical joints and connections should be of proper construction with respect to conductance, insulation, mechanical strength and protection.

Where necessary for safety purposes, suitable warning signs and/or notices should be provided.

b. Initial verification

For new installations (or additions and alterations) appropriate inspection and testing must be carried out during erection and on completion by competent persons to verify the requirements of *BS 7671* have been met. Part 6 of *BS 7671* and this Learning Guide provide further details relating to initial inspection and testing.

Appropriate certification must be issued in line with the requirements of Section 631 and Appendix 6 of *BS 7671* provides model forms for this purpose. The designer of the installation is responsible for making the recommendation in relation to the interval to the first periodic inspection and test.

6. Periodic inspection and testing (Section 135)

Regulation 135.1 recommends that every electrical installation is subjected to periodic inspection and testing. Chapter 62 provides further details in relation to periodic inspection and testing and Appendix 6 provides model forms for reporting.

Further information relating to Chapter 13 Fundamental principles can be found in:
- *BS 7671* Chapters 13
- Electrical Safety Council Technical Manual articles A13-1, B37-5 and P153-1
- IEE Guidance Note 1

notes

CHAPTER 13 FINAL REVISION EXERCISE

13.1 Which of the following would not necessarily be required to be taken into consideration when additions or alterations are being made?
- ☐ a. The rating of any existing equipment.
- ☐ b. The condition of existing equipment.
- ☐ c. The existing earthing and bonding arrangements.
- ☐ d. Existing final circuits are protected by rewireable fuses.

13.2 Which person makes the recommendation for the interval to the first periodic inspection and test of an electrical installation?
- ☐ a. The person ordering the work.
- ☐ b. The designer.
- ☐ c. The installer.
- ☐ d. The person carrying out the initial verification.

Things to do and find

1. Name four ways of determining the supply characteristics.

2. Where on an Electrical Installation Certificate would you insert the recommendation to the next periodic inspection and test?

Part 2
Definitions

Part 2 Definitions including earthing systems, external influence and Index of protection (IP) ratings

1. Introduction

Part 2 of *BS 7671* contains definitions of terms used throughout the Regulations. It is extremely important that anyone requiring a knowledge of *BS 7671* reviews this part of the Regulations as the exact terminology used to define specific words or phrases in Part 2 is critical to an understanding of the rest of the Regulations.

Although there are around 250 definitions in Part 2 some of these are for more specialised use or are infrequently used and, therefore, their meanings only need to be looked up when necessary.

In this part of the Learning Guide commonly used definitions will be covered. It is very important that they are studied and understood as these definitions will reappear many times throughout the Learning Guide (as they do throughout *BS 7671*). Some definitions relating to key topics, listed below, which are used extensively throughout *BS 7671*, are given a more detailed explanation.

- Earthing, bonding and related definitions
- Earthing systems
- Voltage (ranges, bands and types of extra-low voltage systems)
- External influences and IP codes.

In other cases the definitions from *BS 7671* are provided with or without a short explanation. For ease of reference some definitions have been *roughly* grouped.

Symbols used in the Regulations are located at the end of Part 2 of *BS 7671*.

2. Miscellaneous Definitions

An understanding of some definitions is important because they are used widely throughout *BS 7671*. These include:

- Danger
- Electrical installation
- Origin of an installation
- Safety service
- Wiring system
- Electrical Equipment
- Accessory
- Luminaire

Exercise 2.1
(1). Review the above definitions by referring to Part 2 of *BS 7671* (2). Which term does the following definition describe? 'The temperature of the air or other medium where equipment is to be used' (3). What is the definition for a flexible cord and how is it defined by size?

3. Protection Against Electric Shock

There are many definitions connected with the principles of shock protection.

PART 2
Definitions

Before an understanding of the requirements of *BS 7671*, particularly Part 4, can be understood, it will be worth spending time reviewing the definitions related to protection against electric shock including the following:

- Arm's reach,
- barrier,
- basic protection,
- electric shock,
- enclosure,
- fault protection
- simultaneously accessible parts

Exercise 2.2

(1). Which term does the following definition describe? 'A person who distributes electricity to consumers using electrical lines and equipment that he owns or operates' (2). Review the definitions in Part 2 for circuit, distribution circuit, ring final circuit and line conductor (3) Does the definition 'live part' include a neutral conductor?

4. Overcurrent protection and related definitions

An understanding of the definitions relating to overcurrent protection, such as circuit-breaker, fault current, overcurrent, overload and short-circuit current is important and these terms are specifically addressed in Chapter 43 of this Learning Guide.

Exercise 2.3

(1) Which definition does the following describe? 'A circuit condition in which current flows through an abnormal or unintended path. This may result from an insulation failure or a bridging of insulation. Conventionally the impedance between live conductors or between live conductors and exposed- or extraneous-conductive-parts at the fault position is considered negligible' (2) What does the abbreviation RCD stand for?

5. Inspection, testing and reporting definitions

Operatives employed in inspection, testing, reporting and/or certification should be aware of the definitions relating to this area of work. The terms inspection, reporting, testing and verification are all defined in Part 2 of *BS 7671*.

6. Types of insulation and separation - definitions

Within *BS 7671* not only is the term insulation defined but several classes or types of insulation are also defined. For more information relating to the requirements and application of different types of insulation see Sections 412, 413 and 414 of this Learning Guide. The terms basic insulation, reinforced and supplementary insulation have specific definitions and an understanding of the different 'classes' of equipment (Class I, II and III) is important.

7. Personnel definitions

BS 7671 defines persons depending upon their knowledge, experience, relevant practical skills or control and these definitions are used extensively throughout the Regulations. Personnel are classed as competent, instructed, ordinary or skilled. The category an operative falls under will determine the areas of electrical work he should be capable of carrying out safely.

Exercise 2.4

(1). Give an example of a typical wiring system. (2). Give an example of a typical safety service. (3). What are the three practices, listed in *BS 7671*, that verification is comprised of? (4). Give an example of a Class I and Class II piece of equipment.

8. Earthing, Bonding and Related Terms

Within *BS 7671* terms relating to earthing and bonding are used extensively. The following diagram illustrates the main earthing and bonding components of an electrical installation. Earthing and bonding are covered in detail in this Learning Guide in Part 4 and Chapter 54.

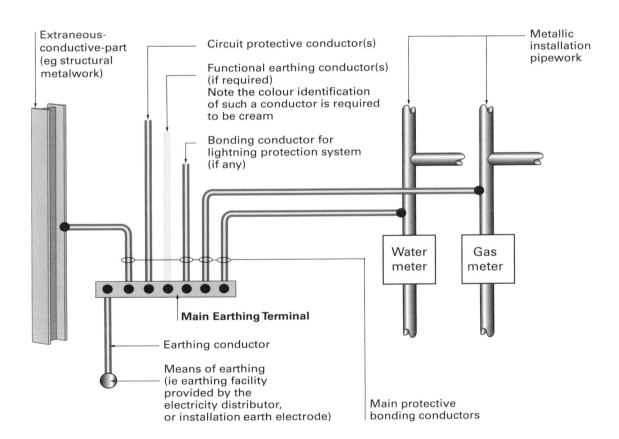

Fig 2.1 Main earthing terminal (MET) and protective conductors (see also Fig 2.1 of *BS 7671*)

It is important to understand the definition of a **Protective conductor** as this is a generic term which includes many other earthing and bonding conductors.

PART 2
Definitions

Exercise 2.5

1) List four types of protective conductor and two types of conductive-parts that may require connecting to the earthing system.

To understand how the principles of protective earthing and protective equipotential bonding work it is essential that several other definitions are understood including the following:

- Earth
- Earth fault loop impedance (see also Section 411 of this Learning Guide)
- Earthing
- Earthing conductor
- Equipotential bonding
- Exposed-conductive-parts
- Extraneous-conductive-parts
- Protective bonding conductor

9. Types of Systems and Earthing Arrangements

a. Introduction

The main earth terminal of an electrical installation is required to be connected with Earth by one of the methods described in Regulations 542.1.2 to 542.1.4.

Four distinct types of earthing arrangements are identified in Chapter 54: TN-S, TN-C-S, TT, and IT, each having different regulatory requirements in respect of matters such as protection against electric shock, protection against overcurrent, and isolation and switching. There is also a fifth arrangement (TN-C) but Regulation 8(4) of the Electricity Safety, Quality and Continuity Regulations 2002 prohibits the use of PEN conductors in consumers' installations.

A 'system' is defined in Part 2 of *BS 7671* as:

'An electrical system consisting of a single source or multiple sources running in parallel of electrical energy and an installation. For certain purposes of the Regulations, types of system are identified as follows, depending upon the relationship of the source, and exposed-conductive-parts of the installation, to Earth:......

The above definition then goes on to describe the different systems (TN-C, TN-S, TN-C-S, TT and IT) and these are outlined in the text below.

Part 3 of *BS 7671* requires the type of earthing arrangement to be determined. It is therefore essential for safety reasons that the electrical designer and electrical contractor responsible for an installation, or a person carrying out a periodic inspection and test knows with certainty the type of system of which the installation forms part.

Further to the above requirements, a Distributor is also required, on request, to provide a statement on the type of earthing (Reg 28 of the Electricity Safety, Quality and Continuity Regulations 2002) and unless inappropriate for reasons of safety, the distributor is required to make available his supply neutral conductor or protective conductor for connection to the consumer's earth terminal (Reg 24).

The five types of system are distinguished from one another by the specific methods used to earth the source and the installation, and also by whether the neutral and protective functions of the system are performed by separate conductors, combined conductors, or a mixture of the two (in different parts of the system). *BS 7430*, Code of practice for Earthing, is a valuable source of reference.

b. Designated letters related to types of systems and earthing arrangements

It is important to understand the meanings of the letters used to describe the different earthing arrangements. The designations TN-S, TN-C-S, TT, TN-C, and IT apply irrespective of whether the supply is single-phase, multi-phase or d.c., and each letter has the following meaning.

Table 2A Letters relating to types of system and earthing arrangements

SUPPLY system earthing arrangements are indicated by the first letter.	
T	Denotes that one or more points of the source of energy are directly connected to Earth. ('T' stands for terre, the French word for earth.)
I	Denotes that all live parts are isolated from Earth, or that the source of energy is connected to Earth through a deliberately introduced earthing impedance. ('I' stands for isolation.)
The INSTALLATION earthing arrangements are indicated by the second letter.	
T	Denotes that the exposed-conductive-parts of the installation are directly connected to Earth.
N	Denotes that the exposed-conductive-parts of the installation are directly connected to the earthed point of the source of energy. ('N' represents neutral).
The SYSTEM PROTECTIVE AND NEUTRAL CONDUCTOR arrangements are indicated by subsequent letters	
S	Denotes that separate neutral and protective conductors are provided. ('S' stands for separate).
C	Denotes that the neutral and protective functions are both performed by a single conductor, called a combined protective and neutral (PEN) conductor. ('C' stands for combined)

c. TN-S system

The exposed-conductive-parts of the installation are connected to the earthed point of the source of energy, and separate conductors are employed for the neutral and protective functions throughout the system.

The protective conductor between the source and the ends of the electricity distributor's lines on the consumer's premises is commonly provided by means of the lead sheath or wire armouring of the supply cable, although an independent conductor is sometimes provided for this purpose. This armour or lead sheath provides a continuous path back to the star point of the supply transformer.

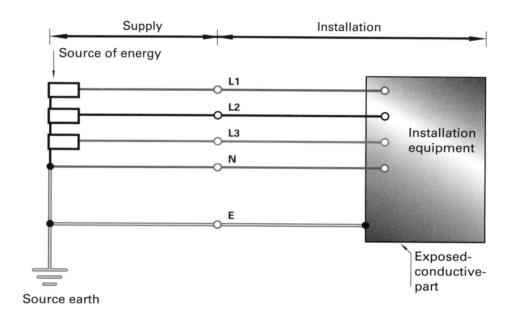

Fig 2.2 TN-S system

d. TN-C-S system

In the TN-C-S system, the exposed-conductive-parts of the installation are connected to the earthed point of the source of energy. In addition, the neutral and protective functions are combined in a single conductor between the source and a point of transition, beyond which separate protective and neutral conductors are provided. The point of transition is usually at the ends of the distributor's low voltage lines on the consumer's premises or, where the source of energy is owned by the customer, at the main switchgear.

There are two variants of the TN-C-S type of system, namely TN-C-S (PME) and TN-C-S (PNB).

e. TN-C-S (PME) system

The more common variant of TN-C-S, known as 'TN-C-S (PME)', is shown in the fig below. This type of distribution is known as Protective Multiple Earthing (PME), and has been used by electricity distributors for most of the new low voltage supplies they have been responsible for installing since the mid-1970s. The Combined Neutral and Earth (CNE) conductor of the distributor's lines is connected to Earth at several points in accordance with the Electricity Safety, Quality and Continuity Regulations 2002, thereby providing low resistance connections between all parts of that conductor and Earth.

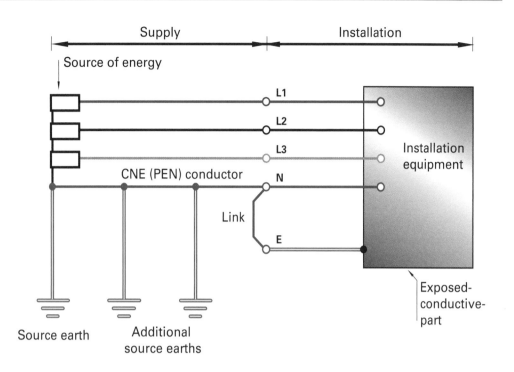

Fig 2.3 TN-C-S system

f. TN-C-S (PNB) system

The other variant of TN-C-S, known as 'TN-C-S (PNB)', is shown in the fig below (PNB stands for Protective Neutral Bonding.) This type of system is normally used only where a single consumer is supplied from a distribution transformer (or other source, such as a generating set). The CNE (or PEN) conductor is connected to Earth at one point only; this being at, or reasonably close to, the source.

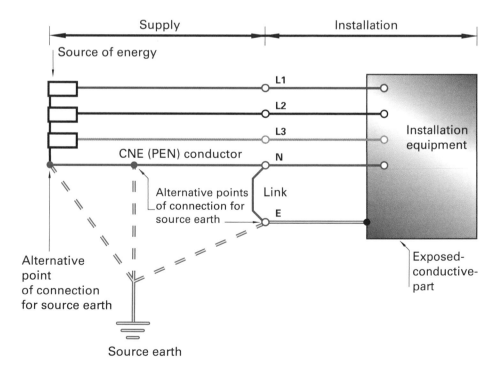

Fig 2.4 TN-C-S (PNB) System

g. TN-C system

The TN-C system is uncommon in the United Kingdom. The neutral and protective functions are combined in a single conductor, known as a PEN conductor, throughout the system (although, the term CNE is sometimes used for such a conductor forming part of the distributor's lines). The exposed-conductive-parts of the installation are connected to the PEN conductor, and hence to the earthed point of the source of energy. As mentioned previously, Regulation 8(4) of the Electricity Safety, Quality and Continuity Regulations 2002 prohibits the use of PEN conductors in consumers' installations.

h. TT system

In the TT system the exposed-conductive-parts of the electrical installation are connected to Earth by means of an installation earth electrode which is electrically independent of the source earth. The protective and neutral functions are provided by separate conductors. It should be noted that the supply to an installation which forms part of a TT system may or may not include a protective conductor. That is to say, the supply could consist of line and neutral conductors only (as in the case of a two-wire overhead supply line). The important thing to appreciate is that, where the installation is to form part of a TT system, the exposed-conductive-parts of the installation must be connected to the installation earth electrode, and not to the supply protective conductor (if any).

TT systems are often employed where the electricity distributor is unable or unwilling to offer an earthing facility for the installation, such as for premises in areas of low population density where the network does not have the required multiple earthing. TT systems are also employed where the use of a PME earthing facility provided by the distributor is inappropriate for statutory or technical reasons, such as for an electrical installation in a caravan or boat, or in an area having a potentially explosive atmosphere. TT systems may be supplied overhead or underground.

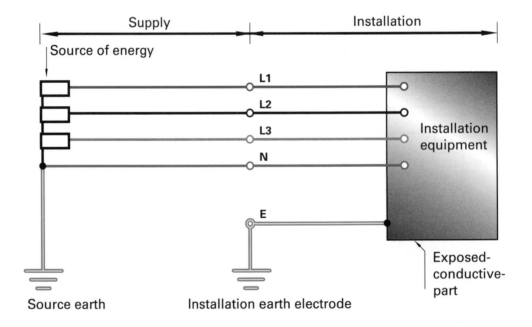

Fig 2.5 TT System

i. IT system

In the IT system the source of supply is either isolated from Earth, or earthed through a deliberately introduced earthing impedance. The exposed-conductive-parts of the installation are connected to Earth by means of an installation earth electrode as in the TT system. The protection of this system is normally by means of devices which monitor the insulation and give an audible or visual alarm and disconnect the supply when a fault occurs. As the source is not directly earthed, this system is prohibited for use in public distribution networks in the United Kingdom by the The Electricity Safety, Quality and Continuity Regulations 2002.

> **Exercise 2.6**
>
> (1) What do the letters T, N, C and S stand for in relating to (earthing) systems? (2) Which type of (earthing) system includes earth electrodes that are independent of the earth electrodes of the source? (3) In which type of (earthing) system are the neutral and protective functions combined in part of the system?

Key Facts
'Understanding the definitions used in *BS 7671* by regular reference to Part 2 helps when more complex regulations are being read'

10. Voltage Terms

Within *BS 7671* there are many references to different voltage categories and ranges. It is important to understand the difference between extra-low voltage and low voltage. **Extra-low voltage does not exceed 50 V a.c. or 120 V ripple-free d.c. (between conductors or to earth) and low voltage exceeds extra-low voltage but does not exceed 1000 V a.c. or 1500 V d.c. between conductors or 600 V a.c. or 900 V d.c between conductors and Earth.** High voltage exceeds the above value for low voltage.

The term *reduced low voltage system* relates to a system in which the nominal line to line voltage does not exceed 110 V (three-phase 63.5 V to earthed neutral, single-phase 55 V to earthed mid-point). These systems are often used on construction sites (see Section 704 of this Learning Guide for further information) and other locations where a reduced voltage system is considered beneficial.

Voltage Bands relate to the above nominal voltage categories although types of electrical installations and equipment are also included within these definitions. The definition for voltage bands is shown below along with Fig 2.6 illustrating the voltage between conductors for bands I and II.

> **Band I.** *Band I covers:*
>
> - *installations where protection against electric shock is provided under certain conditions by the value of voltage;*
> - *installations where the voltage is limited for operational reasons (e.g. telecommunications, signalling, bell, control and alarm installations).*
> *Extra-low voltage (ELV) will normally fall within Band I.*
>
> **Band II.** *Band II contains the voltages for supplies to household, and most commercial and industrial installations.*
> *Low voltage (LV) will normally fall within Band II*

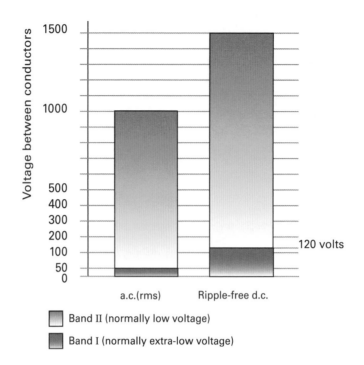

Fig 2.6 Voltage bands

SELV, PELV and FELV

As the letters suggest SELV, PELV and FELV are extra-low voltage (ELV) systems. The prefix used before the 'ELV' differentiates the differences between these systems. The source of the supply and whether the system meets specific requirements determines whether they are SELV, PELV or FELV. For more information relating to SELV and PELV see Section 414 of this Learning Guide. For more information relating to FELV see Section 411 of this Learning Guide.

Exercise 2.7

(1). Refer to Part 2 to review the definitions for SELV, PELV, FELV and reduced low voltage systems

11. EXTERNAL INFLUENCE

The term external influence is defined as:

'Any influence external to an electrical installation which affects the design and safe operation of that installation'

The term external influence is used extensively throughout *BS 7671*. The main references to external influence are Regulation Group 512.2, Section 522 and Appendix 5. However, there are many other sections and individual regulations contain requirements relating to external influences. It is important to note that there is some correlation between some external influence classifications and codes and IP Codes (see IP Codes below). IP codes relates to the protection provided by equipment against specific external influences.

Appendix 5 gives the classification and codification for external influences. Each category has two letters, followed by a number, for example AD6.

notes

The first letter indicates the general category of external influence either:

- A – Environment
- B – Utilisation
- C – Construction of the building

The second letter relates to the nature of the external influence (such as, ambient temperature, water or corrosion). These categories are also designated A, B and C, etc.

The designated number relates to the class within each external influence and normally reflects the prevalence, severity or level of responsibility. The designated number (1, 2, 3 etc) follow the general category and external influence letters.

Example 1. Classification AA5. The first letter 'A' signifies this classification relates to the *environment*, the second 'A' relates to Ambient Temperature and the '5', in this case, relates to an ambient temperature in the range +5 ^{O}C to +40 ^{O}C.

Example 2. Classification BE2. The first letter 'B' signifies this classification relates to Utilisation, the second letter 'E' relates to Nature of processed or stored materials and the '2' tells us this relates to *fire risks* (because the location contains manufacturing, processing or storage of flammable materials including presence of dust. Typical locations are barns, woodworking shops and paper factories).

Now refer to Appendix 5 to complete the following exercise.

Exercise 2.8

(1). What does the classification and external influence code AD5 relate to? (2). What does the classification and external influence code BA4 relate to? (3). What does the classification and external influence code CA2 relate to?

12. INTERNATIONAL PROTECTION CODE (IP CODE)

a. General

The IP Code is a system given in *BS EN 60529* – Degrees of protection provided by enclosures (IP code), applying to the enclosure of electrical equipment of rated voltage not exceeding 72.5 kV. The purpose of the IP Code is to indicate the degrees of protection provided by an electrical equipment enclosure against:

- Access to hazardous parts
- Ingress of solid foreign bodies *and*
- Ingress of water.

Most of the references in *BS 7671* refer to requirements to meet external influences. However, in some cases the requirements relate directly to the IP rating. The IP rating of equipment and the external influence are directly related, the IP rating being an equipment standard that meets the required external influence.

b. IP code lettering/numbering system

The degrees of protection provided by an enclosure are indicated by a designation consisting of the letters 'IP' followed by two characteristic numerals and up to one additional letter and one supplementary letter, as indicated in Table 2A below and further explained in Table 2B below.

PART 2
Definitions

The first characteristic numeral of an IP Code designation indicates (a) the degree of protection of persons against access to hazardous parts and (b) the degree of protection of equipment within the enclosure against the ingress of solid foreign objects. Where the first characteristic numeral is not required to be specified, it is replaced by the letter 'X'.

The second characteristic numeral of an IP Code designation indicates the degree of protection of equipment within the enclosure against the ingress of water. Where the second characteristic numeral is not required to be specified, it is replaced by the letter 'X'.

Additional letters are optional and they indicate the degree of protection of persons against access to hazardous parts. Additional letters are used where:

> • the actual protection against access to hazardous parts is greater than that indicated by the first characteristic numeral (for example, where greater protection is provided by barriers, suitable shape of openings or distances inside the enclosure), *or*
>
> • Only protection against access to hazardous parts is indicated, the first characteristic numeral then being replaced by the letter 'X'.

Table 2B **IP code numbering/lettering system**

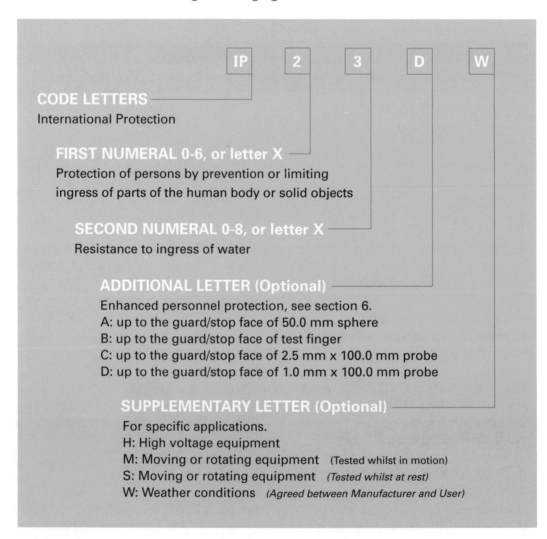

c. Commonly used IP codes

Common examples of IP codes (first letter – protection against solid foreign objects) are IP2X and IP4X which are used on switchgear and electrical enclosures generally. IP2X is often referred to as the 'finger test'. When required in relation to electrical equipment in *BS 7671* the intention is to stop direct contact with live parts by ensuring equipment is effectively sealed from all usual directions of access. IP4X is a stricter requirement and is, for example, a requirement for the top horizontal surface of a barrier or enclosure (to stop small objects falling inside electrical equipment enclosures). Common examples of the second letter (protection against harmful ingress of water) can be found extensively throughout the Regulations and in particular in Part 7, for example the requirements for equipment in bathrooms or swimming pools.

Table 2C illustrates IP codes along with practical examples relating to each code.

1st figure

0	No protection
1	Protected against solid bodies of 50 mm and greater (e.g. accidental contact with the hand)
2	Protected against solid bodies of 12.5 mm and greater (e.g. finger)
3	Protected against solid bodies of 2.5 mm and greater (e.g. tools, wires)
4	Protected against solid bodies larger than 1 mm (e.g. thin tools and fine wires)
5	Protected against dust (no harmful deposits)
6	Completely protected against dust

2nd figure

0	No protection
1	Protected against vertically falling drops of water (condensation)
2	Protected against drops of water falling upto 15° from the vertical
3	Protected against drops of water falling upto 60° from the vertical
4	Protected against splashing water from all directions
5	Protected against jets of water from all directions
6	Protected against powerful jets of water from all directions
7	Protected against the effects of temporary immersion in water
8	Protected against the continuous effects of immersion in water under pressure

Additional letter

B	Test finger penetration to a maximum of 80 mm must not contact hazardous parts

PART 2
Definitions

d. International mechanical protection code (IK code)

In addition to the commonly encountered IP code there is also the International Mechanical Protection Code, known as the IK code. The IK code is used mainly in electrical product specifications and covers most types of electrical equipment incorporating an enclosure, such as for switchgear, controlgear, accessories, luminaires and electrical machines. It offers uniformity in the method of describing the protection provided by enclosures against external mechanical impacts and in the tests employed by manufacturers and test laboratories to verify such protection.

Exercise 2.9

What degree of protection is required by (1) An enclosure used with the protective measure double or reinforced insulation where the lid or door of the enclosure can be opened without the use of a key or a tool? (2) A cable trunking system containing non-sheathed cables? (3) A door giving access to electrical equipment used for outdoor lighting installations, highway power supplies or street furniture where the door is less than 2.5 m above ground level? (4) Electrical equipment in zone 0 of a swimming pool? (5) Electrical equipment for use in a temporary electrical installation at a fairground?

Further information relating to Definitions can be found in:
- *BS 7671* Part 2
- *BS 7430*, Code of practice for earthing
- Electrical Safety Council Technical Manual articles E45-33, E157-5, E157-9, E157-49, I39-5, I41-1, I41-5, E169-9 and V29-5 (This is only a selection for other references search by word)
- IEE Guidance Note 1

PART 2 DEFINITIONS FINAL REVISION EXERCISE

2.1 The description 'A part providing a defined degree of protection against contact with live parts from any usual direction of access' is the definition for which of the following?
- ☐ a. Barrier
- ☐ b. Accessory
- ☐ c. Insulation
- ☐ d. Enclosure

2.2 Which one of the following is not a general category of external influences?
- ☐ a. Construction of the building
- ☐ b. Ambient temperature
- ☐ c. Utilization
- ☐ d. Environment

2.3 The definition 'Conductive part of equipment which can be touched and which is not normally live, but which can become live when basic insulation fails' describes which of the following?
- ☐ a. Extraneous-conductive-part
- ☐ b. Exposed-conductive-part
- ☐ c. Live part
- ☐ d. Protective conductor

2.4 The definition 'A conductive part liable to introduce a potential, generally earth potential, and not forming part of the electrical installation' describes which of the following?

☐ a. Extraneous-conductive-part
☐ b. Exposed-conductive-part
☐ c. Live part
☐ d. Protective conductor

2.5 A residual current device offers protection against which of the following?

☐ a. Earth fault current
☐ b. Overload
☐ c. Short-circuit current
☐ d. Live to neutral faults

2.6 Where equipment is to be installed that must be capable of being submersed in water and withstand a temperature range of -25°C to +5°C the categories of classification of external influences for this equipment must be which of the following?

☐ a. AE3 and AA1
☐ b. AD7 and AA5
☐ c. AD8 and AA3
☐ d. AK2 and BE4

PART 2
Definitions

notes

Things to do and find

1. List the systems or services that will typically require main protective bonding.

2. What is the correct defined term for the part of a fuse designed to melt when the fuse operates?

3. What is the difference between overload and overcurrent?

4. The definition 'installations where protection against electric shock is provided under certain conditions by the value of voltage; installations where the voltage is limited for operational reasons (e.g. telecommunications, signalling, bell, control and alarm installations' describes what category of voltage?

5. What is the difference between Class I and Class II equipment?

6. What earthing system does PME relate to?

7. What is the difference between extra-low voltage and low voltage?

8. Review the earthing systems TN-C-S, TN-S and TT and consider how these systems are installed practically?

Part 3

Assessment of general characteristics

1. Introduction.

Part 3 of *BS 7671* deals with the need for the designer or installer of an electrical installation to assess the general characteristics of the supply and electrical installation. Six chapters, within Part 3, outline the areas that must be assessed and taken into account when protective measures and electrical equipment are being selected and installed. The following table outlines the areas covered by the six chapters in Part 3:

Table 3A

CHAPTER	CHARACTERISTICS TO BE CONSIDERED
Chapter 31	Purpose, Supplies and structure
Chapter 32	Classification of external influences
Chapter 33	Compatibility
Chapter 34	Maintainability
Chapter 35	Safety Services
Chapter 36	Continuity of Service

2. Chapter 31. Purpose, supplies and structure

Before commencing work, whether the work is on a new site or an alteration or addition, it is essential to comply with the requirements of Chapter 31 and esure that specific issues are considered. Failure to address these issues could lead to problems later.

a. Maximum demand and Diversity (311.1)

Maximum demand is the maximum anticipated load of the installation plus an allowance for any future loading. If maximum demand is not determined appropriately the installation or part of it could become overloaded.

Diversity is the factor that allows for the fact that not all electrical equipment in an installation will be in use at the same time. Experience of circuit and equipment usage will help the designer to make informed judgments in relation to expected loads. The following factors should be taken into account:

- Time profiles of electrical loads
- Coincidence of electrical loads
- Mechanical loading of electric motors
- Seasonal changes in loading (particularly heating, lighting and cooling)
- Any special requirements for the particular installation (for example, multiple shower cubicles in public changing rooms).

Maximum demand and diversity are related by the following equation:

Maximum demand = Connected load X Diversity factor

b. Arrangement of live conductors and type of earthing arrangement

The number and type of live conductors for both source and each circuit within the installation (e.g. single-phase, three-phase etc) and the type of earthing (e.g. TN-S, TN-C-S, TT etc) are to be determined when assessing the suitability of a supply and the related installation.

c. Supplies (313.1)

Regulation 313.1 requires the designer of an installation to assess the characteristics of the incoming supply, prior to carrying out new work, alterations or additions. This requirement applies whether the supply is from a Distributor or from a private source (for example a private generator). The characteristics must be determined by calculation, measurement, enquiry or inspection. The following characteristics need to be determined:

(i) The nominal voltage (s) (In most cases this will be 400 V and/or 230 V)

(ii) The nature of the current and frequency (In most cases a.c. and 50 Hz)

(iii) The prospective short-circuit current at the origin of the installation (this subject is covered in Section 434 and Part 6 of this Learning Guide)

(iv) The earth fault loop impedance of that part of the system external to the installation (this is known as the external earth loop impedance (Z_e); this subject is covered in Section 411 and Part 6 of this Learning Guide).

(v) The suitability for the requirements of the system, including maximum demand and

(vi) The type and rating of the overcurrent protective device(s) acting at the origin of the installation.

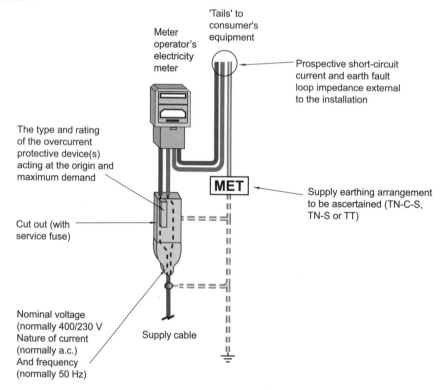

Fig 3.1 Origin of the installation showing the characteristics that need to be identified

d. Supplies for safety services and standby systems

Where an installation has standby safety services such as an emergency lighting system, sprinkler system, standby generator, smoke extract system etc, the requirements for these systems should be separately assessed to ensure the supplies have adequate capacity, reliability, and the correct changeover time for the operation specified.

(This subject is covered along with the requirements of Chapter 35 in Chapter 56 of the Learning Guide).

Fig 3.2 Sprinkler pump house

Key Facts
'Before commencing any new electrical work, alterations or additions, it is essential the type of earthing arrangement is determined'

3. Division of the installation

a. Requirements relating to division of circuits

Regulation Group 314 requires an installation to be divided into circuits, as necessary. Dividing an installation into circuits helps to avoids hazards, facilitates safe inspection, testing and maintenance and minimizes the inconvenience in the event of a fault.

It is imperative, therefore, that careful consideration is given to how many circuits are required for a given electrical installation. It is also important to select the most appropriate overcurrent and fault protection devices and to position them to ensure, as far as possible, that the only circuits to be disconnected are the ones where a fault has occurred.

Exercise 3.1

(1) List three reasons for dividing an installation into circuits (in addition to the ones mentioned above).

---

b. Separate circuits

Separate circuits are required for the following reasons:

(i) So that parts of an installation which are required to be controlled separately, are not affected by the failure of other circuits

(ii) So that the required number of circuits and the number of points supplied by any final circuit meet the requirements of:

- Chapter 43 (Overcurrent protection),
- Section 537 (Isolation and switching) and
- Chapter 52 (Current carrying capacity of conductors).

(iii) So that in a distribution board that has more than one circuit, each final circuit should be connected to a separate way in a distribution board and electrically separate from that of every other circuit to avoid indirect energizing of another final circuit intended to be isolated. In Fig 3.3 below a separate neutral for each circuit is provided and is connected in correct sequence in the distribution board. Fig 3.4 illustrates an incorrectly connected neutral.

Part 3
Assessment of general characteristics

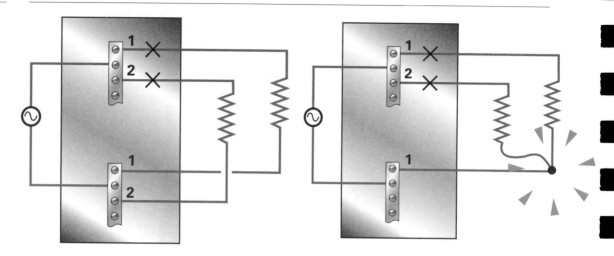

Fig 3.3 Separate neutral connection   Fig 3.4 'Borrowed' or 'crossed' neutral

---

4. Chapter 32 External Influences

An electrical installation or item of equipment should be selected and installed according to the external influences the installation or equipment may be subjected to, e.g. extreme temperatures, exposure to sunlight, water, vibration etc.

For more information relating to External Influences see Part 2 and Section 522 of this Learning Guide.

Exercise 3.2

Write down why you feel Fig 3.4 does not comply with Section 314. What is the solution?

---

5. Chapter 33 Compatibility

The operation of one item of electrical equipment can affect other items of electrical equipment. The harmful effects could be generated internal or external to the installation. Where equipment is liable to have adverse effects on the supply, the distributor should be consulted. An assessment, therefore, has to be made of any characteristics of equipment likely to have harmful effects upon other equipment or services.

Chapter 33 lists 11 different characteristics to be assessed including:

- transient overvoltages
- undervoltages
- unbalanced loads
- starting currents
- harmonic currents
- excessive protective conductor current.

Exercise 3.3

You should now refer to Regulation 331 – make a list of the 6 remaining characteristics not listed above. Select one and find a practical example.

Several of the above items are covered in more depth in other sections within this Learning Guide. For example, the effects of harmonic currents are covered in Appendix 11 and excessive protective conductor currents (not due to a fault) are covered in Section 543.7.

Another factor to be considered when installing electrical equipment is electromagnetic compatibility or EMC. EMC relates to the electromagnetic radiation generated from equipment which can cause other equipment in the vicinity to malfunction or create noise or voltage disturbances. More information relating to EMC can be found in Chapter 44 along with information relating to the effects of voltage disturbances (overvoltages and undervoltages).

6. Chapter 34 Maintainability

Chapter 34 brings to our attention the need for assessing the requirements in relation to the frequency and quality of maintenance, periodic inspection, and testing. This is so that the protective measures, reliability of equipment, and intended life of the installation can be maintained.

7. Chapter 35 Safety services

Further information relating to safety services can be found in Section 56 of this Learning Guide. However it is worth noting that Chapter 35 lists the recognised sources for safety sources:

• Storage batteries
• Primary cells
• Generator sets independent of the normal supply
• A separate feeder of the supply network, independent of the normal supply

8. Chapter 36 Continuity of supply

Chapter 36 requires an assessment to be made for each circuit to determine if there is a need for continuity of service during the intended life of the installation.

An example of this would be a life-support system. For these systems it is important to consider the characteristics relating to the earthing system and protective devices in order to achieve discrimination. The number of circuits, requirements for multiple power supplies and use of monitoring devices are also required to be considered.

Further information relating to Part 3 Assessment of general characteristics can be found in:
• *BS7671* Part 3 and for Safety Services Chapter 56
• Electrical Safety Council Technical Manual articles C121-1, D61-1, E157-9, M29-1, M53-1, M53-5, S13-11, S13-14, S13-17, S13-20 and S13-23
• IEE Guidance Note 1
• NICEIC Snags and solutions Part 2 Wiring systems

PART 3 FINAL REVISION EXERCISE

3.1 Which of the following items of information might you be required to supply to the distributor prior to receiving a connection?
  ☐ a. Maximum demand
  ☐ b. Nominal voltage
  ☐ c. Type and rating of the overcurrent devices at the origin
  ☐ d. External earth fault loop impedance

Part 3
Assessment of general characteristics

3.2 Which one of the following is not a reason given in *BS 7671* for dividing circuits?
- ☐ a. To avoid hazards and minimize inconvenience
- ☐ b. prevent the indirect energizing of a circuit intended to be isolated
- ☐ c. facilitate safe inspection, testing and maintenance
- ☐ d. To make it easier for the owner to carry out functional switching

3.3 Which one of the following is not a characteristic to be considered under the heading compatibility?
- ☐ a. d.c. feedback
- ☐ b. continuity of conductors
- ☐ c. starting currents
- ☐ d. transient overvoltages

3.4 Which one of the following is not recognized as a source for safety services?
- ☐ a. Separate feeder
- ☐ b. Storage batteries
- ☐ c. Distributor's supply without back-up
- ☐ d. Generator sets independent of the normal supply

Things to do and find

1. Make a list of the characteristics to be considered for continuity of service.

2. Give an example of where starting currents may occur.

3. Outline the requirements for the connection of line conductors, related neutrals and circuit protective conductors into a distribution board.

4. When using RCDs in a TT system as the sole measure for earth fault protection, where there are numerous circuits being supplied, what type of RCDs should be provided and where should they be fitted?

5. Describe the problems associated with the dangerous practice of 'borrowing' neutrals.

6. Give four characteristics of the supply that should be determined by calculation, measurement, enquiry or inspection. Which characteristic would the distributor require prior to providing a new connection or alteration/addition?

Part 4
Protection for safety

1. Introduction

Chapter 41 deals with protection against electric shock as applied to electrical installations. This chapter is probably the most difficult of all the chapters in *BS 7671* to understand. However, as Chapter 41 is extremely important it is essential that students spend the time to familiarise themselves with this part of *BS 7671*.

This introductory section of the Learning Guide is intended to cover some of the general principles relating to Chapter 41 and at the same time help to make some of the later sections relating to the specific protective measures easier to understand.

Chapter 41 is based on the internationally accepted document *IEC 61140*, which is the basic safety standard that applies to the protection of persons and livestock. *BS EN 61140* outlines the fundamental rule of protection against electric shock, which is that **hazardous-live-parts must not be accessible** and **accessible conductive parts must not be hazardous live; either under normal conditions without a fault or under single fault conditions.**

The above requirements introduce the concept that to protect persons or livestock against electric shock we need to ensure we protect against two possible types of hazard. In the 16th edition of *BS 7671* these two methods were called direct and indirect contact protection. The 17th edition applies very similar concepts – these now being called basic and fault protection. In line with *BS EN 61140, BS 7671* outlines the methods for protection under fault-free (or normal) conditions this being by basic protective provisions **(basic protection)**, and protection under single fault conditions which is provided by fault protective provisions **(fault protection)**. Alternatively, protection against electric shock may be provided by an enhanced protective provision which provides both basic and fault protection.

Chapter 41 outlines the protective measures that can be applied to ensure the requirements for basic and fault protection have been met. Most of the measures are for general use. However, there are some measures that are only applicable when the installation is controlled or under the supervision of skilled or instructed persons; these measures are covered collectively in Sections 417 and 418 of this Learning Guide.

In addition to the above protection provisions (basic and fault protection) **Additional protection** will be required under certain conditions of external influence and in certain special installations or locations. Additional protection can be provided by residual current devices (RCDs) and/or supplementary equipotential bonding. RCDs may be required to provide additional protection in the event of failure of provision for basic protection and/or the provision for fault protection or carelessness by users. Supplementary equipotential bonding is considered as being additional to fault protection provisions. This subject is discussed further in Section 415 of this Learning Guide.

Before discussing some of the main protective measures it is worth considering the fundamental principles first and establish, in practical terms, what we are trying to protect against.

Key Facts
'Understanding the terms basic protection and fault protection is essential'

2. Basic protection

The information relating to basic protection is outlined in Section 416. However, it is important to have an understanding of these concepts prior to looking at the main protective measures outlined in Section 410; therefore, Section 416 is covered in this section of the Learning Guide. As discussed above, basic protection relates to a protective provision under fault-free (or normal) conditions. This means we need to protect persons or livestock from contact with live parts and therefore prevent them receiving an electric shock.

Chapter 41
Protection against electric shock (Sections 410 and 416)

Direct contact electric shocks are normally of two types; contact with a live conductor whilst in contact with Earth or contact with live conductors at different potentials. The diagrams below illustrate these situations:

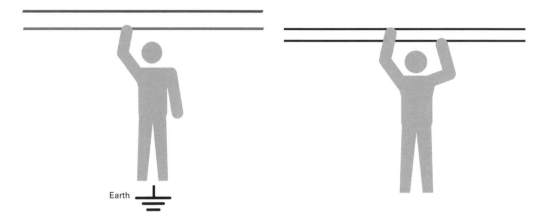

Fig 410.1 Contact with a live conductor whilst in contact with Earth conductors

Fig 410.2 Contact with live conductors at different potentials

To protect against persons or livestock receiving shocks by contact with live parts (as illustrated above) the normal methods are to either insulate the live parts or to prevent contact with live parts by providing a barrier or enclosure.

a. Basic insulation of live parts

Live parts must be completely covered with insulation which can only be removed by destruction and which is capable of durably withstanding the electrical, mechanical, thermal and chemical stresses to which it may be subjected in service.

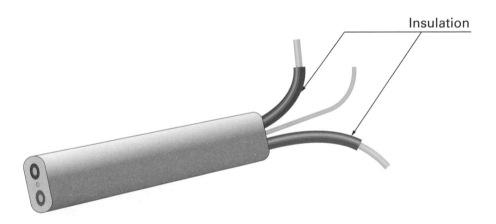

Fig 410.3 Basic protection provided by insulation of conductors

The insulation of factory-built equipment should comply with the relevant product standard. Factory-built equipment includes items such as switchgear, busbars, controlgear, luminaires and accessories. Most factory-built low-voltage equipment is either pre-assembled, or designed for assembly on site in accordance with the manufacturers' instructions. Special consideration needs to be given whenever factory-built equipment is modified.

b. Barriers or enclosures

The principle of this provision is to place live parts behind a barrier or inside an enclosure, the intention being to prevent contact with live parts by persons or livestock. A barrier or enclosure is required to provide basic protection if it contains live parts, except where such protection is provided by other means. Examples of such other means are SELV or insulation of the live parts.

A **barrier** provides protection from contact with live parts from any **usual** direction of access; an **enclosure** provides protection from contact with live parts from **any** direction.

Distribution board having bare live parts placed behind barriers

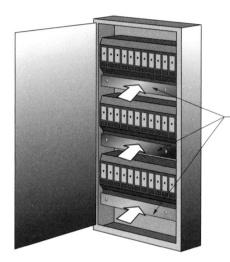

Barriers provide basic protection from contact with live parts from any **usual** direction of access

Fig 410.4 Protection by barriers

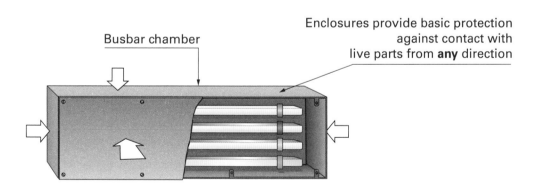

Busbar chamber

Enclosures provide basic protection against contact with live parts from **any** direction

Fig 410.5 Protection by enclosures

The definitions for barriers or enclosures in *BS 7671* actually talks about *'protection against certain external influences'*. External influences are covered in detail in Part 2 of this Learning Guide and Section 522 and Appendix 5 of BS 7671. It may be worth referring to the Part 2 before continuing although a brief explanation of the subject, specifically relating to barriers or enclosures, is given below.

Chapter 41
Protection against electric shock (Sections 410 and 416)

A degree of protection of at least **IP2X** or **IPXXB** is required by the Regulations where a barrier or enclosure is to provide basic protection. Furthermore, a degree of protection of at least **IPXXD** or **IP4X** is required for any readily accessible horizontal top surface of a barrier or enclosure. These requirements are summarized in the table below:

Table 410A (Learning guide table) IP codes for barriers or enclosures

Applicable surface(s) of the enclosure or barrier	IP Code designation	Brief description of protection provided against access to live parts
All except a readily accessible top surface	IP2X or IPXXB	Protection against access to live parts with a finger or a solid object of 12.5 mm diameter and greater. Protection against access to live parts with a test finger at least 12 mm in diameter and 80 mm long.
Readily accessible top surface	IP4X or IPXXD	Protection against access to live parts with a straight wire or strip of more than 1.0 mm diameter or thickness

Where, for operational or maintenance purposes, it is necessary to remove a barrier, open an enclosure or remove a part of an enclosure at least one of the following requirements should be met:

- Removal or opening is possible only by the use of a key or a tool,
- An arrangement such as a door-interlocked isolator is provided to prevent live parts being accessible,
- An intermediate barrier is provided, affording degree of protection of at least IP2X or IPXXB and only removable by the use of a tool.

Exersise 41.1

(1) What should be fitted where an item of equipment that may retain a charge is installed behind a barrier or in an enclosure? (2) What is the required IP degree of protection for an horizontal top surface of a barrier or enclosure?

If, behind a barrier or in an enclosure, an item of equipment, such as a capacitor is installed which may retain a charge after it has been switched off, a warning label should be provided.

3. Fault protection

Part 4 does not contain a specific section relating to fault protection, the requirements being given in the sections covering each protective measure. This Learning Guide will also explain the fault protection requirements separately in the different sections covering the protection measures. However, below is a short explanation of the general principles relating to fault protection.

Fault protection is defined as:

'Protection against electric shock under single fault conditions'

From the above it can be seen that fault protection is a provision that is applicable once a fault has occurred. The diagram below shows a typical situation where a fault has occurred between a live part and an exposed-conductive-part (see Part 2 of *BS 7671* for definitions of live part and exposed-conductive-part).

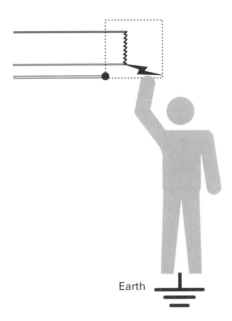

Fig 410.6 Typical situation requiring fault protection

The fault protection provisions used in Part 4 of *BS 7671* to protect against electric shock vary and need to be studied in relation to each protective measure. In the most common protective measure, automatic disconnection of supply, the circuit is designed to ensure that a large enough current flows when a fault occurs and the protective device opens very quickly (apart from a single fault in IT systems). With the protective measure double or reinforced insulation, equipment is insulated to a degree such that a fault in the basic insulation cannot result in a person receiving a shock. These protective measures and others will be discussed in Sections 411, 412, 413 and 414 of this Learning Guide.

Exercise 41.2

Refer to *BS7671* Regulation 410.3.9. - List three items of metalwork which are part of an electrical installation but do not require fault protection provision.

---

4. Protective measures

Four main protective measures are listed in Chapter 41 of *BS 7671*. These protective measures must consist of:

- An appropriate combination of a provision for basic protection and an independent provision for fault protection, *or*
- An enhanced protective provision which provides both basic and fault protection

From the above it can be seen that both basic and fault protection must be provided. Some protective measures have two distinct and separate measures providing basic and fault protection; other measures will provide for both basic and fault by a combined measure.

The four main protective measures are:

- Automatic disconnection of supply (Section 411)
- Double or reinforced insulation (Section 412)
- Electrical separation for the supply of one item of current-using equipment (Section 413)
- Extra-low voltage provided by SELV or PELV (Section 414)

Information relating to the protective measures can be found in Sections 411, 412, 413 and 414 of this Learning Guide. However, the following chart provides an outline of all the safety measures listed in Chapter 41 **(except for measures and provisions that are only allowed where the electrical installation is controlled or supervised by skilled or instructed persons).**

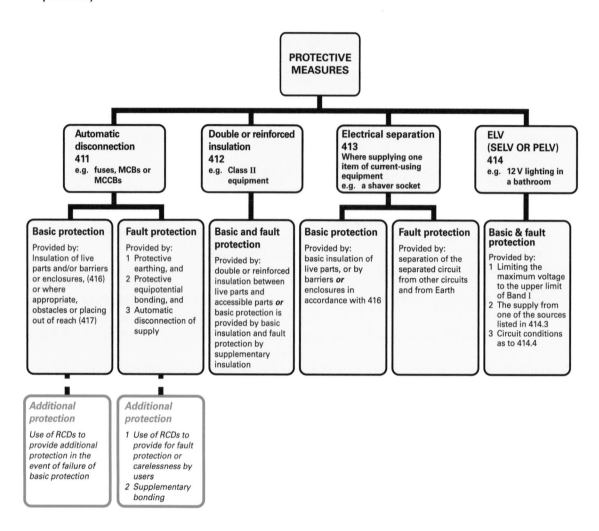

Further information relating to Protection against electric shock can be found in:

- Chapter 41 of *BS 7671*
- Electrical Safety Council Technical Manual articles: D41-1, D41-5, E65-1, E65-5, I41-5 and P153-1
- IEE Guidance Note 5

CHAPTER 41 FINAL REVISION EXERCISE

41.1 **Which of the following provides basic protection?**
- ☐ a. Protective bonding
- ☐ b. RCDs
- ☐ c. FELV
- ☐ d. Insulation of live parts

41.2 **Which of the following is not a protective measure?**
- ☐ a. Placing out of reach
- ☐ b. SELV
- ☐ c. Electrical separation
- ☐ d. Automatic disconnection of supply

41.3 **Which of the following is not a basic protection provision?**
- ☐ a. Placing out of reach
- ☐ b. Insulation of live parts
- ☐ c. Protective bonding
- ☐ d. Barriers or enclosures

41.4 **Which of the following may provide additional protection?**
- ☐ a. Placing out of reach
- ☐ b. Insulation of live parts
- ☐ c. Non-conducting location
- ☐ d. RCDs

41.5 **A barrier or enclosure requires a degree of protection to at least:**
- ☐ a. IP2X
- ☐ b. IPX2
- ☐ c. IP4X
- ☐ d. IP44

41.6 **For basic protection provision a readily accessible top surface requires a degree of protection to at least:**
- ☐ a. IP2X
- ☐ b. IPX2
- ☐ c. IP4X
- ☐ d. IP44

Things to do and find

1. What are the two types of provision that are required by a protective measure?

2. Provide an example of where the protective provision insulation of live parts might be used.

3. Provide an example where the protective provision barriers might be used.

notes

4. List the four main protective measures.

5. What are the specific requirements in relation to personnel where obstacles and placing out of reach are to be used?

6. Name three examples of coverings/coatings that are not acceptable for provision for basic protection.

1. Introduction

Automatic disconnection of supply is by far the most commonly used protective measure. As discussed previously in Section 410, for all protective measures to be effective they must provide elements for both basic and fault protection.

The protective measure automatic disconnection of supply provides basic protection by basic insulation of live parts or barriers or enclosures (see Section 410 of this Learning Guide).

Automatic disconnection of supply provides fault protection by protective earthing, protective bonding and automatic disconnection in the case of a fault. In the 16th edition of *BS 7671* this protective measure was referred to as EEBAD, this is now likely to be referred to as ADS (Automatic Disconnection of Supply) which is a protective measure description in *BS 7671*. It is very important that the theory behind the measure ADS is understood.

> ### Exercise 411.1
>
> Before continuing it is suggested that you should now refer to the section covering Part 2 (Definitions) and review the definitions for 'exposed-conductive-parts', 'extraneous-conductive-parts' along with TN-C-S, TN-S and TT earthing systems.

For this measure to work effectively when an earth fault occurs, the current must be large enough to operate the protective device (e.g. fuse, circuit-breaker, residual current device, etc) disconnecting the circuit in which the fault occurs within a specified time.

The protective measure automatic disconnection of supply has three elements that work together to reduce the risk of electric shock. The three elements are:

- Protective earthing
- Protective equipotential bonding
- Automatic disconnection in case of a fault

Protective earthing of exposed-conductive-parts maintain the exposed-conductive-parts at, or as close as possible to Earth potential, and provide an effective low-impedance path for any earth fault current to return safely to its source.

Protective equipotential bonding is established by connecting extraneous-conductive-parts to the main earthing terminal by use of protective bonding conductors. The purpose of bonding is to minimize potential differences between exposed-conductive-parts and extraneous-conductive-parts during an earth fault.

Automatic disconnection of supply is required to take place when an earth fault occurs. The disconnection should take place within prescribed maximum times, thus limiting the duration for which a potentially hazardous fault condition might exist.

When a fault of negligible impedance occurs between a line conductor and an exposed-conductive-part or a protective conductor in a circuit or equipment, the potential of the metalwork is raised to a level which is likely to be dangerous. It is for this reason that Regulation 411.3.2.1 requires the protective device to automatically interrupt the supply to the line conductor connected to a circuit or equipment.

The diagram below illustrates a line to earth fault. For simplification the effects of the external supply are ignored in this case.

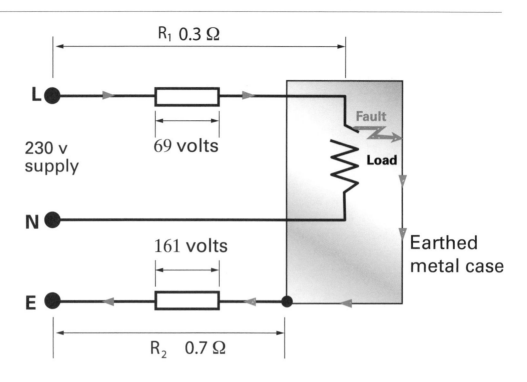

Fig 411.1 Line to earth fault on a simple circuit

Current flow on fault:

$$I = \frac{V}{R_1 + R_2} = \frac{230}{0.3 + 0.7} = 230 \text{ A}$$

Volt drop across line conductor, $R_1 = I \times R_1$

$$= 230 \times 0.3 \quad = \quad 69 \text{ VOLTS}$$

Volt drop across protective conductor, $R_2 = I \times R_2$

$$= 230 \times 0.7 \quad = \quad 161 \text{ VOLTS}$$

Fig 411.1 and related calculation above, illustrate that the line and protective conductors form what is known as a potential divider. In some cases, such as flat twin and earth cables, the circuit protective conductor will have a smaller cross-sectional area than the associated line and neutral conductors. A smaller cross-sectional area means a higher resistance and this in turn leads to a higher proportion of the total supply voltage appearing across the circuit protective conductor under fault conditions. It is important to ensure, therefore, that rapid disconnection occurs. The following text will outline how we design the earthing system to ensure it works effectively under earth fault conditions.

Note: For some circuits and locations there may be a requirement for additional protection by the use of residual current devices (RCDs) and/or supplementary equipotential bonding. For further information relating to additional protection see Section 415 of *BS 7671* or this Learning Guide.

2. Protective earthing and protective equipotential bonding (411.3.1)

It is important to note that the protective measure automatic disconnection of supply requires both protective earthing and protective bonding to work effectively. This is an important consideration for both new installations and alterations and additions.

> **Exercise 411.2**
>
> You should now refer to Regulation 131.8. What are the requirements for earthing and bonding in relation to alterations and additions?

a. Protective earthing

All metalwork, that is defined as an exposed-conductive-part, is required to be connected to a protective conductor. Simultaneously accessible exposed-conductive-parts should be connected to the same earthing system individually, in groups or collectively.

The term protective conductor is the generic term covering all types of protective conductors, such as earthing conductor, circuit protective conductor, protective bonding conductor and supplementary equipotential bonding conductor. Further information relating to protective conductors can be found in Chapter 54 of *BS 7671* and this Learning Guide and it is worth reviewing this Chapter before continuing.

Apart from suspended lampholders, having no exposed-conductive-parts, a circuit protective conductor should be run to and terminated at each point in the wiring and at each accessory.

b. Protective equipotential bonding

Chapter 54 (Section 544) provides the details relating to the sizing of protective bonding conductors. The requirement for the connection of protective bonding conductors between the main earthing terminal (MET) and extraneous-conductive-parts is provided in Regulation 411.3.1.2.

As discussed previously, the term 'extraneous-conductive-part' is defined in Part 2. The definition is given below as a reminder:

> 'Extraneous-conductive-part: A conductive part liable to introduce a potential, generally earth potential, and not forming part of the electrical installation.

There are two elements that need to be satisfied for an item to be classed as an 'extraneous-conductive-part'. First, it must be conductive and second it must be liable to introduce a potential. It is important to understand this principle, as decisions often need to be made as to which items in an installation require protective equipotential bonding.

Within an installation, the following items are likely to be classed as extraneous-conductive-parts and will, therefore, require a protective bonding connection (between the extraneous-conductive part and the main earthing terminal):

(i)   Water installation pipes

(ii) Gas installation pipes

(iii) Other installation pipework and ducting (such as oil tank incoming pipework)

(iv) Central heating and air conditioning systems*

(v)   Exposed metallic structural parts of the building

(vi) Lightning protective system (in accordance with *BS EN 62305*)

Section 411
Protective measure: Automatic disconnection of supply

Where an installation serves more than one building the above requirement should be applied to each building.

To comply with the requirements of *BS 7671* it is also necessary to apply bonding to any metallic sheath of a telecommunications cable. However the consent of the owner or operator of the cable must be obtained.

*This will normally only apply where the central heating system is entering the property from outside (such as combined heat and power schemes), but not where the central heating pipe-work is fed from the water and/or gas service pipes and they have already been connected to protective bonding conductors.

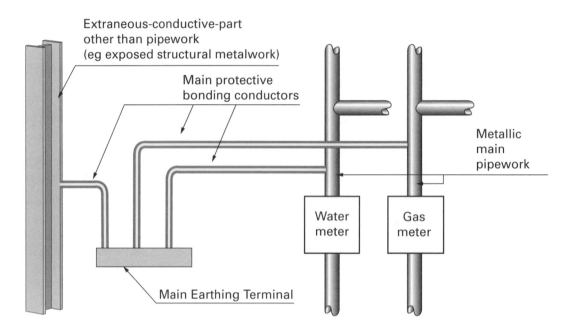

Fig 411.2 Typical connections of Main protective bonding conductors between extraneous-conductive-parts and the main earthing terminal

3. Automatic disconnection in case of a fault (411.3.2)

a. Introduction

Regulation Group 411.3, relating to automatic disconnection in case of a fault, provides some general conditions. This is followed by specific requirements relating to:

- TN systems (411.4)
- TT systems (411.5)
- IT systems (411.6)
- Functional Extra-low Voltage (FELV) (411.7) and
- Reduced low voltage systems (411.8)

The above Regulation Groups will be covered within this topic (411), with each item being given a separate section.

b. Maximum disconnection times

Table 41.1 of *BS7671* (reproduced below) provides the maximum disconnection times for final circuits not exceeding 32 A. It should be noted that the previous requirements for different disconnection times relating to circuits supplying fixed and non-fixed (portable) equipment no longer exists.

Table 41.1 (Reproduced from *BS 7671*) Maximum disconnection times (Regulation 411.3.2.2)

System	50 V < U_O ≤ 120 V seconds		120 V < U_O ≤ 230 V seconds		230 V < U_O ≤ 400 V seconds		U_O > 400 V seconds	
	a.c	d.c	a.c	d.c	a.c	d.c	a.c	d.c
TN	0.8	Note 1	0.4	5	0.2	0.4	0.1	0.1
TT	0.3	Note 1	0.2	0.4	0.07	0.2	0.04	0.1

U_O is the nominal a.c. rms or d.c. line voltage to Earth.

Note 1: Disconnection is not required for protection against electric shock but may be required for other reasons, such as protection against thermal effects.

Note 2: Where compliance with this regulation is provided by an RCD, the disconnection times in accordance with Table 41.1 relate to the prospective residual fault currents significantly higher than the rated residual operating current of the RCD (typically 2 $I_{\Delta n}$).

From Table 41.1 it can be seen that for a TN system between 120 V and 230 V (a.c.) the maximum disconnection time is given as 0.4 seconds. For a TT system (at the same voltage) this would be 0.2 seconds. However, in a TT system where the disconnection is achieved by an overcurrent device and protective equipotential bonding is connected to all extraneous-conductive-parts within the installation, the times can be the same as a TN system.

Exercise 411.3

You should now refer to Table 41.1. Q1. What is the maximum disconnection time for an a.c. circuit with a nominal voltage of 110 V connected to a TT system?
Q2. What is the maximum disconnection time for an a.c. circuit with a nominal voltage of 390 V in a TN system?

It should be noted that:

• In a TN system where a circuit is not covered by Regulation 411.3.2.2 and Table 41.1 (e.g. a final circuit exceeding 32 A or a distribution circuit), a disconnection time not exceeding 5 s is permitted.

• In a TT system where a circuit is not covered by the above Regulation (e.g. a final circuit exceeding 32 A or a distribution circuit), a disconnection time not exceeding 1 s is permitted.

• In circuits where, following a fault to a protective conductor or earth, the output voltage of the source is reduced to 50 V a.c. or 120 V d.c., in not more than the time required by the above Table or notes, automatic disconnection is not required. However, there may be reasons why disconnection is required for reasons other than electric shock (for example protection against fire).

• Where the disconnection times prescribed in Section 411.3 cannot be achieved by Regulation 411.3.2.2, 411.3.2.3 and 411.3.2.4 supplementary bonding must be installed.

c. Earth fault loop impedance

In the above section, disconnection times were outlined for different earthing systems, voltages and types of circuit. Designers, installers or inspectors of electrical installations have to ensure that the required times will be met. The correct disconnection time of each type and size of protective device is related to the earth fault loop impedance (Z_S), measured in ohms (Ω). Earth fault loop impedance (Z_S) is a characteristic vital to the protective measure Automatic Disconnection of supply (ADS). The value of the earth fault loop impedance will determine the current that will flow when an earth fault occurs and this (the value of the current) will determine the time taken for the protective device to disconnect (*automatic disconnection*).

Earth fault loop impedance (Z_S) is the impedance of the intended path of an earth fault current (known as the earth fault loop) starting and ending at the point of the fault to earth.

d. Composition of the earth fault loop

The earth fault loop comprises the following, starting at the point of the fault:

(i) the circuit protective conductor (cpc),

(ii) the Main Earthing Terminal (MET) and earthing conductor of the installation,

(iii) for TN systems, the metallic return path,

(iv) for a TT system, the return path through the conductive mass of Earth,

(v) the path through the earthed neutral point of the transformer (or other source of energy, such as a diesel generator set or uninterruptible power supply (UPS)),

(vi) the transformer winding (or the equivalent in another source of energy), and

(vii) the line conductor from the transformer (or other source of energy) to the point of fault.

As indicated in items (iii) and (iv), the nature of the return path to the source of energy differs fundamentally, depending on whether the installation forms part of a TN system or part of a TT system. Note: (Different earthing systems are covered in Part 2 of *BS 7671* and this Learning Guide)

We can now look at some diagrams illustrating the earth loop impedance path for the most common earthing arrangements.

e. TN Systems (411.4)

In a TN system, the return path is metallic, and is formed by the protective conductor of the supply network - either a combined protective and neutral (PEN) conductor (TN-C-S or TN-C system) or a dedicated protective conductor (TN-S system). The diagrams below illustrate the earth loop impedance path for each earthing arrangement.

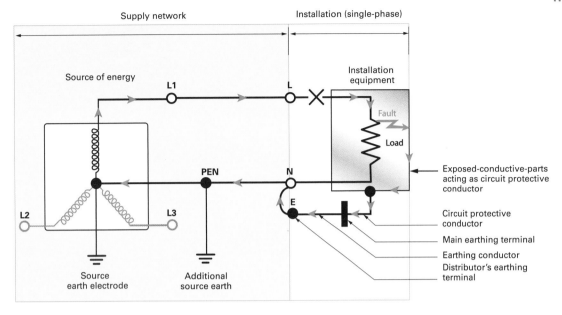

➤   Denotes path of fault current
✗   Denotes circuit-protective device (overcurrent)

Fig 411.3 TN-C-S earth fault loop (showing earth fault path)

As stated earlier, the earth fault loop of a TN-C-S system, as shown in the figure above, is typical of the earth fault loop of all types of TN system, in that it is wholly made up of metallic conductors.

The earth fault loops of the other types of TN system (TN-C and TN-S), whilst still being wholly metallic, differ from that of a TN-C-S system in the following respects:

• In a TN-C system, the circuit protective conductor is combined with the neutral conductor of the installation in a PEN conductor. However, as the Electricity Safety, Quality and Continuity Regulations (ESQCR) prohibit the use of PEN conductors in consumers' installations, no further reference will be made to this system in this section.

• In a TN-S system, the return path to the source of energy is through a dedicated protective conductor of the supply, not through a combined protective and neutral (PEN) conductor.

Section 411
Protective measure: Automatic disconnection of supply

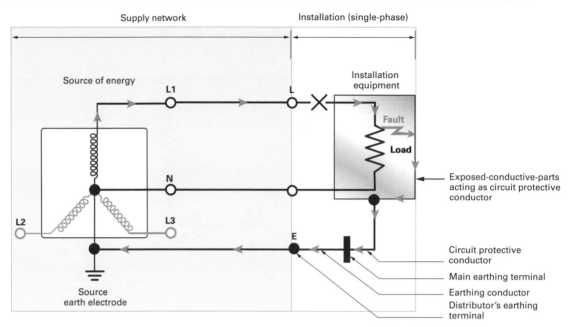

> Denotes path of fault current
X Denotes circuit-protective device (overcurrent)

Fig 411.4 TN-S earth fault loop (showing earth fault path)

As can be seen from the above diagram the earth return and supply neutral are separate conductors.

f. Maximum value of earth fault loop impedance

The ohmic value of the earth fault loop impedance at the most remote point of each circuit is required to not exceed the limiting (or maximum) value permitted by the application of Regulation 411.4.5. which includes the following formula:

$$Z_s \times I_a \leq U_o$$

Where:

Z_s is the impedance in ohms (Ω) (as outlined in 3d above),

I_a is the current in amperes (A) causing the automatic operation of the disconnecting device within the time specified in Table 41.1 of Regulation 411.3.2.2 or as appropriate Regulation 411.3.2.3. For an RCD acting as the disconnecting device the current Ia is the rated residual operating current providing the disconnection times required by Table 41.1 or Regulation 411.3.2.3

U_o is the nominal a.c. rms or d.c. line voltage to Earth in volts (V)

The intention is that, in the event of an earth fault of negligible impedance, between a line conductor and an exposed-conductive-part, the fault current will be of sufficient magnitude to cause the protective device to automatically disconnect the supply to the faulty circuit within the maximum time permitted by the Regulations. To save time having to apply the above calculation, **Tables 41.2, 41.3, and 41.4** have been produced in Section 411 of *BS 7671* for common overcurrent protective device types and sizes. Disconnection times for a range of overcurrent protective devices can also be ascertained by checking the time/current characteristic curves in Appendix 3.

Table 41.2 relates to fuses, with values of earth fault loop impedance for a nominal voltage U_o of 230 V and a maximum disconnection time of 0.4 seconds.

Exercise 411.4

You should now refer to Table 41.2. What is the maximum Z_S value for a 20 A *BS 1361* fuse? What is the maximum Z_S value for a 32 A *BS EN 60269-2* fuse? Now check these values by looking at the curves in Appendix 3.

Table 41.3 relates to circuit-breakers to *BS EN 60898* and the overcurrent element of RCBOs to *BS EN 61009* for a nominal voltage of 230 V. The maximum values of earth fault loop impedance provided in this table will provide for disconnection of the circuit-breaker or RCBO in what is known as the 'instantaneous operation' which is 0.1 second. The three types of circuit-breakers to *BS EN 60898* (Type B, C & D), have different characteristics and, therefore, three different values of maximum earth fault loop impedance are required.

Exercise 411.5

You should now refer to Table 41.3. What is the maximum Z_S value for a 32 A Type B circuit-breaker? What is the maximum Z_S value for a 32 A Type C circuit-breaker?
What is the maximum Z_S value for a 63 A Type D circuit-breaker

Table 41.4 relates to fuses and the values of earth fault loop impedance are for a nominal voltage U_O of 230 V for a maximum disconnection time of 5 seconds.

Exercise 411.6

You should now refer to Table 41.4. What is the maximum Z_S value for a 20 A *BS 1361* fuse? What is the maximum Z_S value for a 32 A *BS 88-2* fuse? How do these values compare to the values obtained from Table 41.2? Why are they different?

It should be noted that if the above values are being measured and the conductors are not at their normal operating temperature, a note below Tables 41.2, 41.3 and 41.4, indicates that these measured values will need to be adjusted accordingly. The adjustment factor will depend on the type of cable being tested and the temperature of the conductor at the time of the test. A typical example would be where an allowance is made for a variation between the temperature of conductors when tested (not loaded or lightly loaded) at 20 $^\circ$C and the normal operating temperature at 70 $^\circ$C (for a thermoplastic (PVC) cable). This example would require the tested figure to be divided by 0.8 and this (higher) figure checked against the tables in *BS 7671*.

g. TT systems (411.5)

In a TT system, the return path to the source of energy is the earth return path, comprising the installation earth electrode, the conductive (or general) mass of Earth and the source earth electrode.

Section 411
Protective measure: Automatic disconnection of supply

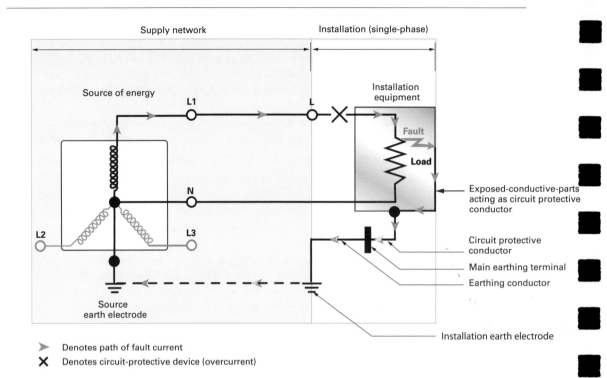

Fig 411.5 TT system - earth fault loop impedance path

In a TT system, shown above, fault current will flow through the exposed-conductive-part, through the circuit protective conductor to the Main Earthing Terminal (MET) and through the earthing conductor to the means of earthing. In the case of a TT system, the means of earthing is an installation earth electrode. The fault current return path to the source of the supply continues via the general mass of Earth and the source earth electrode because a TT system has no direct metallic connection between the MET of the electrical installation and the earthed point of the source of supply.

In most cases, due to the high resistance of the earth fault current path via the general mass of Earth, it will usually not be possible to fulfill the disconnection time requirements of Table 41.1 for automatic disconnection by means of an overcurrent protective device. Under such conditions, Regulation 411.5.2 requires protection to be provided by an RCD.

Where an RCD is used for fault protection in a TT system, Regulation 411.5.3 states in addition to the disconnection requirements of 411.3 the conditions of the following formula must be met:

$$R_A \times I_{\Delta n} \leq 50 \text{ V}$$

Where:

R_A is the sum of the resistances of the earth electrode and the protective conductor(s) connecting it to the exposed-conductive-part

$I_{\Delta n}$ is the rated operating current of the RCD

Table 41.5, derived from Table 41.5 of *BS 7671*, illustrated below, provides maximum values of earth loop impedance (Z_S) to ensure RCD operation in accordance with Regulation 411.5.3 for non-delayed type RCDs to *BS EN 61008* and *BS EN 61009* for final circuits not exceeding 32 A.

Table 41.5 (Learning Guide Table) Maximum values of earth fault loop impedance for RCDs

Rated residual operating current (mA)	Maximum earth fault loop impedance Zs (ohms)		
	$50\ V < U_o \leq 120\ V$	$120\ V < U_o \leq 230\ V$	$230\ V < U_o \leq 400\ V$
30	1667*		1533*
100	500*		460*
300	167*		153*
500	100		92

* It should be noted that the earth electrode resistance should be kept as low as practicable and a value not exceeding 200 Ω is recommended.

h. IT System (411.6)

An IT system is defined as a system having no direct connection between live parts and Earth, the exposed-conductive-parts of the electrical installation being earthed. Because IT systems are only used for special applications it will not be covered in detail in this Learning Guide.

Although IT systems are covered by *Protective measure: automatic disconnection of supply (Section 411),* in the event of a single fault to an exposed-conductive-part automatic disconnection of supply is not required, provided certain conditions are met. These conditions include limiting the voltages between line conductor(s) and exposed-conductive-parts and monitoring and/or protective devices.

> **REFER to BS7671**
>
> For further information relating to IT systems refer to Regulation Group 411.6

i. Functional Extra-low voltage (FELV) (411.7)

The term Functional Extra-Low Voltage (FELV) was referred to in Part 2 Definitions. Where an extra-low voltage system does not meet all the requirements of SELV or PELV systems, supplementary provisions are required. This combination of provisions is known as FELV. In a FELV system, extra-low voltage is used for purely functional reasons although its use may have safety benefits.

The source for a FELV system should be either as per SELV or PELV requirements or be supplied from a transformer with at least simple separation.

The protection against electric shock requirements are generally the same as for low-voltage circuits. Basic protection is provided by either basic insulation or barriers or enclosures (see section 410 of this Learning Guide or Section 416 of *BS 7671*). Where the primary circuit is subject to protection by automatic disconnection of supply, the exposed-conductive-parts of the equipment of FELV circuit should be connected to the protective conductor of the primary circuit of the source.

j. Reduced low voltage systems

Where for functional reasons the use of extra-low voltage is impracticable and there is no requirement for SELV or PELV, a reduced low voltage system may be used. These systems are often used on construction and demolition sites as well as for supplies to equipment in industrial installations.

Section 411
Protective measure: Automatic disconnection of supply

The definition of a reduced low voltage system was covered in Part 2 (definitions). In these systems the nominal voltage is limited to 110 V a.c. rms between phases and this means the maximum voltage to earth is 63.5 V for a three-phase system and 55 V for a single phase system.

Basic protection is required and should be provided by basic insulation and/or barriers or enclosures.

Fault protection by automatic disconnection of supply follows the requirements for low voltage systems with an overcurrent protective device in each line conductor or by a residual current device and all exposed-conductive-parts being connected to earth.

A maximum disconnection time of 5 seconds is required at every point of utilization (including socket-outlets). Where a circuit-breaker is used, the maximum earth fault loop impedances values can be derived by the formula in 411.4.5 or, for the most common overcurrent device types and ratings, Table 41.6 provides the maximum earth fault loop impedance values for U_O of 55 V and 63.5 V. Where a fuse is used Table 41.6 should be used for a disconnection time of 5 seconds.

Exercise 411.7

You should now refer to Table 41.6 of *BS 7671* What is the maximum Z_S value for a 32 A Type C circuit breaker (U_O of 55 V)? What is the maximum Z_S value for a 20 A *BS 88-2.1* fuse (U_O of 63.5 V)?

Plugs, Socket-outlets, LSC, DCL and cable couplers of a reduced low voltage system must have a protective conductor contact and not be compatible with any plug, socket-outlet or cable coupler for use at any other voltage or frequency in the same premises.

Further information relating to Protective measure: Automatic disconnection of supply can be found in:
- *BS 7671 Section 411*
- Electrical Safety Council Technical Manual articles E13-5, E57-9, E57-13, E57-19, F13-14, I17-15 and R101-29
- *IEE Guidance Note 5*

SECTION 411 FINAL REVISION EXERCISE

411.1 The maximum disconnection time for a TT system where shock protection is provided by an RCD with a nominal voltage of 230 V a.c. is which of the following:
- ☐ a. 0.2 s
- ☐ b. 0.4 s
- ☐ c. 1 s
- ☐ d. 5 s

411.2 The maximum disconnection time for a TN system with a nominal voltage of 400 V a.c. is which of the following:
- ☐ a. 0.2 s
- ☐ b. 0.4 s
- ☐ c. 1 s
- ☐ d. 5 s

411.3 The maximum earth fault loop impedance for 0.4 s disconnection time with U_o of 230 V for a *BS 1361* 20 A fuse is which of the following:
- ☐ a. 1.15 Ω
- ☐ b. 1.7 Ω
- ☐ c. 1.77 Ω
- ☐ d. 2.80 Ω

411.4 The maximum earth fault loop impedance for 0.4 s or 5 s disconnection time with U_o of 230 V for a *BS EN 60898* Type C 32 A circuit-breaker is which of the following:
- ☐ a. 0.36 Ω
- ☐ b. 0.57 Ω
- ☐ c. 0.72 Ω
- ☐ d. 1.44 Ω

411.5 The maximum earth fault loop impedance for 5 s disconnection time with U_o of 230 V for a *BS 88* 160A fuse is which of the following:
- ☐ a. 0.19 Ω
- ☐ b. 0.25 Ω
- ☐ c. 0.33 Ω
- ☐ d. 0.70 Ω

411.6 The maximum earth fault loop impedance to ensure RCD operation in accordance with Regulation 411.5.3 for a non-delayed RCD to *BS EN 61008* with a rated residual operating current of 100 mA with U_o of 230 V is which of the following:
- ☐ a. 100 Ω
- ☐ b. 460 Ω
- ☐ c. 500 Ω
- ☐ d. 1667 Ω

notes

Things to do and find

1. List four examples of extraneous-conductive-parts that may require protective bonding.

2. What types of basic protection are generally used with the protective measure automatic disconnection of supply?

3. In which Chapter of *BS 7671* would you find the information in relation to the sizing of protective conductors?

4. List the items that constitute an earth fault loop for a TN-S system.

5. Which table in Appendix 3 covers Type C circuit-breakers to *BS EN 60898*?

6. Give two examples of locations you might expect to find a reduced low voltage system.

7. In what way does a FELV supply differ from a SELV supply?

8. What is the maximum earth fault loop impedance (5 s disconnection time) for a circuit with a Uo of 55 V protected by a *BS EN 60898* Type C 63 A circuit-breaker?

9. Refer to Appendix 3. What is the disconnection time of a 45 A BS 3036 semi-enclosed fuse carrying 580 A?

1. Introduction

The protective measure double or reinforced insulation relies on the use of equipment, meeting certain requirements, and having no exposed metal parts on which a dangerous voltage could appear in the event of a failure in the basic insulation of a live part. The requirements relating to double or reinforced insulation can be found in Section 412 of *BS 7671*.

Generally, the measure applies to individual items of equipment, such as luminaires, other current-using equipment, and assemblies of switchgear and controlgear, meeting the requirements. Where it is intended to use double or reinforced insulation as the sole protective measure in an installation it must be under effective supervision in normal use so that no change is made that would impair the effectiveness of the protective measure.

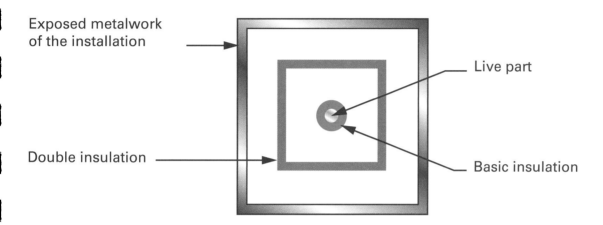

Fig 412.1 Illustration of double insulation

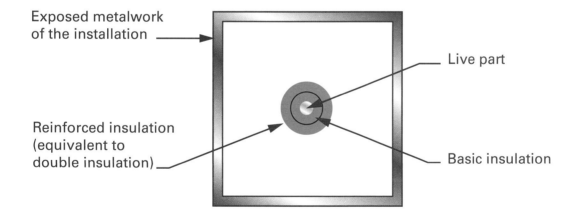

Fig 412.2 Illustration of reinforced insulation

2. Basic and fault protection

Where basic and fault protection are considered separately for some protective measures, in the case of double or reinforced insulation the two can be considered together. There are two ways that basic and fault protection can be provided depending upon the type of insulation that has been applied to the electrical equipment (see above illustrations). In the first case basic protection is provided by basic insulation and fault protection is provided by supplementary insulation. In the second case both basic and fault protection is provided by reinforced insulation (between live parts and accessible parts).

Section 412
Protective measure: Double or reinforced insulation

3. Electrical equipment and enclosures

Normally, electrical equipment will be manufactured and marked to the relevant product standard and it is important that the type of insulation is ascertained and any installation instructions are followed. The following symbol identifies equipment that has been type-tested as Class II (electrical equipment having double or reinforced insulation)

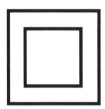

Fig 412.3 Class II equipment construction mark

Where electrical equipment only has basic insulation, supplementary* or reinforced insulation* will have to be applied to the equipment in the process of erecting the electrical installation or the equipment will have to be contained in an insulating enclosure.

*Where supplementary or reinforced insulation has been applied in the process of erecting electrical equipment with basic insulation the following symbol should be fixed in a visible position on the interior or exterior of the enclosure to indicate that the equipment should not be connected to a protective conductor.

Fig 412.4 Symbol -Do not connect circuit protective conductor

> **Exercise 412.1**
>
> Refer to *BS7671* and Regulations 412.2.1.2 and 412.2.1.3 and Regulation Group 412.2.2 for more information relating to insulation applied during erection and enclosures.

Apart from where this protective measure is used as the sole protective measure within an installation, a circuit supplying one or more items of Class II equipment should have a circuit protective conductor run to and terminated at each point in wiring and at each accessory. This provision is intended to take account of possible future changes from Class II to Class I equipment.

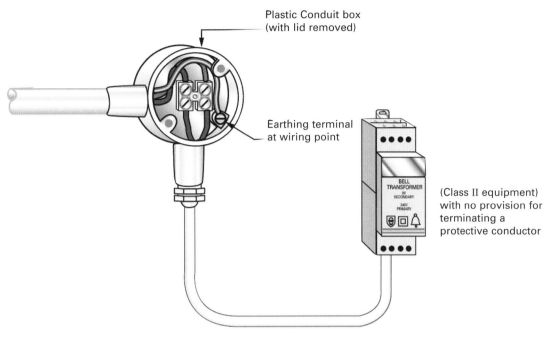

Plastic Conduit box
(with lid removed)

Earthing terminal
at wiring point

BELL
TRANSFORMER
8V
SECONDARY

240V
PRIMARY

(Class II equipment)
with no provision for
terminating a
protective conductor

**Fig 412.5 Circuit protective conductor run to and terminated
at Class II equipment**

4. Wiring systems-cables having a non-metallic sheath or a non-metallic enclosure

Cables having a non-metallic sheath or a non-metallic enclosure are considered to meet the requirements of *BS 7671* for protection by use of Class II equipment or equivalent insulation. The wiring system has to be installed in accordance with the requirements of Chapter 52 of *BS 7671*.

Types of cable having a non-metallic sheath include, for example, thermoplastic (pvc) insulated and sheathed cables to *BS 6004*. Examples of non-metallic enclosures include plastic conduit systems, plastic trunking or ducting systems, and enclosures formed by non-metallic accessories having non-metallic back boxes.

Exercise 412.2

(1) What is the symbol that identifies Class II equipment? (2) How would you terminate a cpc at a plastic dry lining box used in conjunction with a switch with no provision for a cpc connection?

notes

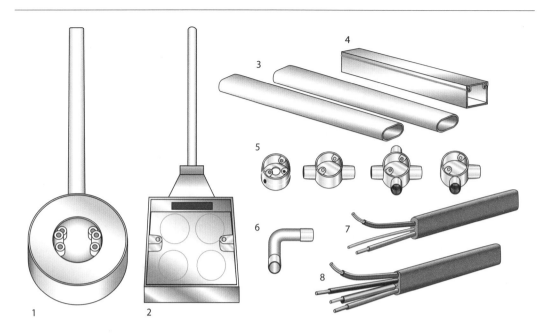

1 Plastic lighting point box   4 Plastic trunking   7 & 8 Insulated and sheathed cable

2 Plastic switch box   5 Plastic conduit boxes

3 Plastic oval conduit   6 Plastic conduit

Fig 412.6 Typical examples of non-metallic sheathed cable and non-metallic enclosures

Exercise 412.3

Now refer to Regulation 531.4.1 to review how a single RCD at the origin of the installation relates to the requirements for protection by the use of Class II equipment or equivalent.

Further information relating to Protective measure: Double or reinforced insulation can be found in:

• *BS 7671 Section 412*

• Electrical Safety Council Technical Manual articles C93-5, I17-3, I17-4

• *IEE Guidance Note 5*

SECTION 412 FINAL REVISION EXERCISE

412.1 What does the following symbol relate to?
- ☐ a. Class I equipment
- ☐ b. Class II equipment
- ☐ c. Class III equipment
- ☐ d. Earthing connection

412.2 Where a lid or an insulating enclosure can be opened without the use of a tool or key and conductive parts are accessible if the lid or door is open, an insulating barrier should be provided with a minimum degree of protection of which of the following?
- ☐ a. IPXXB or IP2X
- ☐ b. IPXXB or IP4X
- ☐ c. IPXXD or IP2X
- ☐ d. IPXXD or IP4X

412.3 The following symbol is intended to inform equipment installers and operators that the equipment should:
- ☐ a. Be connected to earth
- ☐ b. Be connected to an earth electrode
- ☐ c. Not be connected to earth
- ☐ d. Not be insulated

Things to do and find

1. Where the protective measure double or reinforced insulation is being used as a sole protective measure what additional requirements need to be met?

2. What is required to be run to and terminated at each point in wiring and at each accessory?

3. Why is it imperative that where double or reinforced insulation is used as a sole protective measure (for an whole installation) it must be verified that the installation will be under effective supervision in normal use.

1. Introduction

Electrical separation is a protective measure that works by separating one system from another, normally by use of an isolating transformer. The most common example of electrical separation is a shaver supply unit complying with *BS EN 61558-2-5.*

The requirements relating to electrical separation can be split into two distinct sets of regulations. The first concerns the Regulations (within Section 413) relating to one unearthed source with simple separation, supplying one item of current-using equipment (covered in this section of the Learning Guide). The regulations relating to situations where more than one item is supplied from a single source are located in Section 418. Section 418 relates to measures that are only applicable where the installation is controlled or under the supervision of skilled or instructed persons.

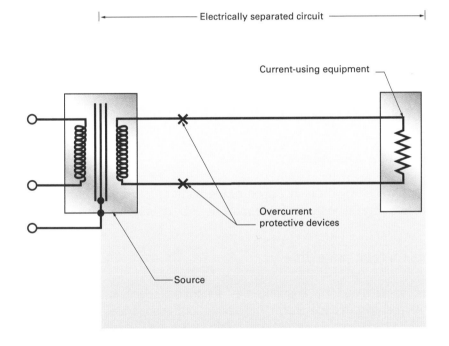

Key Facts
'Ensure you choose the correct type of shaver unit for use in a bathroom or shower room'

Fig 413.1 Electrically-separated system

Fig 413.1 above shows a typical system providing electrical separation. As the secondary winding is not connected to Earth it is not possible to get a shock to Earth as there is no return path for current to flow. Fig 413.2 below illustrates a shaver supply unit complying with *BS EN 61558-2-5.* It can be seen that although there is a fault to the shaver casing there is no return path to Earth through the radiator.

notes

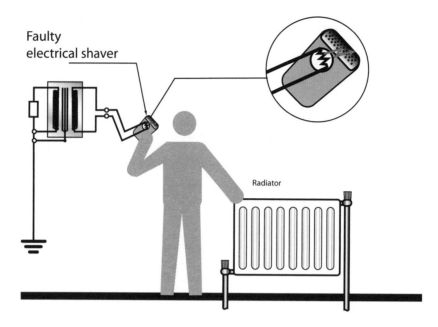

Fig 413.2 Shaver with an electrical fault

2. Requirements for basic protection

Basic protection is provided by basic insulation of live parts or barriers or enclosures (see Section 410 of this Learning Guide for more information), or by double or reinforced insulation.

3. Requirements for fault protection

a. Fault protection is provided by ensuring the separated circuit is supplied through a source with at least simple separation. The voltage of the separated circuit should not exceed 500 V.

b. Live parts of the separated circuit should not be connected at any point to another circuit or to Earth or to a protective conductor.

c. Flexible cables and cords should be visible throughout any part of their length which may be liable to mechanical damage.

d. No exposed-conductive-parts of the separated circuit should be connected either to the protective conductor or exposed-conductive-parts of other circuits, or to Earth.

e. Consideration needs to be given to wiring systems used for separated circuits, especially if they are to be routed with other circuits in the same wiring system.

Exercise 413.1

Refer to Regulation 413.3.5 to review the additional requirements where separated circuits are routed with other circuits

Further information relating to Protective measure: Electrical Separation can be found in:
- *BS 7671* Section 413
- Electrical Safety Council Technical Manual articles E89-1 and E 65-1
- *IEC Guidance Note 5*

SECTION 413 FINAL REVISION EXERCISE

413.1 The maximum voltage of a separated circuit:
- ☐ a. 60 V a.c.
- ☐ b. 120 V a.c.
- ☐ c. 230 V a.c.
- ☐ d. 500 V a.c.

413.2 Apart from where an installation is controlled or under the supervision of skilled or instructed persons, how many items of current-using equipment can be supplied from an unearthed source with simple separation is which of the following?
- ☐ a. 1
- ☐ b. 2
- ☐ c. 4
- ☐ d. An unlimited number

Things to do and find

1. What is the most significant difference between the protective measure SELV and electrical separation?

2. In a system where electrical separation is the protective measure, how are basic and fault protection provided?

3. What should **not** be done with an exposed-conductive-part of a separated circuit?

1. Introduction

This protective measure relates to protection by extra-low voltage systems by use of either SELV or PELV, the letters SELV standing for separated extra-low voltage, and PELV for protective extra-low voltage.

These two systems are defined by voltage limitations, specified sources, and strict conditions relating to their installation and use. As a result of these specific requirements, SELV or PELV systems can be used in all situations, although in some special installations or locations the maximum voltage is limited, and in some cases additional basic protection may be required.

Protective separation of the SELV or PELV system is required from all circuits (other than SELV or PELV circuits) and basic insulation is required between the SELV or PELV system and other SELV or PELV systems. For SELV systems only, basic insulation is required between the SELV system and earth.

2. SELV

SELV is defined as:

> 'An extra-low voltage system which is electrically separated from Earth and from other systems in such a way that a single fault cannot give rise to the risk of an electric shock'.

To ensure that this measure is installed and operates safely the strictly prescribed criteria of Section 414 of *BS 7671* needs to be followed carefully. As can be seen from Fig 414.1 below, it is not possible to receive a shock to Earth from this system, as there is no return path to Earth.

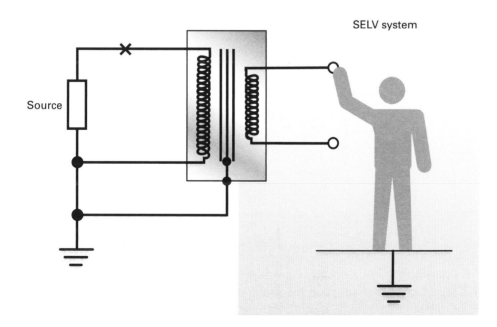

Fig 414.1 SELV source and illustration that a shock to Earth cannot occur for a single fault

notes

The source of supply to the SELV system is an important consideration and several types of SELV sources are recognized by *BS 7671* in Section 414.3. Acceptable sources must meet the requirements for voltage and separation in relation to other electrical systems.

The upper limit for a SELV system is 50 V a.c or 120 V ripple-free d.c. However, in some cases, for example in some special installations or locations such as locations containing a bath or shower or swimming pools, the upper voltage limits may be reduced further.

a. Examples of SELV sources (these sources are the same for PELV).

The most common source for SELV systems is a safety isolating transformer complying with *BS EN 61558-2-6*.

> **Key Facts**
> 'The three main things to remember when designing or installing SELV or PELV systems are voltage limits, electrically separated sources and adherence to strict installation criteria'

Separated Extra-Low Voltage (SELV)

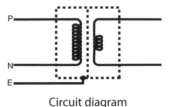

Circuit diagram

Symbol

Fig 414.2 Safety isolating transformer in accordance with BS EN 61558-2-6

A SELV source could also be provided by a motor-generator with a generator winding that meets the requirements for voltage and electrical separation equivalent to that of a safety isolating transformer.

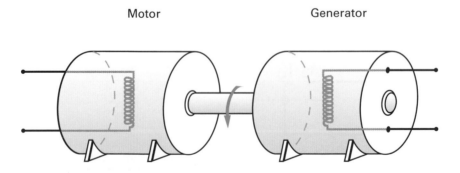

Motor   Generator

Fig 414.3 Motor-generator meeting the requirements for a SELV source

A SELV source may also be an electrochemical source (such as a battery) or another source independent of a higher voltage circuit (such as an engine-driven generator). The source must meet the standard requirements relating to voltage and separation from other systems.

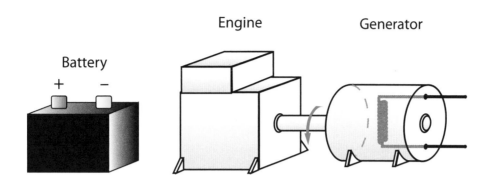

Fig 414.4 Independent sources such as a battery or an engine-driven generator meeting the requirements for a SELV source

Certain electronic devices such as insulation testing equipment and monitoring devices may also meet the required criteria for SELV sources.

3. PELV

A PELV system is defined as:

'An extra-low voltage system which is not electrically separated from Earth, but which otherwise satisfies all the requirements for SELV'.

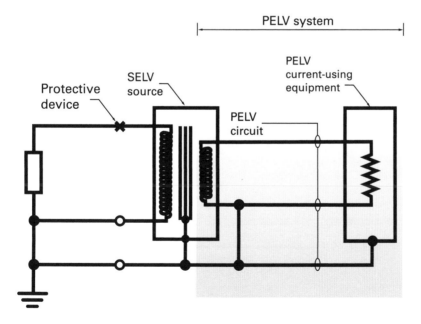

Fig 414.5 A simple PELV system

notes

The source for a PELV system must be a safety source as is required for a SELV system (see above Figs 414.2, 414.3 and 414.4). However, a PELV system is not required to be electrically separated from earth. In many cases, this will mean that one point of the source and/or exposed-conductive-parts of the system are connected to earth, as can be seen in Fig 414.5 above.

4. Basic and fault protection for SELV and PELV

Both basic and fault protection provisions will be met where:

- the nominal voltage cannot exceed 50 V a.c and 120 V ripple-free d.c., and
- the supply is from one of the sources listed in 414.3 and
- the conditions of Regulation Group 414.4 are fulfilled.

Where the nominal voltage exceeds 25 V a.c. or 60 V d.c., or if the equipment is immersed, basic protection will be required by the provision of insulation and/or barriers or enclosures. Insulation and/or barriers or enclosures may also be required below 25 V a.c. or 60 V d.c where there are wet conditions or where specific conditions for PELV are not met.

5. Wiring systems

In cases where the SELV or PELV source supplies a single piece of equipment the possibilities for the integrity of the system to be infringed are restricted. However, where wiring systems are installed within a building the possible detrimental effect of other circuits on the SELV or PELV systems must be considered. To ensure the whole system is effective, it is important that any wiring systems taken from SELV or PELV sources are not compromised by other circuits that are at a higher voltage or do not emanate from a source equal to that required by SELV or PELV systems.

Regulations 414.4.1 and 414.4.2 outline the insulation and installation requirements relating to SELV and PELV circuitry.

Where SELV or PELV socket-outlets and luminaire support couplers are installed they should not be dimensionally compatible with those used for any other system in use in the same premises. Plugs and socket-outlets in a SELV system must not have a protective conductor contact.

Exercise 414.1

You should now refer to Regulations 414.4.1 and 41.4.2 to review the requirements for SELV and PELV circuits

Further information relating to the protective measure SELV or PELV can be found in:
- *BS 7671 Section 414*
- Electrical Safety Council Technical Manual E161-9, E161-11, E161-13, E161- 17 and S9-1
- *IEE Guidance Note 5*

notes

SECTION 414 FINAL REVISION EXERCISE

414.1 The maximum nominal voltage for a SELV or PELV system is which of the following?
- ☐ a. 25 V a.c and 60 V ripple-free d.c.
- ☐ b. 50 V a.c and 60 V ripple-free d.c.
- ☐ c. 50 V a.c and 120 V ripple-free d.c.
- ☐ d. 120 V a.c and 60 V ripple-free d.c.

414.2 Insulation and/or barriers or enclosures must be provided for SELV or PELV circuits if the equipment is immersed or if the nominal voltage exceeds which of the following?
- ☐ a. 25 V a.c and 60 V ripple-free d.c.
- ☐ b. 50 V a.c and 60 V ripple-free d.c.
- ☐ c. 50 V a.c and 120 V ripple-free d.c.
- ☐ d. 120 V a.c and 60 V ripple-free d.c.

414.3 Which of the following cannot be used as a source for a SELV or PELV system?
- ☐ a. Autotransformer.
- ☐ b. Safety isolating transformer
- ☐ c. An electrochemical source
- ☐ d. Specific electronic devices

Things to do and find

1. What do the terms SELV and PELV mean?

2. What makes a PELV system different from a SELV system?

3. When is basic protection required for SELV or PELV systems?

4. List four methods of protective separation between SELV or PELV wiring systems and wiring systems of other circuits.

5. List four types of source that may be suitable for a supply to a SELV or PELV system.

1. Introduction

Additional protection is generally required where there is a possibility of increased risk of electric shock.

Two types of additional protection are outlined in Section 415 of *BS 7671*:

• Residual current devices (RCDs)
• Supplementary equipotential bonding

The main areas specified in BS 7671 as requiring additional protection relate to special locations or installations, certain conditions of external influence (including in some cases concealed wiring) and socket-outlets. However, these are not the only areas specified.

2. Additional protection: Residual current devices (RCDs)

The use of RCDs with a rated residual operating current ($I_{\Delta n}$) not exceeding 30 mA and an operating time not exceeding 40 ms at a residual current of $5I_{\Delta n}$, is recognized in a.c. systems as additional protection in the event of:

• failure of the provision for basic protection and/or fault protection or
• carelessness by users.

The following table reiterates the above requirements.

Table 415 A (Learning Guide Table) RCD requirement for additional protection

Rated residual operating current $I_{\Delta n}$	Operating time	Required residual current to provide 40 mS operation
Maximum 30 mA	Maximum 40 mS	$5I_{\Delta n}$ (150 mA for $I_{\Delta n}$ = 30 mA)

It should be noted that one of the protective measures in Sections 411 to 414 of *BS 7671* (providing basic and fault protection) is still required and RCDs cannot be used as a sole means of protection.

Many sections of Part 7 (Special installations or locations) require additional protection by RCDs and careful consideration needs to be given to all special locations or installations at the design stage.

Regulation 411.3.3 requires additional protection by means of an RCD for:

• all socket-outlets where their rated current does not exceed 20 A, they are used by ordinary persons (as defined in Part 2) and where the socket-outlet is intended for general use.
• Additional protection is also required for mobile equipment with a current rating not exceeding 32 A for outdoors use.

An exception to the above is permitted for socket-outlets for use under the supervision of skilled or instructed persons, e.g. in some commercial or industrial locations where the installations of an RCD may cause nuisance tripping (Regulation 531.2.4 refers) or where a specific labelled or otherwise suitably identified socket-outlet is provided for connection of a particular item of equipment.

Section 415
Additional protection

Except where the installation is not intended to be under the supervision of a skilled or instructed person, additional protection by means of an RCD is also required where the zoning requirements of 522.6.6 cannot be met and or where certain cables, such as PVC insulated and sheathed cables, are installed in a wall or partition, the internal construction of which includes metallic parts (other than fixings etc).

It should be noted that additional protection by means of RCDs, as required by Section 415, does not include the requirements for RCDs to reduce the risk of fire.

Exercise 415.1

You should now refer to Regulations 411.3.3, 522.6.7 and 522.6.8 to review the requirements for RCDs

3. Additional protection: Supplementary bonding

Supplementary bonding is considered as an addition to fault protection. Supplementary bonding may involve the entire installation, a part of the installation, an item of equipment, or a location. Several sections in Part 7, Special installations or locations require supplementary bonding.

Supplementary bonding is accomplished by connecting together all simultaneously accessible exposed-conductive-parts of fixed equipment and extraneous-conductive-parts. The Supplementary bonding system should also connect to the protective conductor of all equipment (within the area requiring supplementary bonding) including those of socket-outlets. The diagram below illustrates the general requirements.

> **Key Facts**
> 'Ensure you fit the correct rated RCDs where required. Also, instruct occupiers to tests RCDs at least every quarter'

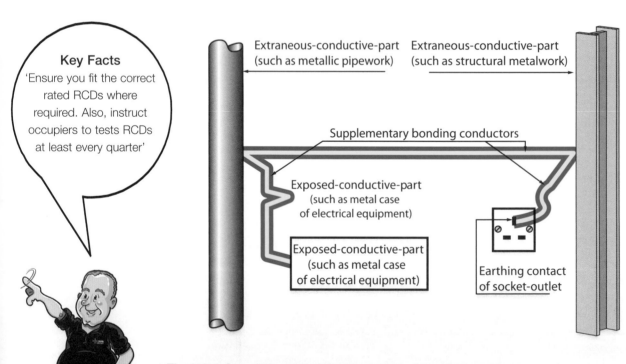

Fig 415.1 Supplementary bonding, general requirement

The following diagram shows typical supplementary bonding connections in a room containing a bath or shower. The diagram is not meant to suggest that this is a requirement in all cases or that all the points connected by supplementary bonding conductors will require a connection.

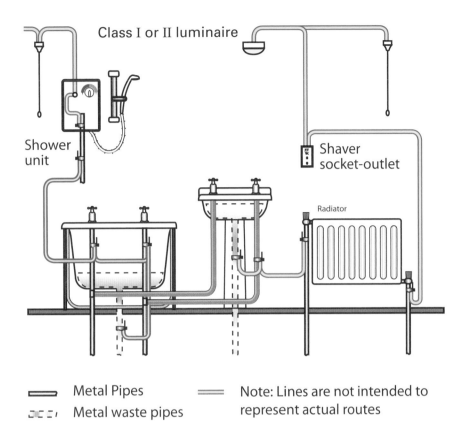

Class I or II luminaire

Shower unit

Shaver socket-outlet

Radiator

━━ Metal Pipes
⊐⊏⊐⊏ Metal waste pipes

═══ Note: Lines are not intended to represent actual routes

Fig 415.2 Supplementary equipotential bonding practical example

In locations that require supplementary equipotential bonding an assessment must be made to ascertain the exposed-conductive-parts and extraneous-conductive-parts that may require a bonding connection. The decision as to whether supplementary equipotential bonding is required can be confirmed by establishing the value of resistance between simultaneously accessible exposed-conductive-parts and extraneous-conductive-parts and ensuring that the resistance fulfils the following conditions:

$R \leq 50 \text{ V}/I_a$ in a.c. systems or

$R \leq 120 \text{ V}/I_a$ in d.c systems

Where Ia is the operating current in amperes of the protective device – for RCDs this should be at $I_{\Delta n}$ and for overcurrent devices, the 5 second operating current.

Example 1: An a.c circuit is protected by a 32 A Type B circuit-breaker. From Appendix 3 or by calculation from Table 41.3, the current required to operate a 32 A Type B circuit-breaker in 5 seconds is 160 A. Putting this figure into the above equation gives:

$R \leq 50/160 = 0.31 \ \Omega$

Example 2: A 30 mA RCD protects an a.c. circuit. The rated residual operating current is 30 mA. Putting this figure into the above equation gives:

$R \leq 50/0.03 = 1666 \ \Omega$.

notes

Exercise 415.2

For further information relating to the connection and sizing of supplementary bonding conductors see Section 544 of *BS 7671*.

Further information relating to additional protection can be found in:
- *BS 7671 Section 415*
- Electrical Safety Council Technical Manual articles B37-65 and D41-13
- *IEE Guidance Note 5*

SECTION 415 FINAL REVISION EXERCISE

415.1 To provide additional protection an RCD must have which of the following characteristics?
- ☐ a. Rated residual current 30 mA and operate in 200 ms when tested with 150 mA.
- ☐ b. Rated residual current 300 mA and operate in 40 ms when tested with 150 mA.
- ☐ c. Rated residual current 30 mA and operate in 200 ms when tested with 30 mA.
- ☐ d. Rated residual current 30 mA and operate in 40 ms when tested with 150 mA.

415.2 The operating time for an RCD providing additional protection when tested at a residual current of 5 $I_{\Delta n}$ is which of the following?
- ☐ a. 30 ms
- ☐ b. 40 ms
- ☐ c. 150 ms
- ☐ d. 300 ms

415.3 An a.c circuit is protected by a 20 A Type C circuit-breaker and supplementary bonding may be a requirement. In relation to the accessible exposed-conductive-parts of this circuit and extraneous-conductive-parts, what would be the maximum resistance that would determine the requirement for supplementary equipotential bonding?
- ☐ a. 0.25 Ω
- ☐ b. 0.5 Ω
- ☐ c. 1.0 Ω
- ☐ d. 2.0 Ω

415.4 An a.c circuit is protected by a 45 A *BS 1361* fuse and supplementary bonding may be a requirement. In relation to the accessible exposed-conductive-parts of this circuit and extraneous-conductive-parts, what would be the maximum resistance that would determine the requirement for supplementary equipotential bonding?
- ☐ a. 0.21 Ω
- ☐ b. 0.96 Ω
- ☐ c. 1.04 Ω
- ☐ d. 4.8 Ω

notes

Things to do and find

1. Identify three examples where RCDs are required for additional protection.

2. Identify three examples where supplementary equipotential bonding may be required.

3. An a.c. circuit is protected by an RCD with a rated residual operating current of 300 mA, what is the maximum resistance that would determine whether supplementary equipotential would be required?

4. An a.c. circuit is protected by a 20 A Type C circuit-breaker, what is the maximum resistance that would determine whether supplymentary equipotential would be required?

5. List three special locations or installations that require 30 mA RCD protection.

Section 417 and 418
Protective measures applicable only when the installation is controlled or under the supervision of skilled or instructed persons

106

1. Introduction

notes

Sections 417 and 418 relate to protective measures that are only applicable to installations that are controlled or under the supervision of skilled or instructed persons. The use of these measures is, therefore, restricted. As these measures are uncommon the guidance provided in this section of the Learning Guide only provides an outline of the requirements.

Section 417 contains two methods that can be used for basic protective provision; that is, obstacles and placing out of reach. These two terms have very specific meanings (defined in Part 2) relating to their use in electrical installations.

Section 418 contains three protective measures; that is, non-conducting location, earth-free local equipotential bonding and electrical separation (where more than one item of current-using equipment is supplied). The first two, non-conducting location and earth-free local equipotential bonding are only applicable to installations that are controlled or under the supervision of skilled or instructed persons. Electrical separation also comes under this restricted category when this measure is used to supply two or more items of current-using equipment.

> **Exercise 417/418.1**
>
> Refer to Part 2 and Fig 417 of *BS 7671* to review the definition and dimensions for arm's reach

2. Section 417 General - Obstacles and placing out of reach

The basic protection provisions, obstacles and placing out of reach, are not frequently encountered. This is because they are intended only for application where the use of the more conventional measures of basic protection - namely, protection by insulation, and/or protection by barriers or enclosure - is impracticable. In the case of obstacles and placing out of reach, live parts do not require to be covered with insulation or protected by a barrier and/or enclosure but there are set requirements that must be met.

Key Facts
'Where electrical installations fall within the remit of Sections 417 or 418 careful scrutiny of *BS7671* and special advice may be required'

3. Obstacles

The application of protection by obstacles is limited to locations accessible only to certain authorized personnel, and is not permitted (apart from one exception) in installations or locations of increased shock risk. An example of an obstacle providing basic protection would be an unenclosed switch or mains panel in a normally locked switchroom. The principle of protection by obstacles is to place an obstacle, such as a handrail, mesh or screen in front of, or around, live parts, in such a manner that a person cannot unintentionally approach or touch live parts.

The regulations require an obstacle to prevent:

• unintentional bodily approach to a live part and
• unintentional contact with a live part when operating energized equipment

An obstacle, where used, must be secured so as to prevent its unintentional removal, although it is permitted to be removable without the use of a tool or key. For example, the handrail illustrated in the diagram below may be located into sleeved sockets sunk into the floor.

notes

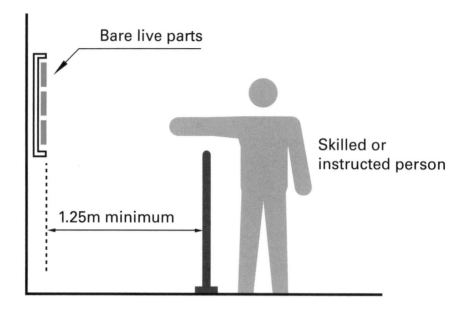

Fig 417.1 A typical example of how a handrail may be used as an obstacle for basic protection

4. Placing out of reach

Like obstacles, the application of protection by placing out of reach is infrequent and restricted in its use.

The principle of protection by placing out of reach is to locate live parts in a suitable position where they cannot normally be touched, thus preventing 'unintentional' contact. Such location of live parts is referred to as 'placing of conductors' in the Electricity at Work Regulations 1989 (EWR) as amended. In practice this term often relates to overhead lines, but it may also be employed in locations accessible only to certain authorized personnel. For these reasons, protection by placing out of reach is not permitted in some installations or locations of increased shock risk.

Examples of placing out of reach providing basic protection could be an overhead travelling crane or controlgear supplying a large electroplating plant. For overhead lines heights and clearance distances, the requirements of the Electricity Safety, Quality and Continuity Regulations 2002 must be followed.

a. Distances from live parts

Bare live parts, other than an overhead line, must not be within arm's reach, nor within 2.5 m of the following:

(i) An exposed-conductive-part

(ii) An extraneous-conductive-part

(iii) A bare live part of any other circuit

The term arm's reach is defined as:

> 'A zone of accessibility to touch, extending from any point on a surface where persons usually stand or move about to the limits which a person can reach with a hand in any direction without assistance.'

The limit of arm's reach is normally taken to be 1.25 m horizontally (where certain conditions are met) and 2.5 m vertically. However, these distances must be increased appropriately where bulky or long conducting objects may be handled, such as metallic ladders or scaffolding.

Fig 417.2 below illustrates an example for the vertical case, 417.3 illustrates the horizontal case (which is the same as for obstacles above).

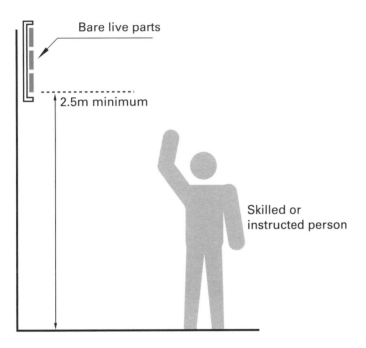

Fig 417.2 Placing out of reach for basic protection (vertical plane).

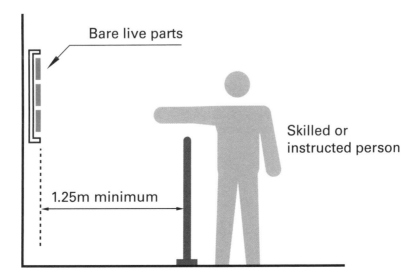

Fig 417.3 Placing out of reach for basic protection (horizontal plane).

109

Section 417 and 418
Protective measures applicable only when the installation is
controlled or under the supervision of skilled or instructed persons

5. Section 418 General – Non-conducting locations, earth-free local equipotential bonding and electrical separation (for the supply to more than one item of current-using equipment)

The three protective measures listed above are infrequently encountered. Their applications are specialized and, as mentioned previously, these systems must be controlled or under effective supervision.

Where these installations are to be designed, installed or inspected and tested, further reading will be necessary. The following is a very brief outline of each protective measure.

6. Non-conducting locations

This method of protection is not recognized by *BS 7671* for *general* application. The principle of a non-conducting location is that, in the designated location, there is effective separation between conductive-parts (whether they are extraneous-conductive-parts or exposed-conductive-parts) even when there has been a failure in the basic insulation of live parts. Further to this, the walls and floors of the location are of electrically insulating material, such that the resistance of every point to Earth (under specified conditions) is not less than a specified value. Also, there must be no protective conductors in the location and precautions need to be taken to ensure that the system is not compromised where the use of mobile or portable equipment is envisaged. Finally, precautions are required to ensure that extraneous-conductive-parts cannot cause a potential to appear external to the location concerned. Methods for measuring the impedance or resistance of insulating floors and walls can be found in Appendix 13 of *BS 7671*.

7. Protection by earth-free local equipotential bonding

The use of this protective measure is permitted but only under effective supervision and only in special situations which are earth-free. Use of the measure is prohibited in some of the installations and locations of increased shock risk covered in Part 7 of *BS 7671*.

Protection by earth-free local equipotential bonding is intended to prevent the appearance of a dangerous voltage between simultaneously accessible parts in the event of a failure in basic insulation.

The main principles underlying the measure are that:

- An unearthed protective bonding conductor connects together every simultaneously accessible exposed-conductive-part and extraneous-conductive-parts, to maintain all the parts at substantially the same potential.
- Precautions are taken so that persons entering and leaving the equipotential location cannot be exposed to dangerous potential difference; in particular where a conductive floor insulated from Earth is connected to the earth-free protective bonding conductors.

8. Electrical separation for the supply to more than one item of current-using equipment

The requirements relating to the protective measure electrical separation, where only one item of current-using equipment is being supplied were covered in Section 413 of this Learning Guide.

With one piece of current-using equipment and the occurrence of a single fault, there should be no risk of electric shock. However, a hazard arises on a second fault and the probability of a second fault increases when there is more than one item of current-using equipment connected to the separated circuit. *BS 7671* recognizes the increased hazard when a separated circuit supplies two or more items of current-using equipment and places additional requirements.

These special requirements are too numerous to mention in this Learning Guide. It should be noted, however, that where more than one item of current-using equipment is being supplied by a separated circuit this is recognized only for special situations under effective supervision, where specified by a suitably-qualified electrical engineer.

Precautions need to be taken to protect the separated circuit from damage and insulation failure. All exposed-conductive-parts of the separated circuit, including the terminal of socket-outlets in a separated circuit, should be connected together by insulated, non-earthed protective bonding conductors. Further information relating to disconnection of separated circuits can be found in Regulations 418.3.7 and 418.3.8.

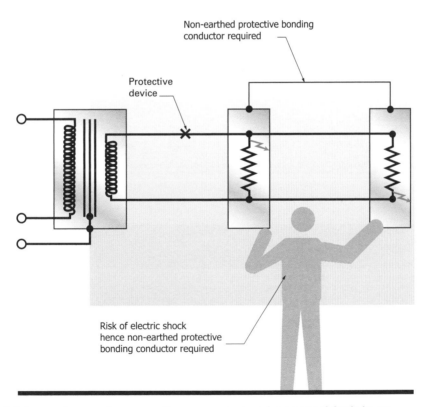

Fig 417.4 A hazard can arise upon the occurrence of a second fault in an electrically-separated system where two or more items of current-using equipment are supplied

Further information relating to the above protective measures can be found in:
- *BS 7671 Section 417 and 418*
- Electrical Safety Council Technical Manual articles D41-9, D41-11, E65-1, E89-1 and I17-9
- *IEE Guidance Note 5*

Section 417 and 418
Protective measures applicable only when the installation is
controlled or under the supervision of skilled or instructed persons

notes

SECTION 417 and 418 FINAL REVISION EXERCISE

417.1 Which of the following provisions for providing basic protection can only
be used in installations that are controlled or supervised by skilled or
instructed persons?
☐ a. Insulation of live parts
☐ b. Enclosures
☐ c. Obstacles
☐ d. Barriers

417.2 Which of the following provisions for providing basic protection can only be used
in installations that are controlled or supervised by skilled or instructed persons?
☐ a. Insulation of live parts
☐ b. Enclosures
☐ c. Placing out of reach
☐ d. Barriers

417.3 The Height in the overhead direction to comply with the requirements for
placing out of reach is which of the following?
☐ a. 1.25 m
☐ b. 1.75 m
☐ c. 2.25 m
☐ d. 2.5 m

Things to do and find

1. What are the protective measures that can only be used where the installation is controlled
    or under the supervison of skilled or instructed persons?

2. What additional precaution should be taken where bulky or long conductive objects are
    normally handled?

3. What are the minimum values of resistance of insulating floors and walls for a 400 V supply?

4. How would bulky or long objects, being used in a location where the provision placing out of
    reach is being provided, affect the dimensions for accessibility to electrical equipment?

5. Under what circumstances is the protective measure electrical separation only permissible
    where the installation is controlled or under the supervision of skilled or instructed persons?

Chapter 42
Protection against thermal effects

1. Introduction

Chapter 42 deals with protection against the thermal effects as applied to electrical installations and equipment with regards to measures for the protection of people, livestock and property.

There are many issues to be considered in relation to the detrimental thermal effects that could result from badly designed or incorrectly installed electrical equipment, including:

- Harmful effects of heat accumulation, heat radiation or hot components or equipment
- Ignition, combustion or degradation of materials
- Flames and smoke (where a fire hazard could be propagated from an electrical installation to other nearby fire compartments)
- Safety services being cut off by the failure of electrical equipment.

Harmful effects of heat or fire may be caused by heat accumulation, heat radiation, hot components or equipment; failure of electrical equipment such as protective devices, switchgear, thermostats, temperature limiters, seals of cable penetrations and wiring systems; overcurrent; insulation faults, arcs, sparks and high temperature particles or harmonic currents.

See Sections 526 of *BS 7671* and this Learning Guide for more information relating to electrical connections and Section 527 in relation to the selection and erection of wiring systems to minimize the spread of fire.

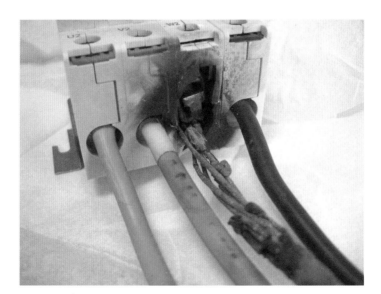

Key Facts
'Deaths can occur from the harmful effects of heat and fire caused by incorrectly designed or installed electrical installations. Chapter 42 should be followed in conjunction with Sections 526, 527 and Appendix 5'

Fig 42.1 Melted insulation due to loose connection

Within Chapter 42 there are three sections. Section 421 deals with the protection against fire caused by electrical equipment, Section 422 provides the requirements for precautions where particular risks of fire exist and Section 423 deals with protection against burns.

2. Protection against fire caused by electrical equipment (Section 421)

Section 421 provides the requirements to help prevent electrical equipment presenting a fire hazard to adjacent material.

The choice of electrical equipment must be made taking into consideration its temperature in normal operation and the effects it could have on any adjacent material. In some cases additional precautions, such as screening or methods to dissipate heat may have to be taken.

Where arcs, sparks or particles at high temperature may be emitted by permanently connected electrical equipment in normal service the requirements of Regulation 421.3 of *BS 7671* should be met.

Exercise 42.1

You should now refer to Regulation 421.3 – Review the options for safeguarding against the effects of arcs, sparks or particles at high temperature.

Fixed equipment causing a concentration of heat must be at a sufficient distance from any fixed object or building element, so that the object or element, in normal conditions, is not subjected to a dangerous temperature (as illustrated in Fig 42.2 below).

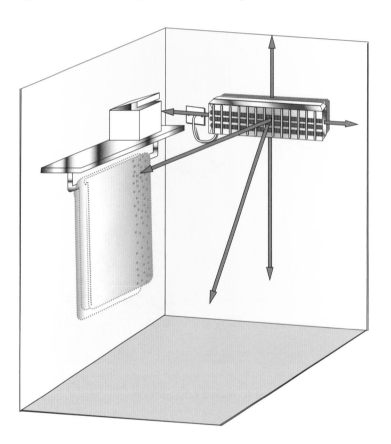

→ Indicates distance from heat source

Fig 42.2 Heat source and adjacent materials or building element

Electrical equipment containing flammable liquids require particular consideration and adequate precautions need to be taken to prevent the spread of liquid, flame and the products of combustion.

Materials used for the construction of enclosures of electrical equipment must comply with the resistance to heat and fire requirements in an appropriate product standard.

Every termination of a live conductor or connection or joint between live conductors must be contained within an enclosure selected in accordance with Regulation 526.5.

(See Section 526.5 of *BS 7671* for further information). It is important to note that all terminations should be enclosed, including extra-low voltage.

> **Exercise 42.2**
>
> You should now refer to Section 526 to review the requirements relating to terminations and enclosures.

3. Precautions where particular risks of fire exist (Section 422)

a. General

In addition to the requirements of Sections 420 and 421, Section 422 outlines further precautions where there is a particular risk of fire.

Additional requirements are required where there are:

• Difficult conditions for evacuation and/or high density occupation and/or
• The risk of fire is increased due to the nature of processed or stored materials

b. Conditions for evacuation in an emergency

The first of the above categories is defined in Appendix 5 as Conditions of evacuation in an emergency. Section 422 lists three categories from Appendix 5: **BD2** (typically, high rise buildings), **BD3** (locations open to the public, such as theatres, cinemas, department stores etc) and **BD4** (high rise buildings open to the public, such as hospitals or hotels).

Where buildings fall into the above categories (BD2, BD3 or BD4) there are restrictions on cable routes, wiring systems, cable types and access to switchgear and controlgear.

c. Locations with risks of fire due to the nature of processed or stored materials

Locations where there is an increased risk of fire due to the nature of processed or stored material are also defined in Appendix 5 of *BS 7671*. Section 422 only refers to **BE2** (**BE1** is classified as no significant risk and **BE3** relates to explosion risks). **BE2** relates to the manufacture, processing or storage of flammable materials including presence of dust. Typical premises would include barns, woodworking shops, flour mills, grain silos and paper or textile factories.

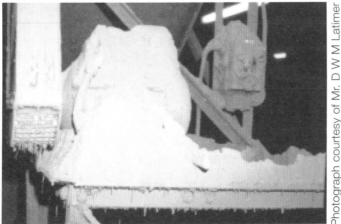

Photograph courtesy of Mr. D W M Latimer

Fig 42.3 Heavy build-up of dust on motor and starter equipment

Chapter 42
Protection against thermal effects

Where buildings fall into the BE2 category there are numerous additional requirements relating to:

- Distances between electrical equipment and combustible materials
- Maximum temperatures of electrical enclosures
- The location of switchgear
- Wiring systems
- Equipment such as motors, motor controls, luminaires, heating appliances
- Overload and fault protective devices
- Provision of RCDs (see * below)

* Except for mineral insulated cables or busbar trunking systems, wiring systems should be protected against insulation faults by an RCD with a maximum residual operating current of 300 mA. Where a resistive fault may cause a fire the rated residual operating current should not exceed 30 mA.

Measures should be taken to prevent the maximum temperature of enclosures of electrical equipment from exceeding 90 °C under normal conditions and 115 °C under fault conditions.

Exercise 42.3

(1) Where there is no recommendation from the manufacturer, in a location with risks of fire due to the nature of processed or stored materials, what is the minimum distance between a 150 W spotlight and combustible material?

d. Combustible constructional materials

Where buildings are mainly constructed of combustible materials, such as wood (Category CA2) the requirements of Regulation Group 422.4 of *BS 7671* should be applied in addition to those in Section 421.

Exercise 42.4

(1) Where there is no recommendation from the manufacturer, in a location constructed of combustible materials, what is the minimum distance between a 100 W spotlight and combustible material?

e. Fire propagating structures

Where a building has a shape and dimensions which facilitate the spread of fire (e.g. chimney effect), such as high rise buildings or a building with a forced ventilation system (Category CB2) the requirements of Section 422.5 of *BS 7671* should be applied in addition to those in Section 421.

4. Protection against burns (Section 423)

The temperature of accessible parts of fixed electrical equipment within *arm's reach* must be limited to protect persons against burns. Apart from equipment for which a Harmonised Standard specifies a limiting temperature, the maximum temperatures given in Table 42.1 (reproduced below) should not be exceeded (or guards fitted so as to prevent accidental contact).

Table 42.1 (Reproduced from *BS 7671*) Temperature limit under normal load conditions for an accessible part of equipment within arm's reach

Accessible part	Material of accessible surfaces	Maximum temperature (°C)
A hand-held part	Metallic Non-metallic	55 65
A part intended to be touched but not hand-held	Metallic Non-metallic	70 80
A part which need not be touched for normal operation	Metallic Non-metallic	80 90

Further information relating to protection against thermal effects can be found in:
- BS 7671 Chapter 42
- IEE Guidance Note 4
- Electrical Safety Council Technical Manual article P153-1

CHAPTER 42 FINAL REVISION EXERCISE

42.1 What is the maximum temperature for an accessible metallic hand-held part of equipment within arm's reach?
- ☐ a. 55 °C
- ☐ b. 65 °C
- ☐ c. 75 °C
- ☐ d. 80 °C

42.2 The code relating to the characteristic, low density occupation, difficult conditions of evacuation is which of the following?
- ☐ a. BD1
- ☐ b. BD2
- ☐ c. BD3
- ☐ d. BD4

42.3 The code relating to the characteristic, manufacture, processing or storage of flammable materials including the presence of dust is which of the following?
- ☐ a. BE1
- ☐ b. BE2
- ☐ c. BE3
- ☐ d. BE4

42.4 The maximum temperature of electrical equipment enclosures in a location with risks of fire due to the nature of processed or stored materials should not exceed which of the following?
- ☐ a. 70 °C under normal conditions and 90 °C under fault conditions
- ☐ b. 90 °C under normal conditions and 70 °C under fault conditions
- ☐ c. 90 °C under normal conditions and 115 °C under fault conditions
- ☐ d. 70 °C under normal conditions and 115 °C under fault conditions

notes

Things to do and find

1. What is the significant lower limit (in litres) for flammable liquids when adequate precautions should be taken?

_____
_____

2. Every termination of live conductors or joint between them must be contained within an enclosure in accordance with which regulation?

_____
_____

3. What is the maximum temperature for a non-metallic part which need not be touched for normal operation?

_____
_____

4. In locations with risks of fire due to the nature of processed or stored materials, the minimum distance between combustible materials and a small 250 W spotlight is?

_____
_____

1. Introduction

Chapter 43 provides requirements for the protection of live conductors from the effect of overcurrent. It describes how live conductors are protected by one or more devices for the automatic disconnection of the supply in the event of:

• Overload current (Section 433)

• Fault current (Section 434)

The requirements of Chapter 43 are intended to protect persons, livestock and property from the hazards that can occur when a circuit is drawing current in excess of its normal operating current.

Co-ordination of overload and fault protection is covered in Section 435 of *BS 7671*. The final section of Chapter 43, Section 436, covers the situation where overcurrent is limited by the characteristics of the supply (e.g. certain bell transformers, certain welding transformers etc).

Sometimes it is necessary to omit a device for protection against overload and fault current for safety reasons (e.g. a supply circuit for a lifting magnet, a fire extinguishing device, or a burglar alarm); Regulation Groups 433.3 and 434.3 respectively, provide guidance in these cases.

2. Definitions and terminologies

Before continuing it may be useful to clarify the meaning of certain terms (as defined in Part 2 of *BS 7671*) relating to Chapter 43:

a. An overcurrent is:

'A current exceeding the rated value. For conductors the rated value is the current-carrying capacity.'

and

b. An overload current is:

'An overcurrent occurring in a circuit which is electrically sound.'

It should be noted that an **'overcurrent' may be** an **overload current** or **a fault current**.

Types of fault current

There are two types of fault current: short-circuit current and earth fault current, as defined in Part 2:

c. A Short-circuit current is:

'An overcurrent resulting from a fault of negligible impedance between live conductors having a difference in potential under normal operating conditions.'

d. An Earth fault current is:

'A fault current which flows to Earth'

Exercise 43.1

(1) Provide examples of each of the following: Overload current, overcurrent, short-circuit current and earth fault current.

---

3. Chapter 43 General requirements.

A protective device must be provided to break any overcurrent in the circuit conductors before the overcurrent causes damage to insulation, connections, joints, terminations or the surroundings of the conductors.

---

4. Protection according to the nature of the circuits and the distribution system (Section 431)

Section 431 of *BS 7671* outlines the requirements relating to the disconnection of line conductors where overcurrent is detected. Detection is required for all line conductors and should cause disconnection of the conductor in which the overcurrent is detected. Disconnection of other live conductors is not necessary, unless the disconnection of one line conductor could cause danger or damage.

Section 431 also outlines the requirements relating to protection of the neutral conductor. It is important to note that no switch or circuit-breaker, except where linked, or fuse must be inserted in an earthed neutral conductor (Regulation 132.14.2 of *BS 7671* refers).

In single-phase circuits the neutral conductor will be the same cross-sectional area as the line conductors and will, therefore, be protected as the line conductors are provided with overcurrent protection. In a three-phase circuit with a truly balanced load the neutral current will be zero and in three-phase circuits with closely balanced loads the neutral current will be less than those in the line conductors. In these cases and where the neutral conductors are the same cross-sectional area as the line conductors the overcurrent protective devices in the line conductor will, as in the single-phase case, provide protection for the neutral conductor. However, in three-phase circuits where a reduced neutral cross-sectional area has been selected (see Section 524 of this Learning Guide for more information relating to reduced neutral csa) or where the neutral current is expected to exceed that in the line conductors (for example because of harmonic currents), overcurrent detection in the neutral conductor is required. The overcurrent detection must cause disconnection of the line conductors but not necessarily the neutral conductor.

---

5. Nature of protective devices (Section 432)

a. Protection against both overload and fault current

To provide this type of protection, except as permitted by Regulation 434.5.1, a device must be capable of breaking, and for a circuit-breaker making, any overcurrent up to and including the maximum prospective fault current at the point where the device is installed.

b. Protection against overload current or fault current only

Protection against overload current only is permissible, although the characteristics of the device used for overload must be co-ordinated with the device providing fault current protection and have a breaking capacity in excess of the energy let-through by that device.

A device providing protection against fault current only, must be installed where overload protection is also provided by other means (e.g. a fuse or a circuit-breaker with short-circuit release) or where Section 433 permits overload protection to be dispensed with. Such a device must be capable of breaking, and for a circuit-breaker making, the fault current up to and including the prospective fault current. This device must satisfy the requirements of Section 434.

c. Characteristics of protective device for overcurrent

BS 7671 recognizes specific overcurrent protective devices, as illustrated below. Other devices are not precluded, however, providing their time/current characteristics provide an equivalent level of protection to the ones listed:

Key Facts
'It is important to understand the terms: overcurrent, overload, fault current, short circuit and earth fault current'

Fig 43.1 Cartridge fuses to *BS88*   **Fig 43.2 Cartridge fuses to *BS 1361***

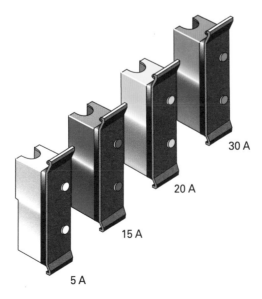

30 A

20 A

15 A

5 A

Fig 43.3 Semi-enclosed (rewireable) fuses to *BS 3036*

Chapter 43
Protection against overcurrent

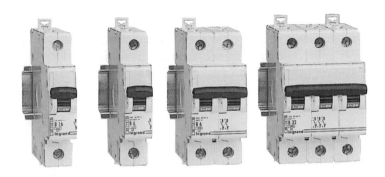

Fig 43.4 *BS EN 60898* Circuit-breakers

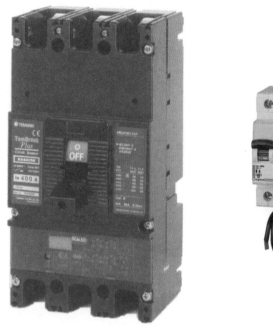

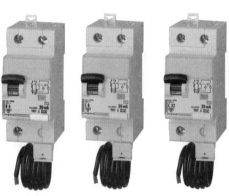

Fig 43.5 *BS EN 60947-2* Circuit breakers

Fig 43.6 RCBO'S to *BS EN 61009-1*

6. Co-ordination between conductor and overload protective device (Section 433.1)

Fig 43.7 below is a block diagram of a circuit, showing the overload protective device (normally a fuse or circuit-breaker), the circuit conductors (cable) and the load.

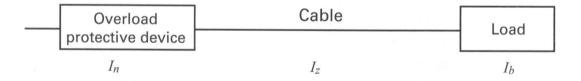

Fig 43.7 Block diagram of a circuit

In the above diagram should an overload occur, the protective device is designed to automatically disconnect the circuit (by blowing the fuse or tripping the circuit-breaker).

Should an overload occur in a circuit where there is no overload protection, the temperature of the circuit conductors could rise excessively, possibly damaging the insulation, joints and terminations of the conductors, and /or their surroundings.

To protect against such damage, the design of the circuit has to properly co-ordinate the current-carrying capacity of the conductors and the anticipated load current with the characteristics of the overload protective device.

Co-ordination will be met, and comply with Regulation 433.1.1 (i) if:

$$I_b \leq I_n \leq I_z \qquad \text{(expression a)}$$

Where: I_b is the design current of the circuit (i.e. the load)

I_n is the nominal current or setting of the protective device

I_z is the current carrying capacity of the conductor
(i.e. a cable, busbar or powertrack)

In other words:

I_b the design current of the circuit must not be greater than

I_n the current rating or current setting of the protective device, and

I_n the current setting of the device must not exceed

I_z the lowest conductor rating of that circuit

Co-ordination will also be met and comply with Regulation 433.1.1 (iii) if :

$$I_2 \leq 1.45 \times I_z \qquad \text{(expression b) overload protective}$$

Where I_2 is the current ensuring effective operation of the overload protective device in the conventional time (e.g. 1 to 4 hours , depending on the standard and rating of the overload protective device)

To summarise the requirements of Regulation 433.1.1 (iii):

The current causing effective operation of the protective device must not exceed **1.45** times the lowest of the current-carrying capacity (I_z) of any of the conductors of the circuit.

If the conditions in Regulation 433.1.1 (i) are satisfied, (i.e. expression a), then the conditions in Regulation 433.1.1 (ii) (expression b) will also be satisfied for recognized protective devices (see 5c above), apart from semi-enclosed (rewireable) fuses to *BS 3036*.

a. Where the protective device is a *BS 3036* fuse

Where the device is a semi-enclosed fuse to *BS 3036*, compliance with condition (ii) above is afforded if its nominal current (I_n) does not exceed 0.725 times the current carrying capacity (I_z) of the lowest rated conductor in the circuit protected.

This is because the characteristics of a *BS 3036* fuse are such that the value of I_2 for the fuse may be up to twice the value of I_n. That means it may require a current twice the rating of the fuse to cause disconnection in the conventional time.

Chapter 43
Protection against overcurrent

To satisfy $\qquad I_2 \leq 1.45 \times I_z$ (expression b)

We have to make $\qquad 2 \times I_n \leq 1.45 \times I_z$

Therefore $\qquad I_n \leq \dfrac{1.45}{2} \times I_z \leq 0.725 \times I_z$

In practical terms, if a *BS 3036* fuse is used as a protective device, it may mean that a larger cable than determined from normal load calculations will have to be selected. This issue is covered in the section of the Learning Guide relating to cable sizing, where the 0.725 factor is used, resulting in larger conductor sizes when rewireable fuses are being considered (Regulation Group 523 and Appendix 4 of *BS 7671* and this Learning Guide refer).

b. Ring final circuits and co-ordination between conductors and overload protective devices

In relation to the requirements outlined above, ring final circuits need to be considered as a special case. The requirements of Regulation 433.1 are complied with, provided that the following conditions are met:

- accessories are manufactured to *BS 1363* and supplied through a ring final circuit with or without unfused spurs, protected by a 30 A or 32 A protective device complying with the Standards mentioned in 5c above *and*
- the circuit must be wired with copper conductors having line and neutral conductors with a minimum cross-sectional area (csa) of 2.5 mm^2 (where 2-core mineral insulated cables complying with *BS EN 60702-1* are used, a csa of 1.5 mm^2 is permitted) *and*
- The current-carrying capacity (I_z) of the cable is not less than 20 A *and*
- The load current in any part of the circuit is unlikely to exceed the current-carrying capacity of the cable for long periods.

c. Position of devices for protection against overload

A device for overload protection is usually required to be placed at the point where a reduction occurs in the current-carrying capacity of the conductors of the installation as illustrated in Fig 43.8 below.

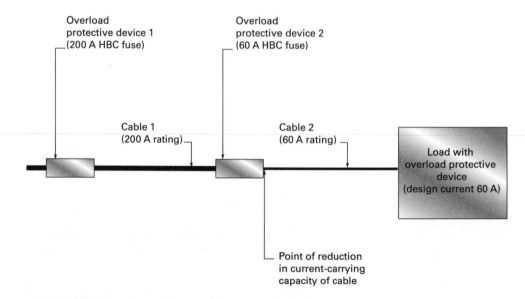

Fig 43.8 Overload protective device positioned at a point of reduction in current-carrying capacity of conductors

If there are no outlets or spurs along the section after the reduction in cross-sectional area, the protective device may be placed along the cable run provided that at least one of the conditions outlined in Regulation 433.2.2 are met.

> **Exercise 43.2**
>
> Review the conditions outlined in Regulation 433.2.2.

d. Omissions of devices for protection against overload

The Regulations provide information relating to the omission of protection against overload in two categories, one for general application, the other for safety reasons.

In relation to general applications there are three situations where a device for protection against overload need not be provided:

(i) Reduction in current-carrying capacity

A device for overload protection is usually required to be placed at the point where a reduction occurs in the current-carrying capacity of conductors. However, this requirement may be relaxed if the conductor is effectively protected against overload by a protective device placed on the supply side of that point. For example, consider a cable having a current-carrying capacity of 100 A carrying a design current of 50 A. If the overload protective device were a 60 A fuse, the current-carrying capacity of the cable could safely be reduced to 60 A at any point along its length, without provision of an overload protective device at that point.

This relaxation is sometimes used where conductors with a larger current-carrying capacity than necessary are used to reduce voltage drop in the circuit and a reduction in cross-sectional area may be necessary to enable the cables to be terminated.

(ii) Characteristics of the load or the supply

Overload protection need not be provided for a conductor which, because of the characteristics of the load or the supply, is not likely to carry overload current.

One example of such a conductor is a flexible cord supporting a lampholder. The flexible cord is not likely to carry overload current because the lampholder will only accommodate lamps up to a certain rating and the lamp current cannot be increased except when there is a fault. Other examples include the conductors of a circuit supplying an electric shower or a water heater where design current cannot be exceeded even at the highest temperature setting. An example of where overload protection need not be provided in relation to the characteristics of the supply would be a generator or battery where the maximum output of the source is limited such that a conductor connected to these devices could not become overloaded.

(iii) Meter tail

The person responsible for an electrical installation need not provide overload protection for the meter tails where the Distributor agrees that their overload device(s) provide(s) overload protection between the origin and the main distribution point of the installation (provided that overload protection is provided at that point).

Chapter 43
Protection against overcurrent

Fig 43.9, below, shows a consumer unit located a short distance from the Distributors overload device. The Distributor will usually agree that their overload device affords protection to the meter tails, provided that certain conditions are met, such as a restriction on the length of the meter tails.

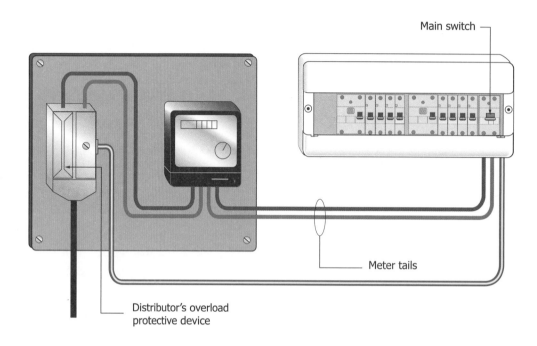

Main switch

Meter tails

Distributor's overload protective device

Fig 43.9 Distributor's equipment may provide overload protection

e. Omission of devices for protection against overload for safety reasons

When considering the omission of a device for overload protection in order to avoid danger from the unexpected disconnection of a circuit, an assessment should be made of the risks involved, taking into account the effects of any foreseeable overload on the equipment and its surroundings. The protective device should not be omitted unless the assessment shows that danger will be prevented as far as reasonably practicable and that unexpected disconnection of the circuit would cause greater danger. In all cases where overload protection is omitted, provision of an overload alarm should be considered. Regulation 433.3.3 gives six examples where the omission of overload protective devices are permitted for safety reasons:

i) Exciter circuits of rotating machines

Danger could be caused by the unexpected disconnection of an exciter circuit of a rotating electrical machine.

ii) Supply circuits of lifting magnets

The unexpected disconnection of the supply circuit of a lifting magnet would cause danger by the unintended release of an object without warning.

Fig 43.10 A lifting magnet

iii) The secondary circuit of a current transformer

The secondary circuit of a current transformer, if open circuited, would result in unacceptably high voltage being induced in the secondary winding, which could cause an insulation failure, fire and electric shock.

iv) A circuit supplying a fire extinguishing device

The consequences of disconnecting a circuit supplying a fire extinguishing device may be more serious than the potential damage to the circuit cable and its surroundings. In this case it would be essential that the extinguishing device continued to operate, for example during a fire, rather than disconnect automatically due to an overload.

v) A circuit supplying a safety service such as a fire alarm or gas alarm

The consequence of disconnecting a circuit supplying a fire alarm or gas alarm may result in safety issues to people or livestock.

vi) A circuit supplying medical equipment used for life support in specific medical locations where an IT system is incorporated.

In medical locations where patients are reliant on life support equipment, such as in intensive care or in operating theatres, the disconnection of a circuit is likely to have serious consequences.

f. Parallel conductors

i) Overload protection of conductors in parallel

Where a single protective device protects two or more conductors in parallel there must be no branch circuits or devices for isolation or switching in the parallel conductors. It should be noted that this regulation does not apply to ring final circuits where spurs are allowed.

notes

ii) Equal current sharing between parallel conductors

Except for a ring final circuit where spurs are permitted, where a single device protects conductors in parallel and the conductors are sharing currents equally, the overall value of current-carrying capacity of the conductors (I_z) is the sum of the current carrying capacities of the parallel conductors (refer to Section 523 of *BS 7671 (523.7)* for further information relating to current sharing).

iii) Unequal current sharing between parallel conductors

Where the use of a single conductor, per phase, is impractical and the currents in the parallel conductors are unequal, the design current and the requirements for overload protection for each conductor must be considered individually.

It should be noted that a difference of greater than 10% between design currents for each conductor is considered unequal. Further information is given in paragraph 2 of Appendix 10 of *BS 7671*.

7. Protection against fault current (Section 434)

Section 434 only considers the case of fault current between conductors belonging to the same circuit.

a. Determination of prospective fault current

The prospective fault current between conductors has to be determined at every relevant point of the installation. It is important to ascertain the highest value of either the line to earth, line to neutral current for a single-phase circuit or line to line for a three-phase circuit. Doubling the line to neutral value would give an approximate value for line to line short-circuit current for a three-phase circuit (where only the line to neutral value is available).

The highest value of prospective fault current will normally be at the origin of the installation. Prospective fault current can be determined by calculation, measurement or enquiry:

- Calculation of the prospective fault current requires information relating to the external supply impedance values.
- The enquiry route involves the Distributor. They will normally quote the maximum value of prospective fault current for a typical installation, not necessarily the one in question. For a domestic property this is most often quoted as 16 kA for a single-phase 100 amp supply.
- The measurement method involves the use of test instruments (normally an earth fault loop impedance tester with the additional provision for line to neutral measurement and prospective fault current settings).

Figs 43.11 and 43.12 below illustrate two types of fault (line to earth and line to line).

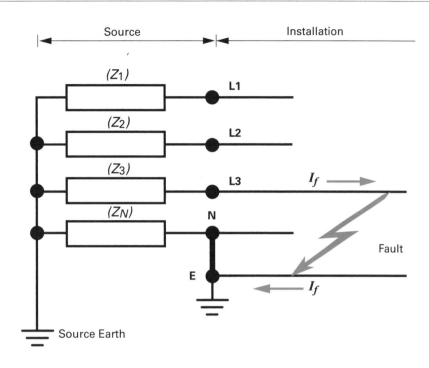

Fig 43.11 Line to earth fault

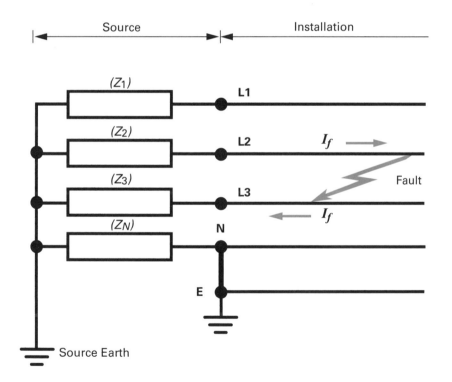

Fig 43.12 Line to line fault

b. Position of devices for fault protection

In the same way that there was a requirement for overload protection, a fault current protective device is also required at the point where a reduction occurs in the value of current-carrying capacity of the conductors (see Fig 43.13 below).

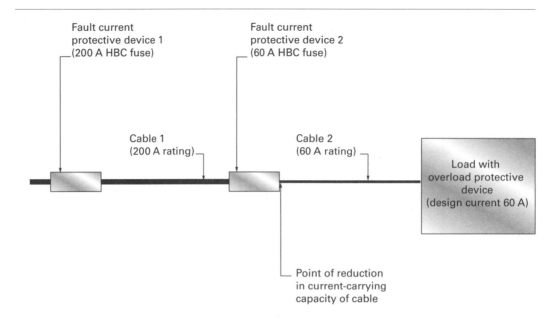

Fig 43.13 Fault current protective device positioned at a point of reduction in current-carrying capacity of conductors

c. Omission of devices for protection against fault current

Just as there was an exception to the requirement for an overload device, there are also exceptions in relation to the requirement to provide a fault current protective device. This exception should not be applied, however, to installations situated in locations presenting a risk of fire or explosion and where the requirements for special installations or locations specify different conditions.

The supply side protective device can be used to provide fault protection where a change occurs (such as cross-sectional area, method of installation, type of cable or environmental conditions), provided that it is ascertained (in accordance with Regulation 434.5.2) that the wiring situated on the load side will not be damaged by the energy let-through of the device.

Another exception relates to the situation which allows the fault current device to be placed on the load side, after the point of reduction in current-carrying capacity, providing the conductor:

• does not exceed 3 m in length, and
• is installed to reduce the risk of fault to a minimum, and
• is installed in a manner to reduce to a minimum the risk of fire or danger to persons.

Fig 43.14 (below) illustrates a typical switchboard arrangement. Normally in this situation the interconnecting cables feeding the outgoing protective devices can be sized in relation to the outgoing devices although they will be connected to a busbar protected by the larger incoming device.

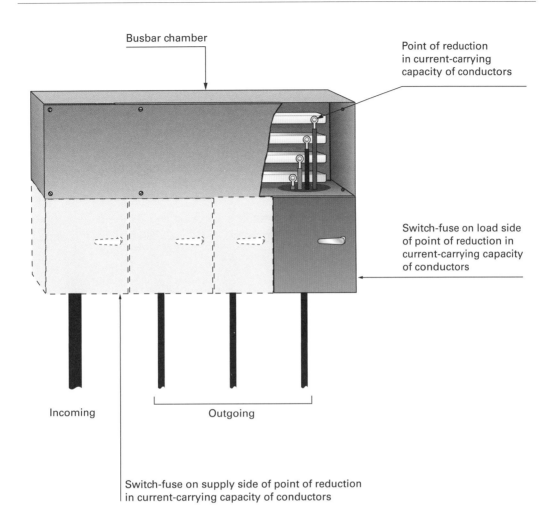

Busbar chamber

Point of reduction
in current-carrying
capacity of conductors

Switch-fuse on load side
of point of reduction in
current-carrying capacity
of conductors

Incoming

Outgoing

Switch-fuse on supply side of point of reduction
in current-carrying capacity of conductors

**Fig 43.14 General arrangement of connections between the busbars and
a switch-fuse of a typical switchboard where there is a reduction in current-carrying
capacity of conductors**

Exercise 43.3

Review Regulation 434.3 for examples where a fault protection device can be omitted.

d. Fault protection of conductors in parallel

A single protective device may protect conductors in parallel against fault currents provided
that the operating characteristic of the device results in its effective operation at the most
onerous position in one of the parallel conductors. Where conductors in parallel are being
installed, Regulation 434.4 and Appendix 10 of *BS 7671* should be reviewed.

e. Characteristics of a fault current protective device

Regulation 434.5.2 states that a fault occurring at any point in a circuit must be interrupted
within a time such that the fault current does not cause the permitted limiting temperature of
any conductor or cable to be exceeded.

Along with the effects of fault currents on conductors, the protective devices themselves also
need to be considered with respect to their breaking capacities. The breaking capacity of the
device must not be less than the prospective fault current at its point of installation.

notes

However, a lower breaking capacity is permitted if another protective device having the necessary breaking capacity is installed on the supply side, and the characteristics of the devices are co-ordinated such that the energy let-through by these two devices does not exceed that current which can be withstood without damage by the device on the load side and the conductors protected by these devices. This is sometimes referred to as 'backup' protection (see Part 2 of *BS 7671* for the definition of *'backup protection'*).

f. Calculation of maximum permissible fault clearance time

Where a protective device is provided for fault current protection up to 5 seconds, the clearance time of the device under fault conditions must not result in the admissible limiting temperature of any live conductors being exceeded. The time *t*, in which a given fault current will raise the live conductors from the highest permissible operating temperature in normal duty to the limiting temperature can, as an approximation, be calculated using the equation given below:

$$t = \frac{k^2 s^2}{I^2}$$

Where:

t   is the duration of the fault, in seconds,

s   is the conductor cross-sectional area in mm^2

I   is the effective fault current, in amperes, expressed for a.c. as the rms value, due account being taken of the current limiting effect of the circuit impedances

k   is a factor, taking account of conductor material, insulation material and the initial and final conductor temperatures

Therefore, as an approximation, for a fault current *I*, the fault current protective device is required to disconnect the faulty circuit in *t* seconds or less, in order to prevent damage to conductors or their insulation.

Table 43.1 of *BS 7671* provides values for **k** for common materials, for calculation of the effects of fault current for disconnection times up to 5 seconds. An example of highest permissible operating temperature (or initial temperature in Table 43.1) and final temperature for a cable (below 300 mm^2) with thermoplastic insulation would be 70 $^{\circ}$C and 160 $^{\circ}$C respectively.

Exercise 43.4

You should now refer to Regulation 434.5.2 and Table 43.1. What does the k stand for in the formula? What is the k value for a 50 mm^2 cable with a copper conductor and 90 $^{\circ}$C thermosetting insulation? What is the k value for 400 mm^2 copper cable with 70 $^{\circ}$C thermoplastic insulation?

8. Co-ordination of overload and fault current protection (Section 435)

In most cases, both fault current protection and overload protection will be provided by a single overcurrent protective device, providing the requirements of Sections 433 and 434 are met and the device has a rated breaking capacity of not less than the value of the prospective fault current at its point of installation.

Where conductors in parallel or certain types of circuit-breaker (e.g. non-current-limiting types) are being used, further checks such as calculations may be required.

Regulation 435.2 requires that where separate devices are used for protection against fault current and overload current, the characteristics of the devices are co-ordinated. The purpose of this requirement is to ensure that the energy let-through by the fault current protective device does not exceed that which can be withstood without damage by the overload current protective device.

Further information relating to overcurrent protection can be found in:
- BS 7671 Chapter 43 and Appendix 11
- Electrical Safety Council Technical Manual articles F13-14, F13-16, F13-17, F13-18, F13-19, F13-20, F13-21, F13-22, F13-29, O57-13, O69-1, O69-5 and P5-5
- IEE Guidance Note 6

CHAPTER 43 FINAL REVISION EXERCISE

43.1 The phrase 'An overcurrent occurring in a circuit which is electrically sound' describes which of the following?
- ☐ a. A short-circuit current
- ☐ b. An earth-fault current
- ☐ c. An overcurrent
- ☐ d. An overload current

43.2 The phrase 'A current exceeding the rated value. For conductors the rated value is the current-carrying capacity' describes which of the following?
- ☐ a. A short-circuit current
- ☐ b. An earth-fault current
- ☐ c. An overcurrent
- ☐ d. An overload current

43.3 In the formula $I_b \leq I_n \leq I_z$, I_n stands for which of the following?
- ☐ a. The design current of the circuit
- ☐ b. The current ensuring effective operation of the protective device
- ☐ c. The nominal current of the protective device
- ☐ d. The current-carrying capacity of the conductor

43.4 In the formula $I_b \leq I_n \leq I_z$, I_b stands for which of the following?
- ☐ a. The design current of the circuit
- ☐ b. The current ensuring effective operation of the protective device
- ☐ c. The nominal current of the protective device
- ☐ d. The current-carrying capacity of the conductor

43.5 In the formula $I_2 \leq 1.45 \times I_z$, I_2 stands for which of the following?
- ☐ a. The design current of the circuit
- ☐ b. The current ensuring effective operation of the protective device
- ☐ c. The nominal current of the protective device
- ☐ d. The current-carrying capacity of the conductor

Chapter 43
Protection against overcurrent

43.6 Where protection for overload is being provided by a BS 3036 fuse, the correction factor that may need to be applied when calculating the required current-carrying capacity of a conductor is which of the following?

- ☐ a. 0.3036
- ☐ b. 0.725
- ☐ c. 0.755
- ☐ d. 1.45

Things to do and find

1. What are the requirements or limitations where protection is required but a reduction in cross-sectional area of a conductor occurs and there is no overcurrent or fault current protection at that point?

2. Give examples of where a device for overload protection may be omitted for safety reasons.

3. List the protective device types outlined in Chapter 43.

4. What are the special conditions or requirements that must be met in relation to ring circuits?

5. Where would you find further information relating to protection of conductors in parallel against overload?

6. Define each of the terms in the formula $t = \dfrac{k^2 s^2}{I^2}$

1. Introduction

Chapter 44 provides requirements for the protection of electrical installations and measures against voltage disturbances and electromagnetic disturbances. These two subjects are referred to in several sections of *BS 7671* and it is worth noting that Chapter 13 Fundamental Principles (Regulation Group 131.6) outlines the general requirements that need to be assessed by electrical designers and installers.

As well as the introductory Section 440 (Section 441 is not used), Chapter 44 of *BS 7671* contains four other sections:

- Section 442 Protection of low voltage installations against temporary overvoltages and faults between high voltage systems and earth
- Section 443 Protection against overvoltages of atmospheric origin or due to switching
- Section 444 Measures against electromagnetic influences (reserved for future use)
- Section 445 Measures against undervoltage.

It should be noted that Section 444, Measures against electromagnetic influences, is 'reserved for future use'. However, a short section is included in this Learning Guide based on the requirements of Regulation 131.6.4 and miscellaneous references throughout *BS 7671*.

The aim of Chapter 44, in addition to Regulation Group 131.6, is to protect persons and livestock against injury and to protect property against the harmful effects as a consequence of:

- A fault between live parts of circuits supplied at different voltages
- Overvoltages such as those originating from atmospheric events or from switching
- Undervoltage and any subsequent voltage recovery.

In summary, Chapter 44 addresses the problems that may occur in consumers' installations as a result of voltage variations, both overvoltage and undervoltage. Voltage disturbances can cause serious damage to electrical installations such as insulation or equipment failure, with the consequential risk of electric shock or fire. An overvoltage, though not defined in *BS 7671*, is a voltage in excess of the normal voltage design range of an item of equipment.

2. Section 442 Protection of low voltage installations against temporary overvoltages due to earth faults in the high voltage system due to faults in the low voltage system.

Faults occurring on both the high voltage (HV) and low voltage (LV) distribution network may have an impact on and compromise the safety of the consumers' low voltage installation. Although *BS 7671* only covers low voltage systems, Section 442 of *BS 7671* also requires the effects of faults on the high voltage system to be considered.

It is worth noting that both HV and LV distribution networks can be supplied from either a Distributor or from a private source.

Section 442 outlines four situations that can have an effect on the safety of the LV installation by creating temporary overvoltages:

- Faults between the HV system(s) and Earth in the transformer substation that supplies the LV installation. (Regulation Group 442.2)
- Loss of the supply neutral. (Regulation 442.3)

Chapter 44
Protection against voltage disturbances and electromagnetic disturbances

• Accidental earthing of a line conductor of an LV IT system. (Regulation 442.4)
• Short circuit between a line conductor and neutral in the LV installation. (Regulation 442.5)

Regulation Group 442.2 provides the requirements where a fault to Earth may occur in the HV side of the substation which may have an affect on the LV side of the substation and connected LV network. Where HV and LV earthing systems are in close proximity, two practices are presently used to reduce the affects of overvoltages on the earthing system, either interconnection of all HV and LV earthing systems or separation of all HV and LV earthing systems. Interconnection of HV and LV earthing systems would be the general method where the combined electrodes are less than 1 Ω and this figure is recommended in *BS 7430* Code of practice for earthing. Where this value cannot be achieved the recommendation is to install separate electrodes with a minimum distance of 3 metres between electrodes. Calculations (provided in Regulation Group 442.2) are also required to assess the magnitude and duration of power frequency stress voltages and power frequency fault voltages that can be produced when HV earth faults occur.

It should be noted that compliance for ensuring the effectiveness and safety of the HV system is normally the responsibility of the substation installer/owner/operator and therefore the calculations required by Section 442 are not normally necessary by the LV system installer. Further to this, Regulation 442.2 and 442.3 are deemed to be fulfilled for installations receiving a supply at LV from a system for distribution of electricity to the public.

Regulations 442.3, 442.4 and 442.5 require consideration to be given to the effects of power frequency stress voltage due to:

• the loss of the neutral in a TN or TT system or,
• an earth fault in an IT system or
• a short-circuit between a line conductor and the neutral conductor.

It should be noted that if a short-circuit occurs in a LV installation between a line and the neutral conductor, the voltage between the other line conductors and the neutral conductor can reach up to 1.45 U_0 for up to 5 seconds.

3. Section 443 Protection against overvoltages of atmospheric origin or due to switching.

a. Protection against overvoltages of atmospheric origin

Section 443 deals with protection of electrical installations against transient overvoltages of atmospheric origin transmitted by the supply distribution system and against switching overvoltages generated by the equipment within the installation.

The term 'overvoltages of atmospheric origin' relates to lightning although direct lightning strikes on the LV lines of supply network or on electrical installations are not taken into account in Section 443. Often, overvoltages of atmospheric origin are induced into overhead lines by nearby lighting strikes or the close proximity and movement of charged clouds.

Fig 44.1 Lightning strike near overhead power lines

Two levels of protection against overvoltage are identified by Section 443:

a. Basic protection, which relies upon the equipment of the installation having an adequate impulse withstand voltage for its intended use. The rated impulse withstand voltage of an item of equipment is the peak value of an impulse voltage of prescribed form and polarity that the equipment can withstand under specified test conditions without failure.

b. Additional protection, usually by provision of surge protection devices. Such protection is not required in the majority of installations in the United Kingdom.

Where an installation is supplied by an LV system containing no overhead lines, no additional equipment protection against overvoltage of atmospheric origin is necessary providing the impulse withstand voltage of equipment is in accordance with Table 44.3. (see below). A suspended cable having insulated conductors with earthed metallic covering is deemed to be an underground cable for the purposes of Regulation 443.2.1.

Where an installation is *supplied by an LV network* which includes overhead lines or where the installation includes an overhead line and in either case the condition of external influence **AQ1** exists, no additional protection against overvoltage of atmospheric origin is required providing the impulse withstand voltage of equipment is in accordance with Table 44.3 (see below). The external influence AQ relates to the number of thunderstorm days per year, AQ1 being 25 or less and AQ2 being more than 25.

Chapter 44
Protection against voltage disturbances and electromagnetic disturbances

Table 44.3 (Reproduced from *BS 7671*) Required minimum impulse withstand voltage

Nominal voltage of the installation V	Required minimum impulse withstand voltage kV*			
	Category IV (equipment with very high impulse voltage)	Category III (equipment with high impulse voltage)	Category II (equipment with normal impulse voltage)	Category I (equipment with reduced impulse voltage)
230/240 or 277/480	6	4	2.5	1.5
400/690	8	6	4	2.5
1000	12	8	6	4

* This impulse withstand voltage is applied between live conductors and PE

The shaded cells in the above table relate to where the nominal voltage (U_0/U) is 230/400 V, as is the case in most installations.

The categories of equipment, mentioned in Table 44.3 above, relate to the type of equipment and their location within an electrical installation. Table 44.4 of *BS 7671* provides examples of equipment falling into categories I to IV.

As an alternative to the above AQ criteria, the use of surge suppression may be based on a risk assessment method. In this case, information relating to the critical length of incoming lines and the level of consequences (the usage and importance of the installation) will be required.

Exercise 44.1

(1) Name three types of fault or incident that could cause a temporary overvoltage. (2) What is the required minimum impulse voltages (in kV) for equipment in Category II?

b. Switching overvoltages generated within an installation

Overvoltage may be generated *within an installation* as the result of switching high current loads, inductive loads, such as motors, transformers or arc welding equipment, or capacitive loads, such as power factor correction equipment. Dependent upon the particular point in the a.c. current waveform at which the switching takes place, an overvoltage in the order of 250 V to 3 000 V can be generated when the current drawn by an inductive load is interrupted.

In addition to the above overvoltages, high frequency transient overvoltage surges can be generated by the operation of electronic switches, such as may be used in speed controllers of electrical plant.

4. Section 444 Measures against electromagnetic influences.

Although Section 444 is reserved for future use, several sections of *BS 7671* refer to electromagnetic influences and the requirement to ensure installations have an adequate level of immunity against their effects.

Electromagnetic compatibility (EMC) is the requirement for the correct design and functioning of equipment to ensure electromagnetic radiation generated from equipment does not cause other equipment in the vicinity to malfunction. Further references in *BS 7671* to electromagnetic influence and electromagnetic compatibility can be found in Regulation 131.6.4, Section 332, Regulation Group 515.3 and Regulation Group 521.5.

notes

Key Facts
'Designers and installers need to consider supply conditions and/or equipment that could affect or be affected by over or under voltages'

5. Section 445 Protection against undervoltage.

Undervoltage on a system is a condition used to describe a reduction or complete loss of supply voltage.

A reduction or loss in voltage may occur to such a level so as to cause failure of equipment or in some cases damage depending on the nature of the equipment connected.

Where a total loss of voltage occurs there is also a danger that equipment may restart unexpectedly on restoration of supply. *BS 7671*, therefore, requires suitable precautions to be taken where a reduction in voltage, or loss and subsequent restoration of voltage, could cause danger. Regulation 445.1.1 refers to Regulation 552.1.3 in relation to *circuits supplying motors*. This latter regulation requires every motor to be fitted with means to prevent automatic restarting after a stoppage due to a drop in voltage or failure of supply, where unexpected restarting of the motor might cause danger. One way to meet this requirement is by the use of starters incorporating undervoltage relays with manual restarting facilities.

Where current-using equipment or any other part of the installation may be damaged by a drop in voltage and it is verified that such damage is unlikely to cause danger, one of the following arrangements shall be adopted:

• Provision of suitable precautions against the foreseen damage

• Consultation with the person or body responsible for the operation and maintenance of the installation to verify that the foreseen damage is an acceptable risk.

An undervoltage protective device may incorporate a suitable time delay if the operation of the equipment to which the protection relates allows, without danger, a brief reduction or loss of voltage. Any delay in the opening or reclosing of a contactor should not impede instantaneous disconnection by a control device or a protective device.

Where the reclosure of a protective device is likely to cause danger, the reclosure should not be automatic.

Exercise 44.2

What type of circuit will nearly always require a means to prevent automatic restarting after a stoppage due to a drop in voltage or failure of supply?

Further information relating to protection against voltage disturbances and electromagnetic disturbances can be found in:
• *BS 7671* Chapter 44
• *BS 7430* Code of practice for earthing
• Electrical Safety Council Technical Manual articles C121-1, M169-1, P153-1, V29-5and V29-9
• IEE Guidance Note 1

notes

CHAPTER 44 FINAL REVISION EXERCISE

44.1 In relation to required minimum impulse withstand voltages; the description 'equipment with normal impulse voltage' describes which of the following?
- [ ] a. Category I
- [ ] b. Category II
- [ ] c. Category III
- [ ] d. Category IV

44.2 Which of the following is the required minimum impulse withstand voltage for Category **II** equipment with a nominal voltage of 230 V?
- [ ] a. 1.5 kV
- [ ] b. 2.5 kV
- [ ] c. 4.0 kV
- [ ] d. 6.0 kV

44.3 Which of the following circuits is most likely to require a means to prevent automatic restarting after a stoppage due to a drop in voltage or failure of supply?
- [ ] a. A lighting circuit
- [ ] b. A water heater circuit
- [ ] c. A floor heating circuit
- [ ] d. A motor circuit

44.4 Following the restoration of supply after a power failure and where the reclosure of a protective device is likely to cause danger, the reclosure should be which of the following?
- [ ] a. Automatic
- [ ] b. Electronic
- [ ] c. Non-automatic
- [ ] d. Solid-state

44.5 Which of the following best describes the external influence code AQ2 (thunderstorm days per year)?
- [ ] a. Negligible
- [ ] b. More than 25 thunderstorm days per year
- [ ] c. Indirect exposure
- [ ] d. Direct exposure

44.6 Where a supply is provided by a suspended cable having insulated conductors with earthed metallic covering, which of the following forms of protection against overvoltage of atmospheric origin is necessary if the impulse withstand voltage of equipment is in accordance with Table 44.3 of *BS 7671*?
- [ ] a. No additional protection is required
- [ ] b. Surge protective devices are required
- [ ] c. Transient voltage devices are required
- [ ] d. Metal oxide varistor are required

Things to do and find

1. List the four faults or events covered by Regulation Group 442.1

2. Which Table in *BS 7671* provides information relating to 'Required minimum impulse withstand voltage'?

3. What is the required minimum impulse withstand voltage for Category III equipment with a nominal installation voltage of 400 V?

4. *'Equipment to be used at or in close proximity to the origin of the electrical installation upstream of the main distribution board, e.g. electricity meter, primary overcurrent device, ripple control unit'* is a description of which impulse equipment category?

Part 5
Selection and erection of equipment

1. Introduction

notes

Chapter 51 deals with the selection of equipment and its erection. It provides common rules for compliance with measures of protection for safety, requirements for proper functioning for intended use of the installation, and requirements appropriate to the external influences.

Every item of equipment should be selected and erected so as to allow compliance with *BS 7671*. Manufacturers' instructions should also be taken into account.

2. Compliance with standards

Each item of equipment used in an electrical installation must comply with the relevant requirements of the applicable current British Standard or Harmonised European standard. Alternatively, if equipment complying with a foreign national standard based on an IEC standard is to be used, the designer or specifier must verify that any differences between these Standards will not result in a lesser degree of safety.

> **Exersise 51.1**
>
> Refer to Regulation 511.1 to review the situation where a British or Harmonized Standard is not being used. What does Regulation 120.4 require in this situation?

3. Operational conditions and external influences

Every item of equipment must be suitable for the:

- Nominal voltage of the system *and*
- The design current allowing for capacitive and inductive effects, *and*
- The current likely to flow in abnormal conditions (the characteristics of the protective device will affect the duration of the current) *and*
- The frequency *and*
- Power characteristics *and*
- Compatibility with other equipment

It should be noted that switchgear, protective devices, accessories etc must not be connected to conductors intended to operate at a temperature exceeding 70 °C unless the equipment manufacturer has confirmed that the equipment is suitable for such conditions. This should be given serious consideration when utilizing for example, steel wire armoured cables that use thermosetting insulation as, when carrying their "maximum rated current", their conductors would be operating at or near 90 °C.

4. External influences

Electrical equipment should be appropriate for the situation in which it is to be installed and used. The conditions likely to be encountered should be considered including any external influences. External influences are covered in Part 2 of this Learning Guide as well as Appendix 5 of *BS 7671*. The correct selection of equipment is important for proper functioning, and to ensure the reliability of the measures for protection for safety.

Chapter 51
Common rules (selection and erection of equipment)

5. Accessibility

All equipment must be installed so that it can be easily operated, inspected and maintained and provide ease of access to any connections. This requirement does not apply to joints in cables where such joints are permitted to be inaccessible as detailed in Section 526.

6. Identification and notices

a. General

Section 514 covers the extensive requirements for identification and notices. This includes advisory and warning notices as well as colour identification of cables and wiring systems. The general requirements are that unless there is no possibility of confusion, each item of switchgear or controlgear should be provided with a label, or some other suitable means of identification, indicating its purpose. Where the operation of the switchgear or controlgear cannot be witnessed by the operator, and where this might lead to danger, a suitable indicator must be installed in a prominent position, clearly visible to the operator.

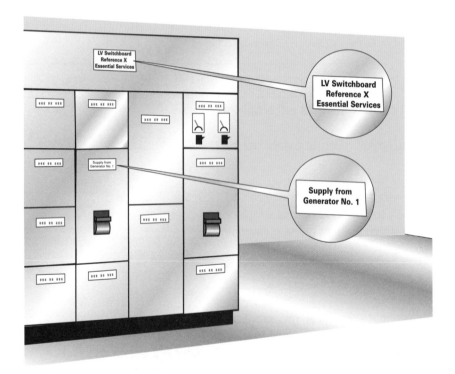

Fig 51.1 Switchboard, showing typical labeling for identification

Wiring must also be arranged and/or marked, so that it can be identified for inspection, testing, repair or alteration of the installation.

51.2 Example of a cable identification marker

b. Identification of conductors and wiring systems

Except where identification is not required, cores of cables should be identified by colour, letters or numbers. Table 51 (reproduced below) of *BS 7671*, provides the details in relation to identification of conductors.

The changes to the colour identification of conductors in fixed wiring were introduced by *Amendment No 2 to BS 7671 : 2001* on 31 March 2004. The new colours are the European harmonised colours. Appendix 7 of *BS 7671* provides further information relating to the changes to colour identification. Where newly installed cables interface with conductors identified to previous versions, the guidance in Appendix 7 of *BS 7671* should be followed.

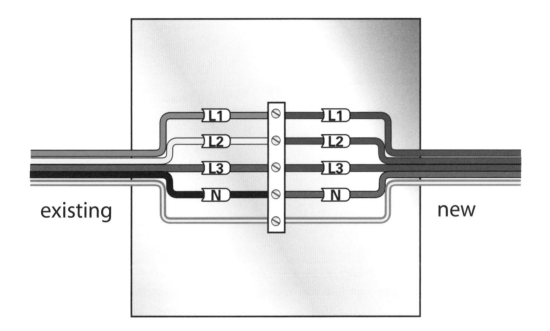

existing   new

Key Facts
'Double check conductor colours, especially on older installations to make sure you have correct polarity'

Fig 51.3 Typical arrangement for colour identification at an interface of different colour coded conductors

---

Exersise 51.2

Refer to Section 514 of *BS 7671* (1) Where cores of cables are marked, where should identification be placed? (2) What should the colour of a conduit be where it is to be distinguished from other services?

Table 51 (Learning Guide table derived from Table 51 of *BS 7671*) Identification of conductors.

TABLE 51 - Identification of conductors

Function		Colour	Alpha numeric
Protective conductors		Green-and-yellow	
Functional earthing conductor		Cream	
a.c. power circuit[1]			
Line of single-phase circuit		Brown	L
Neutral of single- or three-phase circuit		Blue	N
Line 1 of three-phase circuit		Brown	L1
Line 2 of three-phase circuit		Black	L2
Line 3 of three-phase circuit		Grey	L3
Two-wire unearthed d.c. power circuit			
Positive of two-wire circuit		Brown	L+
Negative of two-wire circuit		Grey	L-
Two-wire earthed d.c. power circuit			
Positive (of negative earthed) circuit		Brown	L+
Negative (of negative earthed) circuit[2]		Blue	M
Positive (of positive earthed) circuit[2]		Blue	M
Negative (of positive earthed) circuit		Grey	L-
Three-wire d.c. power circuit			
Outer positive of two-wire circuit derived from three-wire system		Brown	L+
Outer negative of two-wire circuit derived from three-wire system		Grey	L-
Positive of three-wire circuit		Brown	L+
Mid-wire of three-wire circuit[2][3]		Blue	M
Negative of three-wire circuit		Grey	L-
Control circuits, ELV and other applications			
Line conductor		Grey	L

	Brown		Orange		White
	Black		Yellow		Pink, or
	Red		Violet		Turquoise

Neutral or mid-wire[4]		Blue	N or M

NOTES: [1] Power circuits include lighting circuits.
[2] M identifies either the mid-wire of a three-wire d.c. circuit, or the earthed conductor of a two-wire earthed dc circuit.
[3] Only the middle wire of three-wire circuits may be earthed.
[4] An earthed PELV conductor is blue.

Exersise 51.3

You should now refer to Regulation 514.6 to review typical situations where identification by colour or marking may be omitted.

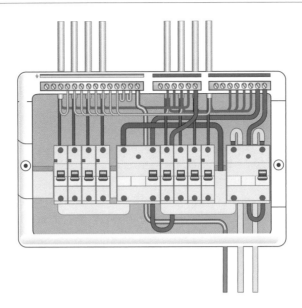

Fig 51.4 Single-phase a.c. colour identification

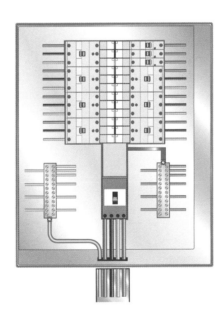

Fig 51.5 Three-phase a.c. colour identification

The colour for protective conductors, as indicated in Table 51, is green-and-yellow, this combination being reserved solely for these conductors. The Regulations also stipulate that, apart from PEN conductors, single-core cables coloured green-and-yellow throughout their length should not be over-marked at their terminations. The green-and-yellow combination should not be less than 30% or more than 70% for each colour. Conductors with green-and-yellow colour identification must not be numbered, other than for the purpose of circuit identification. The single colour green must not be used.

Exersise 51.4

Refer to regulation 514.4.2 to review the identification requirements for bare conductors or busbars used as protective conductors.

Chapter 51
Common rules (selection and erection of equipment)

Where bare conductors are used for line or neutral operation, they should also be identified where necessary, by application of tape, sleeve, paint or disc of the appropriate colour.

c. Identification of protective devices

Circuit protective devices are required to be arranged and identified so that the circuit protected may be easily recognized.

In distribution boards where it is impracticable to individually label protective devices, the protective devices may be identified by means of a durable chart or schedule fitted inside the cover of, or adjacent to, the distribution board. The chart may, for example, show the physical layout of the outgoing ways of the distribution board and identify the circuit associated with each. Alternatively, if each way is given a reference (e.g. 'B1' for *brown phase, way number one*), a schedule listing each way by reference and identifying the associated circuit may be used.

d. Diagrams

A legible diagram, chart or table or equivalent form of information must be provided indicating the following:
* the type, and composition of each circuit (number of points served, number and size of conductors, type of wiring) *and*,
* the method for providing shock protection (which protective measure (such as ADS) has been provided) *and*
* the information necessary for the identification of each device performing the functions of protection, isolation and switching, and its location, *and*
* any circuit or equipment vulnerable to a typical test.

For simple installations the above information may be given in a schedule. A durable copy of the schedule relating to the distribution board must be provided within or adjacent to each distribution board.

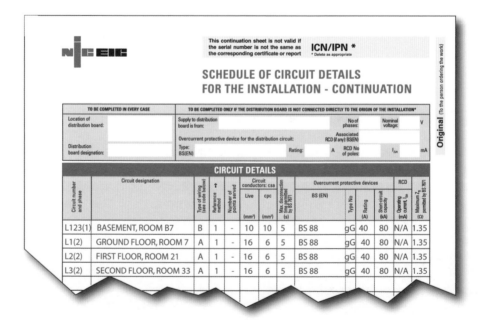

Fig 51.6 An example of the information required for a circuit chart can be found on an electrical installation certificate (test schedule)

e. Advisory and warning notices, general

BS 7671 contains many requirements for notices. Some are for advice or information; many are to provide warnings to operatives and/or the general public. The following text outlines the notices required by Section 514. It should be noted, however, that more specific notices are dealt with in other sections of *BS 7671*.

f. Warning notice – voltage

Where a nominal voltage exceeding 230 volts exists within an item of equipment or enclosure and where the presence of such a voltage would not normally be expected, a warning of the maximum voltage present must be clearly visible before access is gained to a live part.

g. Warning notice - Isolation

Where an item of equipment or an enclosure contains live parts that are not capable of being isolated by a single device and no interlocking arrangement is provided to ensure that all the circuits concerned are isolated prior to gaining access, then Regulation 537.2.1.3 requires a durable warning notice to be provided.

The notice should be permanently fixed in such a position as to warn persons, prior to their gaining access, of the danger of live parts and the need to isolate using the appropriate isolating devices. In addition the notice is required by Regulation 514.11.1 to indicate the location of each appropriate isolation device, unless there is no possibility of confusion.

Danger live parts. Isolate before gaining access by opening the motor starter switch-disconnector for Extractor Fan No. 1 and Extractor Fan No. 2.

Fig 51.7 A typical danger label for an enclosure containing live parts

h. Warning notice - earthing and bonding connections

A permanent label is required to be fixed in a visible position at or near:

• the point of connection of every earthing conductor to an earth electrode, and
• the point of connection of every bonding conductor to an extraneous-conductive-part, *and*
• the main earth terminal, where separate from main switchgear.

The label should comply with *BS 951* which requires the words ***"Safety Electrical Connection - Do Not Remove"*** to be inscribed.

Fig 51.8 A typical warning label supplied with a BS 951 earthing and bonding clamp

i. Warning notice – non-standard colours

If an extension, alteration or repair is made to an installation such that cores of both the old colours, red, yellow, blue & black, and the new colours, brown, black, grey & blue are present, a warning notice must be affixed at or near the appropriate distribution board or consumer unit with the wording as illustrated in Fig 51.9 below.

CAUTION

**This installation has wiring colours
to two versions of BS 7671.**

**Great care should be taken before
undertaking extension, alteration or repair
that all conductors are correctly identified.**

Fig 51.9 Warning notice to indicate old and new colour identification codes

j. Notice - periodic inspection and testing

A notice, which is likely to remain easily legible throughout the life of the installation, should be fixed in a prominent position at or near the origin of every installation upon completion of the work carried out.

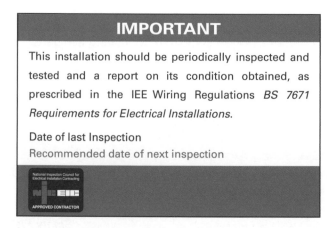

Fig 51.10 Periodic inspection and test notice (label)

k. Notice- RCD quarterly re-test requirement

Where an installation incorporates a residual current device, a notice should be fixed in a prominent position at or near the origin of the installation. The notice should be in indelible characters as shown in Fig 51.11 below

> This installation, or part of it, is protected by a device which automatically switches off the supply if an earth fault develops. Test quarterly by pressing the button marked 'T' or 'Test'. The device should switch off the supply and should then be switched on to restore the supply. If the device does not switch off the supply when the button is pressed, seek expert advice.

Fig 51.11 RCD quarterly retest notice (label)

---

7. Prevention of mutual detrimental influence

a. General

The designer and installer of an electrical installation are required to take account of not only the external influences, but also of influences that are mutually detrimental. These include influences that other services or structural components of the building may have on the electrical installation. Further, the effects of the electrical installation on other services, or indeed other parts of the electrical installation, must also be given due consideration.

The above requirements also corresponds with Regulation 131.1.1 of *BS 7671*, which requires that an electrical installation is arranged in such a way that no mutual detrimental influence will occur between different electrical installations and non-electrical installations of the building, account being taken of electromagnetic interference.

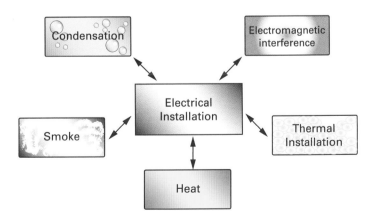

Fig 51.12 Examples of possible mutual detrimental influences acting on, from, or within an electrical installation

Chapter 51
Common rules (selection and erection of equipment)

b. Different voltages and different types of current

Where circuits and equipment of different voltages, or carrying different types of current (such as a.c. or d.c.), are grouped together in a common assembly such as a switchboard, they should be effectively segregated to avoid mutual detrimental influence. This subject is covered further in Section 528 of this Learning Guide.

c. Electromagnetic interference

EMC relates to the electromagnetic radiation generated from equipment which can cause other equipment in the vicinity to malfunction. Electrical equipment should be chosen with sufficiently low emission levels so that it cannot cause unacceptable electromagnetic interference with other electrical equipment by electrical induction or propagation in the air.

Further information relating to *Chapter 51 Selection* and *erection of equipment – Common rules* can be found in:
- BS 7671 Chapter 51
- Electrical Safety Council Technical Manual articles C41-1, I1-1, I1-9, I1-17, I1-21 and M169-1

CHAPTER 51 FINAL REVISION EXERCISE

51.1 Which of the following single colours must not be used to identify conductors?
- ☐ a. Green
- ☐ b. Black
- ☐ c. Yellow
- ☐ d. Blue

51.2 Which of the following is not required on a circuit chart?
- ☐ a. Equipment vulnerable to a typical test
- ☐ b. The information necessary for the identification of each protection device
- ☐ c. The earth fault loop test results
- ☐ d. The type and composition of each circuit

51.3 Which of the following is not specified as a location requiring an earthing and bonding warning notice?
- ☐ a. The point of connection to a residual current device
- ☐ b. The main earthing terminal, where separate from the main switchgear
- ☐ c. The point of connection of every bonding conductor to an extraneous-conductive-part
- ☐ d. The point of connection of every earthing conductor to an earth electrode

51.4 Which of the following is not listed in *BS 7671* as a "warning notice"?
- ☐ a. Where a voltage exceeds 230 V and its presence is not expected
- ☐ b. At points of earthing and bonding connections
- ☐ c. Where both old and new wiring colours exist in an installation
- ☐ d. To indicate the completion and retest dates of an installation

51.5 Line 3 of a three-phase a.c. circuit should be identified by which of the following?
☐ a. Black or L1
☐ b. Black or L2
☐ c. Brown or L2
☐ d. Grey or L3

51.6 Which of the following describes the harmful effects of an electrical installation on the non-electrical installation?
☐ a. Electromagnetic compatibility
☐ b. Mutual detrimental influence
☐ c. External influence
☐ d. Maintainability

Things to do and find

1. List the matters to be considered in relation to suitability of equipment and operational conditions.

2. Where would you find the full list of external influences in *BS7671*?

3. List four different examples of warning notices.

4. What colour should be used to identify a conductor used for the mid-wire of a three-wire d.c. circuit?

5. List the items required for a circuit identification schedule at a distribution board. Where should this schedule be located?

6. What is the correct periodic frequency for insertion on an RCD retest label to inform tenants that the RCD should be operated to ensure continuing mechanical reliability?

7. Which British Standard should the warning notice at an earthing or bonding connection be in compliance with?

8. What types of protective measure would be in place where a warning notice that indicates *'The equipotential protective bonding associated with the electrical installation in this location MUST NOT BE CONNECTED TO EARTH. Equipment having exposed-conductive-parts connected to earth must not be brought into this location'* is used?

1. Introduction to Chapter 52 and Section 520

The correct selection and erection of a wiring system is important to ensure that it is suitable for its intended purpose and that consideration has been given to any external influences that the wiring system may be subjected to.

A wiring system is an assembly made up of bare, non-sheathed or sheathed cables or bus bars and the parts which secure and if necessary enclose the cables or busbars. The term 'wiring system', therefore, covers a large section of what the electrician installs as part of his day-to-day work, both the containment e.g. trunking, conduit, cable tray, basket tray etc and the installed cables (single-core or multicore cables, sheathed or non-sheathed).

It should also be remembered that Chapter 52 also applies to protective conductors, although Chapter 54 of *BS 7671* should also be consulted for further requirements associated with those conductors.

Chapter 52 of *BS 7671* provides requirements in addition to the fundamental principles of Chapter 13 specifically in relation to:

- cables and conductors
- their connections, terminations and/or jointing
- their associated supports or suspensions and
- their enclosures or methods of protection against external influences.

2. Section 521 Types of wiring system

a. General

The installation methods of wiring systems, in relation to the conductors and cables, must be in accordance with Table 4A1 of Appendix 4 of *BS 7671*, provided any external influences are taken into account. Table 4A1 states which installation methods are appropriate to commonly installed conductors and cables.

An example of the use of Table 4A1 is that non-sheathed cables are not permitted to be clipped direct, but are permitted in conduit, trunking and ducting systems.

> **Exercise 520.1**
>
> Refer to Table 4A1. Can a non-sheathed cable (line or neutral conductors) be run on a cable ladder, cable tray or cable brackets?

The installation methods of wiring systems, in relation to the selection of cables for current carrying capacity, are provided in Table 4A2 of Appendix 4. These tables are used by first finding the **installation method**, and then the reference method related to it. The **reference method** is then used when determining the current-carrying capacity of a cable or flexible cord from Tables 4D1A to 4J4A.

Note: The subject current-carrying capacity of cables is covered fully in Section 523 of this Learning Guide.

notes

> **Exercise 520.2**
>
> Refer to Table 4A2: Identify which reference method, in relation to the installation method, is to be used to obtain current-carrying capacity where:
> a) Non-sheathed cables are run in conduit on a wooden or masonry wall
> b) A twin flat and earth cable is clipped direct to a wooden joist above a plasterboard ceiling with thermal insulation not exceeding 100 mm.
> c) Multicore cables are installed on horizontally run wire mesh tray

b. Busbar trunking systems and powertrack systems

Busbar trunking systems are commonly used in buildings in a variety of ways to distribute electricity. In multi-storey commercial or domestic properties they are often used to provide supplies to individual floors (sometimes known as rising-mains). Tap-off boxes then supply distribution boards to feed power and lighting on each floor. Busbar trunking systems (often overhead) are also used to supply machinery, this facility providing flexibility when the connected equipment may require frequent movement. Busbar trunking systems are also used in industrial and commercial premises to provide both distribution and final circuitry by using interconnecting busbar trunking of different ratings. Busbar trunking systems are available with a wide range of current ratings up to several thousand amperes and are designed to be installed in installations where there may be high fault levels.

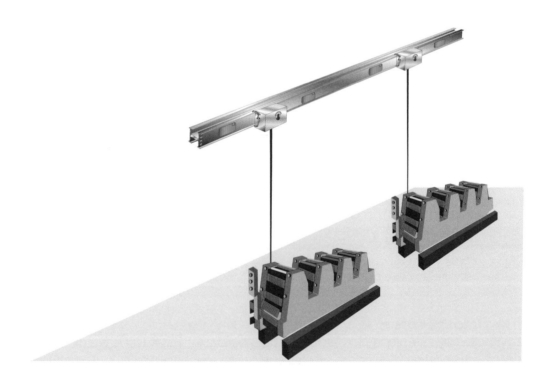

Fig 521.1 Overhead busbar trunking feeding machines

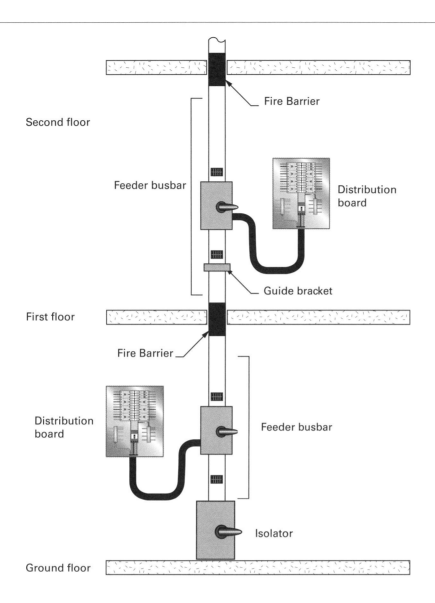

Fig 521.2 Rising main busbar trunking

Busbar trunking systems must be installed in accordance with manufacturer's instructions, taking account of any external influences.

Exercise 520.3

State an external influence that may need be to be considered in relation to:
a) A vertical busbar system within a multi-storey block of dwellings.
b) An overhead busbar system for workshop machinery

Powertrack systems are normally used as supplies to final circuits. They are commonly used for under-floor distribution systems feeding socket-outlets or office furniture or above ceilings to provide supplies and final connection points to luminaires. They have a maximum rating of 63 A.

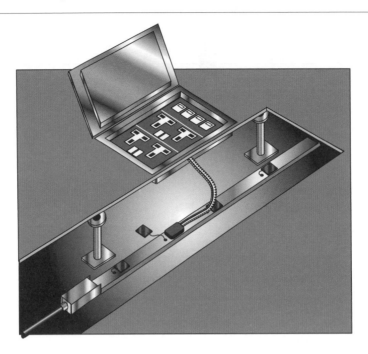

521.3 Under-floor powertrack system

Note: Appendix 8 of *BS 7671* outlines the specific points to note in relation to the current-carrying capacity and voltage drop for busbar trunking and powertrack systems.

c. A.C. circuits – electromagnetic effects

Electromagnetic effects from incorrectly installed cables of alternating current (a.c.) circuits can cause heat to be generated in the metal of ferromagnetic enclosures, such as steel conduit or steel equipment housings. To prevent such heat, which may damage cables and other materials, *BS 7671* calls for the following requirements to be met:

(a)	Single-core cables armoured with steel wire or steel tape must not be used for a.c. circuits
(b)	Conductors of a.c. circuits installed in ferromagnetic enclosures (such as steel conduit, trunking or ducting) must be arranged so that the conductors of all line and the related neutral conductor (if any) and the appropriate protective conductor of each circuit are contained in the same enclosure
(c)	Where such conductors enter a ferromagnetic enclosure, they must be arranged so that they are not individually surrounded by ferromagnetic material, or other provision must be made to prevent eddy (induced) currents.

Every conductor or cable must have adequate strength and be so installed to withstand the electromechanical forces that may be caused by current, including fault current which it may carry in service.

Where single-core cables enter a ferromagnetic enclosure (for example a distribution board) all the conductors of the circuit including line, neutral and any associated protective conductors must pass through the same entry and not enter through separate entries This also applies to cables passing through holes in steel trunking.

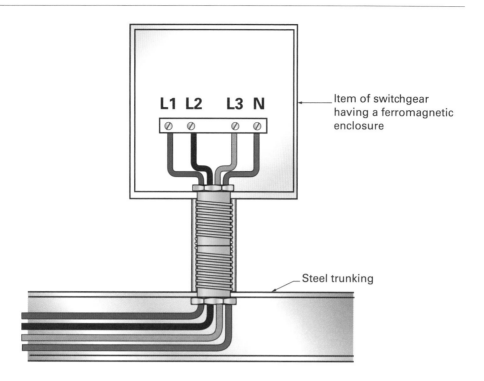

L1 L2   L3 N

Item of switchgear
having a ferromagnetic
enclosure

Steel trunking

Fig 521.4. All cables passing through the same entry/exit hole

The above diagram illustrates the situation where all conductors enter or leave an enclosure by the same entry. Where this is not possible, for example due to the type of wiring system being used, a non-ferromagnetic metal or non-metallic fixing plate can be used (Fig 521.5) or if a ferromagnetic plate is used, a slot can be inserted between conductors, as illustrated (Fig 521.6) below:

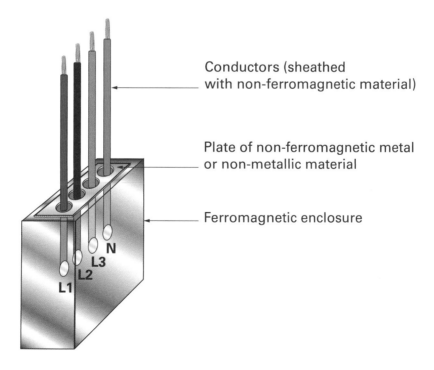

Conductors (sheathed
with non-ferromagnetic material)

Plate of non-ferromagnetic metal
or non-metallic material

Ferromagnetic enclosure

N
L3
L2
L1

Fig 521.5 Non-ferromagnetic metal or non-metallic entry plate

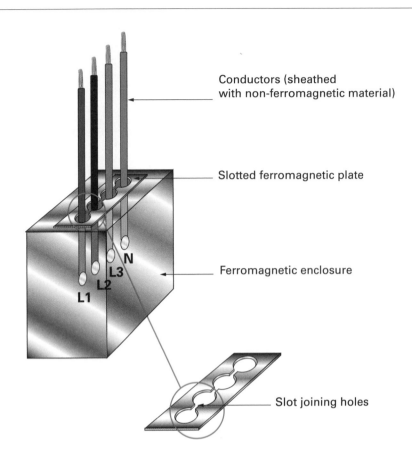

Conductors (sheathed
with non-ferromagnetic material)

Slotted ferromagnetic plate

N
L3
L2
L1

Ferromagnetic enclosure

Slot joining holes

Fig 521.6 Ferro-magnetic fixing plate with slots between conductors

d. Conduit, ducting, trunking and ladder systems

Regulation 521.6 states that two or more circuits are allowed in the same conduit, ducting or trunking system provided that the requirements of Section 528 of *BS 7671* are met. Section 528 considers the proximity of wiring systems to other services and includes requirements to ensure that where a wiring system is installed in the vicinity of services that produce detrimental influences, precautions should be provided to protect the wiring system (see Section 528 of *BS 7671* and/or this Learning Guide for more details).

e. Multicore cables

A multi-core cable must not contain two or more Band I and Band II circuits unless the requirements of Section 528 are met. Section 528 requires, amongst other things, that each conductor of a multicore cable is insulated for the highest voltage present in the cable.

f. Circuit arrangements

The conductors of a circuit must not be distributed over different multicore cables, conduits, ducting, trunking or ladder systems. However, where multicore cables are run in parallel, forming one circuit, this requirement need not be met. If multicore cables are installed in parallel, then each cable must contain one conductor of each line.

The line and neutral conductors of each final circuit must be electrically separate from that of every other final circuit. This is to prevent the indirect energizing of a final circuit intended to be isolated (see also Regulation Group 314).

g. Use of flexible cables or cords

Where a wiring system is selected that supplies equipment that is intended to be moved, flexible cables or cords must be utilised. Stationary equipment which is moved temporarily for the purpose of cleaning or connecting may be supplied by non-flexible cables. Examples of these are cooking equipment that may be moved occasionally or flush mounted floor boxes mounted in an access floor that may be removed for connection or relocation. Any equipment that is subject to vibration must also be connected by a flexible cable or cord.

A flexible cable or flexible cord must be used for fixed wiring only where the relevant provisions of *BS 7671* are met.

h. Installation of cables

The installation of non-sheathed cables for fixed wiring must be installed within conduit, ducting or trunking. Such containment provides the necessary mechanical protection for the unsheathed cables. However, this requirement does not apply to protective conductors that comply with Section 543 of *BS 7671*.

Non-sheathed cables are permitted in a trunking system where it provides at least the degree of protection IP4X or IPXXD or if the cover can only be removed by the use of a tool or a deliberate action.

Exercise 520.4

(1). List two methods to avoid the electromagnetic effects when connecting single-core armoured cables onto a metallic distribution board.
(2). What factors may have to be considered when several circuits are being installed in the same wiring containment system? (3). How would mechanical protection normally be afforded to non-sheathed cables? (4). Give an example of a non-ferromagnetic metal and a non-metallic material suitable for use as a fixing plate on a distribution board.

Further information relating to Selection and erection of wiring systems – Scope and Types of wiring systems can be found in:
- *BS 7671* Sections 520 and 521
- Electrical Safety Council Technical Manual articles E105-1, E157-5, E157-25 and E157-29
- IEE Guidance Note 1

CHAPTER 520 & 521 FINAL REVISION EXERCISE

521.1 Where single-core cables, of the same circuit, enter a ferromagnetic enclosure through separate entries, a slot is required to prevent which of the following?
- ☐ a. Induced voltage disturbances
- ☐ b. Overvoltage transients
- ☐ c. Harmonic currents
- ☐ d. Electromagnetic effects

notes

521.2 A busbar trunking must comply with which of the following standards?
☐ a. *BS EN 60439-2*
☐ b. *BS EN 60947-2*
☐ c. *BS EN 60947-7*
☐ d. *BS EN 61534-1*

521.3 The Table in *BS 7671* that provides acceptable methods of installation in relation to conductors and cables is entitled which of the following?
☐ a. Table 52.1
☐ b. Table 4A1
☐ c. Table 4A2
☐ d. Table 4C1

521.4 The Table in *BS 7671* that provides installation and reference methods for determining the current-carrying capacities of cables is entitled which of the following?
☐ a. Table 52.1
☐ b. Table 4A1
☐ c. Table 4A2
☐ d. Table 4C1

Things to do and find

1. What are the restrictions in relation to the use of flexible cables and cords?

2. What further protection would normally be required when installing non-sheathed cables? Give examples.

3. What are the considerations that must be given to the selection and erection of wiring systems in relation to Chapter 13?

4. What are the conditions that must be met where several circuits are contained within the same enclosure?

5. What do the *BS EN 60670-22* and *BS EN 60947-7* relate to?

1. Introduction

All electrical installations are subject to some form of external influence. It is important, therefore, when selecting a wiring system that all possible detrimental effects are considered. The external influences to be considered can be as straight forward and common as temperature or water, but some of the less common influences may also need consideration. The definition and relevance of the term external influence, along with IP ratings, was covered in Part 2 of this Learning Guide. To recap, the term External Influence is defined as:

> 'An influence external to an electrical installation which affects the design and safe operation of that installation'

The requirements and related information relating to external influences can be found in different parts of *BS 7671*. Regulation Group 512.2 External influences (common rules), requires that electrical equipment should be selected and erected in accordance with the requirements of Appendix 5. If the equipment does not, by its construction, have the characteristics relevant to the external influences of its location, it may be used on condition that it is provided with appropriate additional protection in the erection of the installation.

> **Exercise 522.1**
>
> Refer to Appendix 5 (and Part 2 of this Learning Guide) to review the different classifications of external influence.
> 1. What do the following codes relate to: AD7, AE4 BA4, BE, CA2?

Section 522 provides the requirements that need to be considered when selecting the installation method for the wiring system and the protection against any expected external influences. The introduction to Section 522 provides a reminder about the particular care to be taken at changes in direction in wiring systems and where wiring enters into equipment.

Section 522 of *BS 7671* outlines the external influences, categorised in Appendix 5, that are significant to wiring systems. These are:

- Ambient temperature (AA)
- External heat sources
- Presence of water (AD) or high humidity (AB)
- Presence of solid foreign bodies (AE)
- Presence of corrosive or polluting substances (AF)
- Impact (AG)
- Vibration (AH)
- Other mechanical stresses (AJ)
- Presence of flora and/or mould growth (AK)
- Presence of fauna (AL)
- Solar radiation (AN) and ultra-violet radiation
- Seismic effects (AP)
- Wind (AS)
- Nature of processed or stored materials (BE)
- Building design (CB)

> **Key Facts**
> 'References to external influences are used extensively throughout BS 7671 and it is important you become familiar with Section 522 and Appendix 5'

2. Ambient temperature (AA)

Wiring systems must be selected for the highest and lowest ambient local temperatures they are likely to encounter.

In addition, cables have a limiting temperature in normal operation (see Table 52.1 below) and a limiting temperature in the case of a fault; these values should not be exceeded.

Table 52.1 (Reproduced from *BS 7671*) Maximum operating temperatures for types of cable insulation

Type of insulation	Temperature limit
Thermoplastic	70 °C at the conductor
Thermosetting	90 °C at the conductor
Mineral (Thermoplastic covered or bare exposed to touch)	70 °C at the sheath
Mineral (bare not exposed to touch and not in contact with combustible materials)	105 °C at the sheath

The components of the wiring system including cables and the wiring accessories should only be installed or handled within the temperature limits specified by the manufacturer in their product specification. For example, insulation can be damaged by installing cables in ambient temperatures below that specified by the manufacturer.

3. External heat sources

Heat from an external source, whether radiated, conducted or convected, can be detrimental to wiring systems. Where the effects of heat need addressing, an effective method of protection, such as those listed below, or an equally effective method, must be used:

- shielding
- placing sufficiently far from the heat source
- selecting a system with due regard for the additional temperature rise which may occur
- local reinforcement or substitution of insulating material

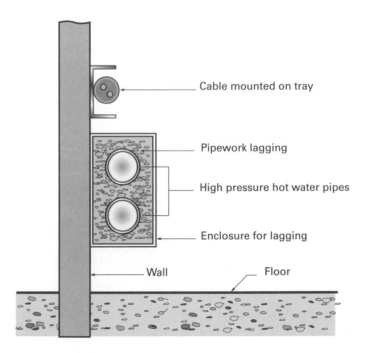

Cable mounted on tray

Pipework lagging

High pressure hot water pipes

Enclosure for lagging

Wall   Floor

Fig 522.1 Protection of cables from an external heat source

Exercise 522.2

(1). Provide at least one practical example of heat from an external source that is: (a) radiated, (b) conducted (c) convected.
(2). What is the maximum operating temperature for a cable with thermosetting (XLPE and EPR) insulation?

Cables and flexible cords that are installed inside accessories, appliances or luminaires must be suitable for temperatures likely to be encountered or additional insulation, suitable for those temperatures, should be provided. Additional insulation (e.g. heat-resistant oversleeving) may be required for example when connecting cooking appliances, heaters and light fittings.

4. Presence of water (AD) or high humidity (AB)

The effects of damage caused by condensation or ingress of water must be considered when selecting, installing, using or maintaining wiring systems. The completed wiring system must comply with the relevant IP degree of protection.

Where water may collect or condensation may form in a wiring system, provision must be made for the escape of water or condensation that may collect in wiring systems. This can be provided in the form of a drain hole, providing any relevant IP degree of protection has been considered.

Protection against mechanical damage must be provided against impact and/or vibration and/or other mechanical stresses if the wiring system is to be subjected to waves (AD6).

5. Presence of solid foreign bodies (AE)

The term solid foreign bodies relates to objects of various sizes ranging from dust to larger objects that might have an effect on the wiring system or electrical equipment. The dangers arising from the ingress of solid foreign bodies should be minimized by appropriate selection and erection of wiring systems. The completed wiring system must comply with the IP degree of protection relevant to the particular location.

Also, where dust is present in significant quantity (AE4), additional precautions must be taken to prevent its accumulation. This is due to the fact that the dissipation of heat from the wiring system could be adversely affected.

Exercise 522.3

(1). Provide an example of where dust would be present in a significant quantity and state how this could be a potential problem to the wiring system. Identify a solution to the problem.
(2) If luminaires were located in a position such that a significant quantity of dust was allowed to settle on them, how could this also be a potential problem?
Why could conductive dust (such as fine metal particles) be an additional hazard?

notes

6. Presence of corrosive or polluting substances (AF)

Where corrosive or polluting substances are present, and they are likely to cause corrosion or deterioration, then the parts of the wiring system that could be affected must be suitably protected or manufactured from a material that is resistant to such substances.

During the erection of the wiring system this may mean that protective tapes, paints or grease have to be applied to protect the wiring system from any corrosion or deterioration. A practical example of where a coating may need to be reinstated is where paint or anti-corrosive coatings have been removed by way of cutting, drilling and fixing components of the wiring system.

It is important that where dissimilar metals, that are liable to initiate electrolytic action, are used, they should not be placed in contact with each other, unless special arrangements are made to avoid the consequences of such contact. Examples of this potential problem are the connections of protective bonding conductors onto water pipes and where earthing conductors are being connected to earth electrodes.

Materials liable to cause mutual or individual deterioration must not be placed in contact with each other. An example of this is ensuring that PVC cables are installed so that they are not in contact with expanded polystyrene.

Exercise 522.4

Give three examples of where paint or anti-corrosive coatings are removed when erecting a wiring system and state what precautions would be necessary to reinstate the protection against external influence.

7. Impact (AG)

a. General

Protecting wiring systems from the damage arising from mechanical stress is a requirement for every electrical installation and the following areas need to be considered during installation, use or maintenance:

- impact
- abrasion
- penetration
- tension or compression

An assessment must be made of the likely impact on wiring systems. *BS 7671* categorises impact into low, medium and high severity (AG1, AG2 and AG3 as outlined in Appendix 5).

Exercise 522.5

(1). Provide two examples of situations where mechanical damage to wiring systems could occur and how this could be prevented. (2) List three methods, recommended in *BS 7671*, for protecting wiring systems where medium or high severity impacts could occur.

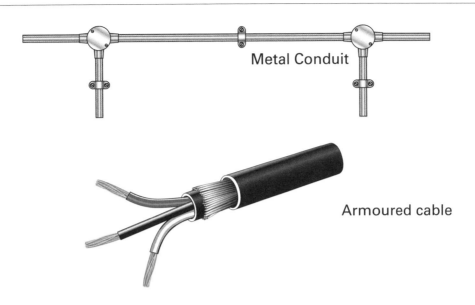

Metal Conduit

Armoured cable

522.2 Typical wiring systems that may be suitable to withstand expected mechanical stresses in an industrial installation

b. Cables buried in a floor

Under floor trunking or ducting systems buried in the floor screed are also liable to mechanical damage due to the loads being placed on the floor caused by the intended use and should, therefore, be sufficiently protected.

c. Cables installed under floors or above a ceiling

Another area where mechanical protection needs careful consideration is where a wiring system is installed under a floor or above a ceiling. Cables in this situation should be run in such a position that they are not liable to damage by contact with the floor or the ceiling or their fixings. The diagram below illustrates the requirements. Generally, the cables should either be 50 mm from the top, or bottom as appropriate, of the joist or batten, incorporate an earthed armour or screen or be provided with mechanical protection to prevent the penetration of the cable by nails, screws and the like.

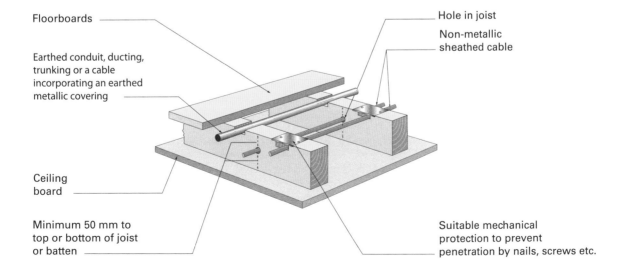

Floorboards

Hole in joist

Non-metallic sheathed cable

Earthed conduit, ducting, trunking or a cable incorporating an earthed metallic covering

Ceiling board

Minimum 50 mm to top or bottom of joist or batten

Suitable mechanical protection to prevent penetration by nails, screws etc.

522.3 Protection for cables under a floor or above a ceiling

Section 522
Selection and erection of wiring systems in relation to external influences

Where wiring systems penetrate an element of building construction which is intended to be load bearing the integrity of the bearing element must be assured after such penetration (see Figs 522.10 and 522.11 below)

8. Cables concealed in walls or partitions

It is extremely important that the requirements relating to the protection of cables in walls and partitions are fully understood. Damage to cables in walls or partitions can often occur, for example, where fixings are being made and drills, screws or nails penetrate the cables. The Regulations outlining the requirements offer several options which must be considered carefully. In many cases where the installation is not intended to be under the supervision of a skilled or instructed person concealed cables will require protection by means of an RCD having the characteristics specified in Regulation 415.1.1

a. RCD protection *not* required

Where a cable is concealed in a wall or partition deeper than 50 mm from the surface of the wall or partition no further protection is required (apart from the exemptions mentioned below under 8b)

Where cables are run **less than 50 mm** from the surface of a wall or partition and one of the following requirements (cables incorporating an earthed metallic covering or mechanical protection against damage sufficient to provide protection against the penetration by nails, screws and the like) are met, RCD protection is not required:

(i) the cable must incorporate an earthed metallic covering *or*
(ii) the cable must be enclosed in earthed conduit satisfying the requirements for a protective conductor *or*
(iii) the cable must be enclosed in earthed trunking or ducting satisfying the requirements for a protective conductor *or*
(iv) the cable must be mechanically protected against damage sufficient to provide protection against the penetration by nails, screws and the like.

b. RCD protection *is* required

Where the requirements for *'Cables buried over 50 mm deep'*, earthed metallic covering (*(i)*, *(ii)* or *(iii)* above) or mechanical protection (*(iv)* above) are **not** met an RCD (having the characteristics specified in Regulation 415.1.1) is required unless the installation is intended to be under the supervision of a skilled or instructed person.

Cable zones as outlined in the 16th edition of *BS 7671* are still required (see Fig 522.4 below), however, in the 17th edition cables require RCD protection even where they are run within the zones (unless the installation is intended to be under the supervision of a skilled or instructed person)

Exercise 522.6

(1) Refer to Regulation 522.6.6 (v) and 522.6.7 to review the zone requirements illustrated in diagram 522.4 below.

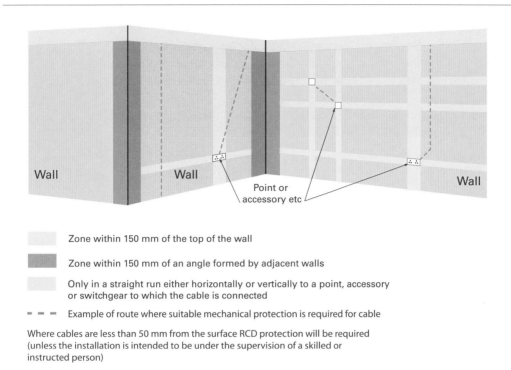

Zone within 150 mm of the top of the wall

Zone within 150 mm of an angle formed by adjacent walls

Only in a straight run either horizontally or vertically to a point, accessory or switchgear to which the cable is connected

- - - Example of route where suitable mechanical protection is required for cable

Where cables are less than 50 mm from the surface RCD protection will be required (unless the installation is intended to be under the supervision of a skilled or instructed person)

Fig 522.4 Zones for concealed cables in walls and partitions. Conditions applying to cables embedded in a wall or partition at a depth of less than 50 mm from surfaces and where mechanical protection or earth screening is not provided.

In addition to the above requirements for zones, where the location of the accessory, point or switchgear can be determined from the reverse side, a zone formed on one side of a wall or partition of 100 mm thickness or less extends to the reverse side. Fig 522.5 below illustrates this condition.

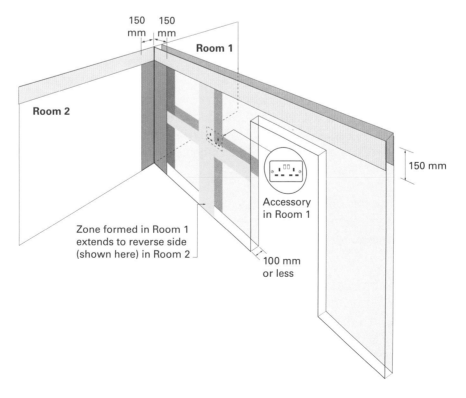

Fig 522.5. An example of where the location of an accessory can be determined from the reverse side of a wall

Section 522
Selection and erection of wiring systems in relation to external influences

Finally, RCD protection is also required where cables are concealed in a wall or partition and the internal construction of the walls or partition include metallic parts (other than metallic fixings e.g. screws or nails). This requirement applies irrespective of the depth of the cable from a surface of the wall or partition. There is an exemption to this requirement where the installation is intended to be under the supervision of a skilled or instructed person.

Table 52.2 (Learning Guide Table) Summary of cables concealed in walls or partitions and not requiring RCD protection

Where more than 50 mm from the surface of a wall or partition. (However, see walls or partitions the internal construction of which includes metallic parts below*)
Where incorporating an earthed metallic covering as specified in Regulation 522.6.6 (i)
Where enclosed in earthed conduit as specified in Regulation 522.6.6 (ii)
Where enclosed in earthed trunking or ducting as specified in Regulation 522.6.6 (iii)
Where mechanically protected as specified in Regulation 522.6.6 (iv)
Where installed in the zones specified in Regulation 522.6.6 (v) and the installation is intended to be under the supervision of a skilled or instructed person.
*Where cables are concealed in a wall or partition where the internal construction include metallic parts (other than metallic fixings e.g. screws or nails) and the installation is intended to be under the supervision of a skilled or instructed person.

Table 52.3 (Learning Guide Table) Summary of cables concealed in walls or partitions requiring RCD protection

Where cables are concealed less than 50 mm from the surface of a wall or partition, and where they are not incorporating an earthed metallic covering or enclosed in earthed conduit, trunking or ducting (as specified in Regulation 522.6.6) and where they are not intended to be under the supervision of a skilled or instructed person.
Where cables are concealed in a wall or partition where the internal construction include metallic parts (other than metallic fixings e.g. screws or nails) and the installation is not intended to be under the supervision of a skilled or instructed person.

9. Vibration (AH)

Structures or equipment supporting wiring systems and subject to vibration of either medium or high severity must be suitable for such conditions, particularly where cables and cable connections are concerned. Cables and connections that are subject to vibration could eventually break or come loose. Anti-vibration connections and the use of flexible cables will usually provide the necessary protection.

Fixed installation of suspended current-using equipment e.g. luminaires, can also be subject to vibration and movement and, therefore, cables with flexible cores should be used in such circumstances.

10. Other mechanical stresses (AJ)

Section 522.8, contains 13 regulations, concerned with the mechanical stresses that a wiring system may be subjected to and how these are to be avoided. A wiring system should be selected and erected to avoid during installation, use or maintenance, damage to the sheath or insulation of cables and their terminations. One way to meet this requirement is to protect the cables from sharp edges in containment systems or accessories by the use of channelling, grommets or grommet strip.

Fig 522.6 Channelling and grommet used to protect cables prior to plastering

Where conduit or ducting systems are buried in the structure of the building, they should be completely erected between access points before the cables are drawn in. Wiring systems intended for the drawing in and out of conductors or cables require adequate access to allow this operation.

The radius of bends, within wiring systems, should be such that conductors or cables do not suffer damage and terminals are not stressed. Cables and conductors must be supported so that they do not suffer damage or strain from the weight of the cable itself (see also Section 526 of *BS 7671* and this Learning Guide). Manufacturers' recommendations should be followed in relation to supports for cables.

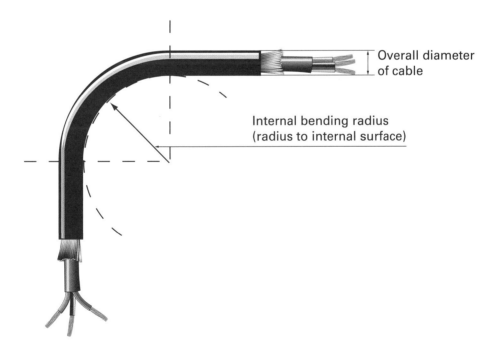

Overall diameter of cable

Internal bending radius (radius to internal surface)

Fig 522.7 Internal bending radius and overall diameter of a cable

Where cables are buried in the ground, unless they are installed within a conduit or duct, the cable must incorporate earthed armour or metal sheath, or both, suitable for use as a protective conductor, or be of insulated concentric construction. The location of buried cables should be marked by cable covers or marking tape, and they should be buried at a suitable depth to avoid damage.

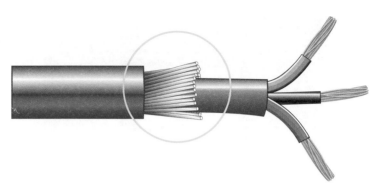

Fig 522.8 Armoured cable

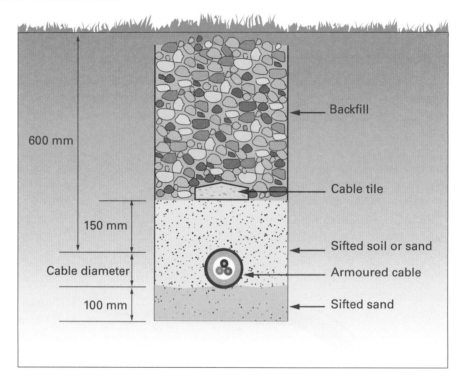

Fig 522.9 Typical section through a buried wiring system

Wiring systems require protection generally from; sharp edges on cable supports and enclosures, damage to cables or conductors from any fixing means and damage from movement in any expansion joints that the wiring system passes across.

Exercise 522.7

Provide examples of how you would: (1) protect a PVC twin cable entering an enclosure (2) Protect a PVC twin cable that is to be buried in plaster from plasterers' tools (3) Ensure single-core cables to be installed in conduit are not damaged, consideration being given to the state of conduit assembly, access points and bends.

In addition to the Regulations relating to damage to cables and conductors, Regulation 522.8.14 outlines the requirements relating to wiring systems and their effect on the building structure. Where wiring systems penetrate an element of the building construction which is intended to be load bearing it must be assured that after such penetration the integrity of the load bearing element is maintained. Building Regulations may need to be consulted for further information relating to alterations to building structures. (Figs 522.10 and 522.11 below illustrate the restrictions relating to walls and floors)

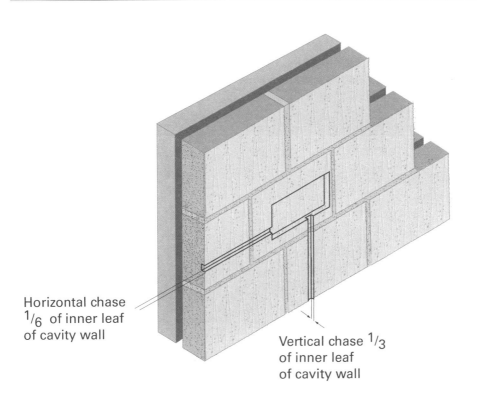

Horizontal chase $^{1}/_{6}$ of inner leaf of cavity wall

Vertical chase $^{1}/_{3}$ of inner leaf of cavity wall

Fig 522.10 Restrictions on the penetration of building construction element (wall)

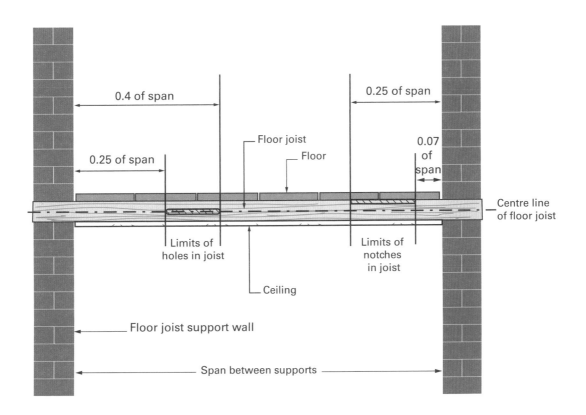

0.4 of span

0.25 of span

0.25 of span

0.07 of span

Floor joist

Floor

Centre line of floor joist

Limits of holes in joist

Limits of notches in joist

Ceiling

Floor joist support wall

Span between supports

Fig 522.11 Restrictions on the penetration of building construction (floors)

11. Presence of flora and/or mould growth (AK)

Where a wiring system is installed in the presence of flora (plants) and/or mould growth, it may be necessary to utilise an installation method that facilitates the removal of such growths, by means of maintenance, or by using a closed type of installation, e.g. conduit or channel. Other preventative measures would be to maintain a distance to plants and regular cleaning. Careful consideration also needs to be made when wiring systems and equipment are attached to growing objects, such as floodlighting installed in trees.

12. Presence of fauna (AL)

Where a wiring system is installed and likely to be in the presence of fauna (animal life), the system should be selected accordingly or special protective measures adopted, for example by:

• the mechanical characteristics of the wiring system, *or*
• the location selected, *or*
• the provision of additional local or general protection against mechanical damage, *or*
• any combination of the above.

This is particularly important on farms, for example where rodents can cause considerable damage to wiring systems.

13. Solar radiation (AN) and ultra violet radiation

A suitable wiring system should be selected where (UV) radiation could be experienced or expected (or shielding should be provided). Solar radiation can increase the ambient temperature in the vicinity of wiring systems and affect the current-carrying capacity of related cables.

Exercise 522.8

If a cable is to be installed along a south-facing wall and is not shielded from the sun, describe two types of wiring system that could be used. Also, identify which wiring system should not be used stating the reason why. What special precaution might be required where an increase in ambient temperature is expected due to solar radiation and plastic conduits are being used?

14. Seismic effects (AP) and Wind (AS)

Where seismic effects or wind may be a particular problem consideration must be given to the design and installation of wiring systems.

15. Nature of processed or stored materials (BE)

See Section 527 and Chapter 42 of *BS 7671* and this Learning Guide in relation to the considerations relating to the selection and erection of wiring systems to minimize the spread of fire.

16. Building design (CB)

Where there are risks due to structural movement, the cable support and protection system should be selected and erected to allow for the expected movement and ensure the wiring system is not subjected to excessive mechanical stress. Flexible wiring systems should be installed in flexible structures or structures intended to move.

> Further information relating to selection and erection of wiring systems in relation to external influences can be found in:
> * Electrical Safety Council Technical Manual articles E157-1, 157-5, 157-9, 157-13, 157-17, 157-21, 157-25, 157-29, 157-33, 157-37, 157-45, 157-49
> * BS7671 Section 522

CHAPTER 522 FINAL REVISION EXERCISE

522.1 The external influence code relating to solid foreign bodies is which of the following?
- ☐ a. AA
- ☐ b. AB
- ☐ c. AD
- ☐ d. AE

522.2 The external influence code relating to impact is which of the following?
- ☐ a. AD
- ☐ b. AF
- ☐ c. AG
- ☐ d. AH

522.3 The external influence code relating to flora or mould growth is which of the following?
- ☐ a. AH
- ☐ b. AK
- ☐ c. AP
- ☐ d. AS

522.4 The external influence code AH relates to which of the following?
- ☐ a. Ambient temperature
- ☐ b. Vibration
- ☐ c. Seismic effects
- ☐ d. Wind

522.5 The external influence code AJ relates to which of the following?
- ☐ a. External heat sources
- ☐ b. Solar radiation and ultra-violet radiation
- ☐ c. Presence of fauna
- ☐ d. Other mechanical stresses

522.6 A cable installed under a floor or above a ceiling, without mechanical protection, should be run at least which of the following?
- ☐ a. 25 mm from the top or bottom of the joist or batten
- ☐ b. 50 mm from the top or bottom of the joist or batten
- ☐ c. 75 mm from the top or bottom of the joist or batten
- ☐ d. 100 mm from the top or bottom of the joist or batten

Section 522
Selection and erection of wiring systems in relation to external influences

Things to do and find

1. Outline the requirement where cables are concealed in a wall or partition of less than 50 mm.

2. List three methods of avoiding the external heating effects on wiring systems.

3. What type of wiring system should be used in a structure intended to move?

4. List three methods that could be adopted where the presence of fauna could constitute a hazard.

1. Introduction

This part of the Learning Guide covers two sections of *BS 7671*, as listed above, as well as Appendix 4. Sections 523 and 525 are related in that the information within these sections is required to carry out cable sizing calculations. Therefore, they will be considered together. Cable sizing, the process of calculating cable cross-sectional area (csa) requires consideration being given to cable current-carrying capacity and voltage drop. References to Appendix 4, Current-carrying capacity and voltage drop for cables and flexible cords is an integral part of the cable selection process, therefore, this part of *BS 7671* will also be covered along with Sections 523 and 525. Examples of cable sizing calculations can be found at the end of this section of the Learning Guide.

2. Section 523 Current-carrying capacities of cables

a. Introduction

Section 523 considers the current-carrying capacities of cables. The current a cable carries will effect the temperature of the conductor and this can have an effect on the insulation. Different types of cable insulation have different limiting temperatures, and it is this factor that dictates the current-carrying capacity of the cable.

The current-carrying capacity of a cable depends upon a number of conditions. When designing circuits and selecting cables and conductors for an electrical installation, it is necessary to give consideration to the effects on the conductors caused by cable construction, conductor operating temperature, method of installation, ambient temperature, grouping, parallel conductors, number of loaded conductors and thermal insulation. (Frequency also affects current-carrying capacity, but this is not covered in this Learning Guide).

b. Cable construction

The type of cable construction, (for example, the materials from which the conductors and insulation are made, the number of cores and whether or not the cable is sheathed and/or armoured), has a significant affect on its current-carrying capacity. Appendix 4 of *BS 7671* includes tables for current-carrying capacity for most types of cables.

> **Exercise 523/5.1**
>
> Refer to *BS7671*: Appendix 4. (1) Find the table relating to multicore 70 °C armoured thermoplastic insulated cables. (2) What is the difference between Tables 4D1A and 4D2A? (3) Which table would you use to find the current-carrying capacity and voltage drop information relating to 'Flat twin and earth' cables?

The current to be carried by any conductor for sustained periods during normal operation should be such that the temperature limit, specified in Table 52.1 of *BS 7671*, is not exceeded. It is important that where a conductor operates at a temperature exceeding 70 °C it should be ascertained that the equipment connected to the conductor is suitable for the resulting temperature at the connection (see also Section 526 of *BS 7671* and this Learning Guide).

The current-carrying capacity of a cable, as outlined in Appendix 4, normally relates to the maximum temperature at which the conductor can operate continuously without causing damage to the cable insulation or sheath, terminations, connected equipment and surroundings (such as building materials).

notes

Exercise 523/5.2

Review Table 52.1 of BS 7671. What is the maximum operating temperature of thermosetting cable insulation?

d. Method of installation

The rate of heat emission and hence the current-carrying capacity of a cable is related to its method of installation. For example, the current-carrying capacity of a cable clipped direct to a surface is generally higher than that of the same cable enclosed in conduit or trunking, as the enclosure inhibits the escape of heat from the cable.

Appendix 4 (Table 4A2) provides an extensive list of different installation methods and their related reference method codes and these should to be consulted when cable current-carrying capacities and voltage drops are being ascertained. Many of these codes can be grouped into generic descriptions. The following table provides a summary of typical installation methods.

Table 523.1 (Learning Guide Table)Typical installation methods and related reference methods

Installation method description	Reference methods
Cables in conduit in a thermally insulated wall. Multicore cables direct in a thermally insulated wall.(For flat twin and earth cables in thermal insulation see Table 4A2) Non-sheathed cables in mouldings, architraves etc.	A
Cables in conduit, trunking, ducting or building voids. Single-core or multicore cables fixed directly under a wooden or masonry ceiling.	B
Clipped direct (including single-core or multicore cable direct in masonry).	C
Cables laid direct in ground or in ductings in ground.	D
Cables on perforated tray, brackets, wire-mesh tray, ladder, suspended from a wire or harness or spaced from a wall (more than 3 x cable diameter)	E or F
Flat twin and earth cables in thermal insulation (see Table 4A2)	100, 101,102 & 103 for cable type covered by 4D5 (Flat twin and earth cables)

Common installation methods are illustrated below in Fig 523.1.

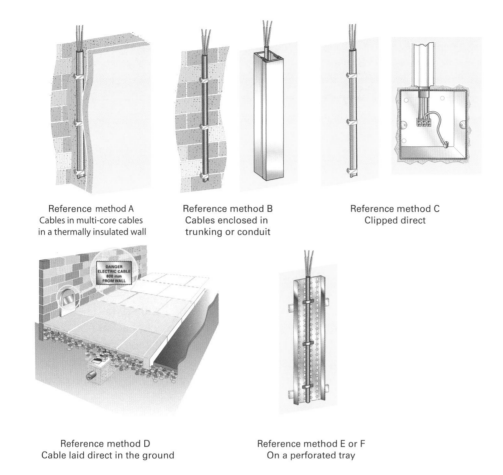

Reference method A
Cables in multi-core cables
in a thermally insulated wall

Reference method B
Cables enclosed in
trunking or conduit

Reference method C
Clipped direct

Reference method D
Cable laid direct in the ground

Reference method E or F
On a perforated tray

Fig 523.1 Commonly used methods of cable installation

Exercise 523/5.3

Refer to *BS7671*: Appendix 4. (1) Which reference method relates to a flat twin and earth cable clipped direct to a wooden joist above a plasterboard ceiling (with a minimum U value of 0.1 W/m^{2}K) and with thermal insulation exceeding 100 mm thickness? (2) What is the difference between this installation method and installation method No 100? (3)What is the reference method for a multicore cable on a ladder?

e. Ambient temperature

The *higher* the ambient temperature of the location where a cable is installed, the *lower* the current-carrying capacity of the cable. The current-carrying capacities in Appendix 4 are based on ambient temperatures for:

• Non-sheathed and sheathed cables in air, irrespective of the installation method – **30 ^{O}C**,

• Buried cables, either directly in the soil or in ducts in the ground **– 20 ^{O}C**.

Where ambient temperatures exceed the above values, the appropriate rating factor given in Tables 4B1, 4B2 and 4B3 should be applied to the current-carrying capacities set out in Tables 4D1A to 4J4A. **Table 4B1** relates **to non-sheathed and sheathed cables in air, Tables 4B2 and 4B3** relate to **buried cables.**

notes

Exercise 523/5.4

Refer to *BS7671*: Appendix 4. (1) What is the rating factor for a 90 °C thermosetting cable in an ambient temperature of 35 °C? (2) What is the rating factor for a thermoplastic (PVC) covered mineral insulated cable (70 °C) in an ambient temperature of 40 °C? (3). If the mineral insulated cable in '2' had a current-carrying capacity of 40 A, prior to the ambient temperature rating factor being applied, what could it carry after applying the factor?

f. Grouping of cables and conductors

(i) General

Where loaded circuits or loaded multicore cables are grouped together (such as being bunched, enclosed in the same conduit or trunking, or clipped adjacent to each other on a surface), the current-carrying capacity of all the conductors is reduced. The reduction in current-carrying capacity is due to the mutual heating effects of the circuits or cables. The derating factor used to take account of this effect is referred to as the grouping factor.

Group reduction factors are applicable to groups of non-sheathed or sheathed cables having the same maximum operating temperature. For groups containing non-sheathed or sheathed cables having different maximum operating temperatures, the current-carrying capacity of all the non-sheathed or sheathed cables in the group must be based on the lowest maximum operating temperature of any cable in the group together with the appropriate group reduction factor.

If, due to known operating conditions, a non-sheathed or sheathed cable is expected to carry a current not greater than 30% of its grouped current-carrying capacity, it may be ignored for the purpose of obtaining the reduction factor for the rest of the group. The factors only apply to grouped cables of similar sizes (same maximum permissible conductor temperature and three adjacent standard sizes). For more information relating to mixed size cables see Appendix 4.

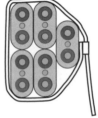

Touching on a perforated tray system

Bunched

On a surface

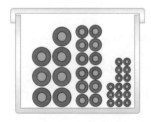
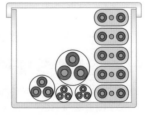

Enclosed

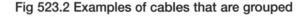

Fig 523.2 Examples of cables that are grouped

For derating factors relating to where loaded circuits or loaded multicore cables are grouped together see Table **4C1** of Appendix 4 (or Table **4C2** for cables laid directly in the ground).

(ii) Number of loaded conductors:

The number of loaded conductors to be considered in a circuit are those carrying a load current. The neutral conductor need not be taken into consideration where the conductors in polyphase circuits carry balanced currents. Under these conditions a four-core cable is given the same current-carrying capacity as a three-core cable having the same conductor cross-sectional area for each line conductor. The neutral conductor should be considered as a loaded conductor in the case of the presence of third harmonic or multiples of third harmonic presenting a total harmonic distortion greater than 15% of the fundamental line current.

Where the neutral conductor in a multicore cable carries current, as a result of an imbalance in the line currents, the temperature rise due to the neutral current is offset by the reduction in the heat generated by one or more of the line conductors. In this case the conductor size should be chosen on the basis of the highest line current. In all cases the neutral conductor should have an adequate csa so that the conductor temperature limit is not exceeded.

g. Cables in thermal insulation:

Thermally insulating material is often used in the walls or ceilings of a building for reasons of energy conservation, or in interfloor spaces to minimize sound transmission. Unfortunately, such material also reduces the current-carrying capacity of any cable it may cover. When a cable will be, or is likely to be covered in thermal insulation, the electrical installation designer must take steps to ensure that the current-carrying capacity of a cable will remain sufficient to meet the requirements of *BS 7671* in relation to the circuit of which the cable forms a part. Otherwise, when the cable is covered in thermal insulation, the operating temperature of the conductors may exceed the applicable rated value (such as 70 $^{\circ}$C for thermoplastic (pvc) insulated conductors), possibly leading to a reduction in the service life of the cable or damage to the insulation of the conductors or adjacent material.

Where a cable is to be run in a space where thermal insulation is likely to be applied, the cable should preferably be fixed so that it will not be covered by the insulation or, where this is not possible, the cross-sectional area of the cable must be increased as appropriate.

Two different cases need to be considered in relation to cables run in or adjacent to thermally insulating material. The cables may be installed either in a thermally insulating wall or above a thermally insulating ceiling, the cable(s) being in contact with a thermally conductive surface on one side or totally surrounded by thermal insulation.

Tabulated current-carrying capacities for various types of cable installed in a thermally insulating wall or above a thermally insulating ceiling - the cable being in contact with a thermally conductive surface on one side - are given in Appendix 4 of *BS 7671*. It is **not** necessary to apply a rating factor for thermal insulation in this case.

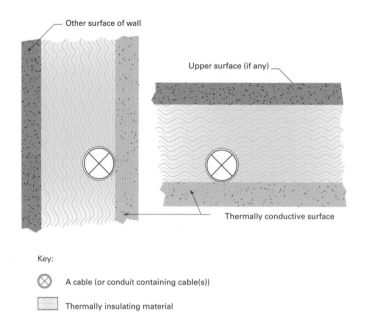

Fig 523.3 A cable in a thermally insulating wall or above a thermally insulating ceiling

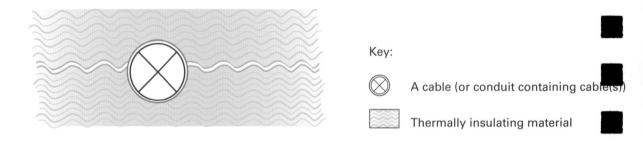

Fig 523.4 A cable totally surrounded by thermally insulating material

For a single cable likely to be totally surrounded by thermally insulating material **over a length of 0.5 m**, the current-carrying capacity must be taken as **0.5** times the current carrying capacity for that cable clipped direct to a surface and open.

Where a cable is to be totally surrounded by thermal insulation **for less than 0.5 m,** the current-carrying capacity of the cable must be reduced appropriately, depending on the size of cable, length in the insulation and thermal properties of the insulation. The derating factors in Table 52.2 are appropriate to conductor sizes up to 10 mm^2 in thermal insulation having a thermal conductivity (λ) greater than 0.04 Wm^{-1} K^{-1}.

Exercise 523/5.5

Review Table 52.2 of *BS 7671*. What is the derating factor for a cable that runs surrounded by thermal insulation for a distance of 200 mm?

h. Conductors in parallel

For more information relating to conductors in parallel see the Section in this Learning guide relating to Appendix 10 of *BS 7671*.

i. Variation of installation conditions along a route:

Heat dissipation can vary from one part of a route to another due to different rating factors etc. In this case the current-carrying capacity of a cable should be taken as the section with the most adverse conditions.

j. Armoured single-core cables

Special precautions need to be taken when single-core aluminium wire armoured cables are being installed. Further guidance should be sought as this subject is outside the scope of this Learning Guide.

k. Protective device or installation condition

The effects of overload protection are not covered in Section 523, but are outlined in Section 433 and Appendix 4 of *BS 7671* and this Learning Guide. Because of the operating characteristics of semi-enclosed (rewireable) fuses to *BS 3036*, a rating factor (C_C) must be applied when cable-sizing calculations are being carried out. This factor (0.725) has the effect of increasing the cross-sectional area when these devices are used. Where cables are buried direct or in a duct in the ground a rating factor (0.9) must also be applied. If a cable is buried direct or in a duct in the ground and protected by a semi-enclosed fuse the factor to be used is 0.653.

3. Section 525 Voltage drop in consumers' installations

When circuit conductors carry load current, a voltage drop is produced in them due to their impedance. This means that the voltage at the load end of the circuit should be expected to be less than that at the supply end. Clearly, it is necessary to limit the voltage drop in a circuit so that the safe and satisfactory operation of current-using equipment supplied through the circuit is not impaired. In order to limit the voltage drop, circuit conductors larger than would otherwise be required may have to be used, depending on the load and the circuit length.

The general requirement of *BS 7671* relating to maximum permitted voltage drop is that under normal operating conditions, the voltage at the terminals of the fixed current-using equipment is required to be greater than the lower limit given in the product standard for the equipment. Where the fixed current-using equipment is not subject to a product standard, the voltage at the terminals has to be such as not to impair the safe functioning of the equipment.

Unfortunately, product standards or other sources providing information about the lowest acceptable voltage at the terminals of fixed current-using equipment may not be readily available. The total voltage drop recommended for an electrical installation is given in Appendix 12 of *BS 7671*. It should be noted, however, that the voltage drop percentages given in Table 12A are between the origin of any installation and any load point. Where there are distribution circuits feeding distribution boards, the total allowable voltage drop will have to be split between the distribution circuit(s) and final circuit(s).

notes

Exercise 523/5.6

Review Table 12A of *BS 7671*. (1) What is the maximum recommended voltage drop percentage for a lighting circuit where the low voltage installation is supplied directly from a public low voltage distribution system. (2) When calculating voltage drop for a given cable, where in *BS 7671* would you find the information relating to volts (millivolts) dropped per ampere per metre of cable?

4. Current-carrying capacity and voltage drop for cables and flexible cords – Calculations.

a. Introduction.

Appendix 4 details the current carrying capacities and voltage drops for cables and flexible cords. Its contents include:

• Circuit parameters (as covered in items 2a to 2k above)
• Schedules of installation methods of cables
• Schedules of appropriate current rating and voltage drop tables
• Rating factors for groups of cables of more than one circuit
• Rating factors for ambient temperature
• Rating factors for protective device or installation condition.

b. Calculations for determining the size of a cable

As discussed previously, there are two calculations that are required when carrying out cable sizing calculations; current-carrying capacity and voltage drop.

(i) Current-carrying capacity

First, it is important to establish the design current of the circuit (I_b) and select the type and size of protective device (I_n) as well as the type of cable to be used.

Any relevant factors (normally derating) are now applied as outlined below using the formula below:

$$I_t \geq \frac{I_n}{C_a \times c_g \times C_i \times C_c}$$

Where:
I_t is the tabulated value of circuit current
I_n is the rated current or current setting of the protective device
C_a is the rating factor for ambient temperature
C_g is the rating factor for grouping
C_i is the rating factor if the cable is surrounded with thermal insulation
C_c is the rating factor depending upon the protective device or installation condition

(ii) Voltage drop calculations

For the following calculations the maximum voltage drop will be in accordance with Appendix 12 (or as stated in the question). The formula for calculating voltage drop is:

Voltage drop = $\dfrac{\text{mV} \times \text{Ib} \times \text{length}}{1000}$

Where the voltage drop is in volts and:

mV   is the millivolts dropped per ampere per metre taken from Tables 4D1A to 4J4A

I_b is the design current of the circuit (the current intended to be carried)

length is the length of the circuit in metres.

(The division by 1000 gives the answer in volts.)

Note: A 3% voltage drop equates to 6.9 volts for a 230 V circuit and a 5% voltage drop equates to 11.5 volts for a 230 V circuit.

It should be noted that the voltage drop can be the overriding factor when calculating conductor csa.

5. Worked Examples.

EXAMPLE 1. Given the following data, calculate the minimum cable size.

A circuit with a load of 6.5 kW at 230 V, is fed by a pvc flat twin and earth cable (thermoplastic 70 $^{\circ}$C), clipped direct. The cable is 20 m long and is protected by a *BS 3036* fuse. The ambient temperature is 35 $^{\circ}$C and there is no thermal insulation or cable grouping. The voltage drop maximum should be taken as 5%.

First, the design current of the circuit (I_b) needs to be calculated

$$I_b = \frac{6500}{230} = \textbf{28.26} \text{ Amperes}$$

The protective device is now chosen (the next largest *BS 3036* fuse is 30 A (I_n) that is $I_n > I_b$).

We now apply the rating factors to I_n

$$I_t \geq \frac{I_n}{C_a \times c_g \times C_i \times C_c}$$

The factor for C_a can be found from Table 4B1. In this example the temperature (35 $^{\circ}$C) and pvc twin with cpc (thermoplastic 70 $^{\circ}$C) gives a factor of **0.94.**

The factor for C_g is not applied in this case as the cable is not grouped with other circuits or conductors.

The factor for C_i is not applied in this case as the cable is not run in thermal insulation.

The factor for C_c is applied (**0.725**) as overcurrent protection is provided by a *BS 3036* (semi-enclosed) fuse.

This gives us:

$$I_t \geq \frac{30}{0.94 \times 0.725} = \textbf{44.02 A}$$

This value (44.02 A) is the one that must be used when selecting a cable from Tables 4D1A to 4J4A. The correct table in this case is Table 4D5. The correct column is the one relating to 'clipped direct' (reference method C). A cable with a current rating over 44.02 A must be selected, which is a 6 mm^2 (rated at 47 A).

A voltage drop check must now be carried out to ensure that both current-carrying and voltage drop parameters are met.

Voltage drop $= \dfrac{\text{mV} \times I_b \times \text{length}}{1000}$

The mV figure from Table 4D5 (for a 6 mm^2 cable) is 7.3. I_b (the design current of the circuit was calculated at 28.26.A. The circuit length is 20 metres. This gives us

Voltage drop $= \dfrac{7.3 \times 28.26 \times 20}{1000} = $ **4.12 V**

As we have allowed a 5% volt drop (11.5 volt) maximum in this case, 4.12 V is well within this criterion.

Having checked both current-carrying capacity & voltage drop calculations it can be confirmed that a 6 mm^2 cable is acceptable.

EXAMPLE 2 Given the following data, calculate the minimum cable size:

A circuit has a 14 kW load fed at 230 V. The cables are thermosetting 90 $^{\circ}$C singles having copper conductors enclosed in conduit, fixed on a wall and run for a length of 36 m. Overcurrent protection is provided by a *BS 88* fuse.

The ambient temperature is 40 $^{\circ}$C and the circuit is grouped with two other of the same/similar size, all circuits being loaded above 30%. The circuit does not run through thermal insulation. The voltage drop maximum should be taken as 5%.

First, the design current of the circuit (I_b) needs to be calculated

$$I_b = \frac{14000}{230} = \textbf{60.87 } \text{Amperes}$$

The protective device is now chosen (the next largest *BS 88* fuse is 63 A (I_n)).

We now apply the rating factors to I_n

$$I_t \geq \frac{I_n}{C_a \times C_g \times C_i \times C_c}$$

The factor for C_a can be found from Table 4B1. In this example the temperature (40 $^{\circ}$C) and thermosetting 90 $^{\circ}$C insulation gives a factor of 0.91.

The factor for C_g can be found from Table 4C1. In this example Item 1 (enclosed) applies and this circuit with two others makes 3 in total. This gives a factor of 0.7.

The factor for C_i is not applied in this case as the cables are not run in thermal insulation.

The factor for C_c is not applied as a *BS 88* fuse is providing overcurrent protection.

This gives us:

$$I_t \geq \frac{63}{0.91 \times 0.7} = 98.9 \text{ A}$$

This value (98.9 A) is the one that must be used when selecting a cable from Tables 4D1A to 4J4A. The correct table in this case is Table 4E1A. The correct column is the one relating to 'Reference Method B enclosed in conduit on a wall'. A cable with a current rating over 98.9 A must be selected, which is a 16 mm^2 (rated at 100 A – single-phase column).

A voltage drop check must now be carried out to ensure that both current-carrying and voltage drop parameters are met.

$$\text{Voltage drop} = \frac{\text{mV x Ib x length}}{1000}$$

The mV from Table 4E1B (over the page) for a 16 mm^2 cable is 2.9. Ib (the design current of the circuit was calculated at 60.87 A). The circuit length is 36 metres. This gives us:

$$\text{Voltage drop} = \frac{2.9 \times 60.87 \times 36}{1000} = 6.354 \text{ V}$$

As we have allowed a 5% volt drop (11.5 volt) maximum in this case, 6.354 V is well within this criterion. Having checked both current-carrying capacity & voltage drop calculations it can be confirmed that a 16 mm^2 cable is acceptable.

EXAMPLE 3 Given the following data, calculate the minimum cable size:

Circuit loading is 2 kW, voltage 230 V. The cable length is 40 m and the cable type is pvc twin with cpc (thermoplastic 70 $^\circ$C), clipped direct (single layer on a wall). The overcurrent protection is provided by a Type B *BS EN 60898* circuit-breaker. The ambient temperature is 30 $^\circ$C and the cable passes through thermal insulation for a distance of 200 mm (totally surrounded). The cable is grouped with one other cable of the same/similar size, including at the point where they pass through thermal insulation. Both circuits are loaded above 30%. The voltage drop maximum should be taken as a lighting load in accordance with Appendix 12.

First, the design current of the circuit (I_b) needs to be calculated

$$I_b = \frac{2000}{230} = \textbf{8.7 Amperes}$$

The protective device is now chosen (the next largest Type B BS EN 60898 circuit-breaker is 10 A (I_n)).

We now apply the rating factors to In

$$I_t \geq \frac{I_n}{C_a \times C_g \times C_i \times C_c}$$

The factor for C_a can be found from Table 4B1. In this example the temperature (30 $^\circ$C) and pvc singles (thermoplastic 70 $^\circ$C) gives a factor of **1** (as this is the normal ambient temperature for this type of insulation).

The factor for C_g can be found from Table 4C1. In this example Item 2 (Single layer on a wall) applies and this circuit with one other makes 2 in total. This gives a factor of **0.85**.

The factor for C_i is taken from Table 52.2 and the distance through thermal insulation of 200 mm in this case gives us a factor of **0.63**.

The factor for C_C is not applied as a *BS EN 60898* circuit-breaker is providing overcurrent protection.

This gives us:

$$I_t \geq \frac{10}{1 \times 0.85 \times 0.63} = 18.7 \text{ A}$$

This value (18.7 A) is the one that must be used when selecting a cable from Tables 4D1A to 4J4A. The correct table in this case is Table 4D5. The correct column is the one relating to 'Reference Method C' (clipped direct). A cable with a current rating over 18.7 A must be selected, which is a 1.5 mm^2 (rated at 20 A).

A voltage drop check must now be carried out to ensure that both current-carrying and voltage drop parameters are met.

$$\text{Voltage drop} = \frac{mV \times I_b \times length}{1000}$$

The mV from Table 4D5 for a 1.5 mm2 cable is 29. I_b (the design current of the circuit was calculated at 8.7 A. The circuit length is 40 metres. This gives us:

$$\text{Voltage drop} = \frac{29 \times 8.7 \times 40}{1000} = 10.1 \text{ V}$$

The criterion for volt drop in this case was (Appendix 12 – lighting circuit) 3% (6.9 V). Unfortunately, the voltage drop for a 1.5 mm^2 cable with a load of 8.7 A run for a length of 40 m is too high at 10.1 V.

The next higher sized cable should now be tried. In this case this will be a 2.5 mm^2. The current-carrying calculation does not need to be carried out as a larger size cable will automatically comply. The voltage drop calculation will, however, need to be re-worked. The mV dropped from Table 4D5 for a 2.5 mm cable is 18 (all other factors remain the same).

$$\text{Voltage drop} = \frac{18 \times 8.7 \times 40}{1000} = 6.26 \text{ V.} \text{ (which is below 6.9 V)}$$

Having checked both current-carrying capacity & voltage drop calculations it can be confirmed that a 2.5 mm^2 cable is acceptable.

Further information relating to current-carrying capacities of cables and voltage drop in consumers' installations can be found in:
- *BS 7671* Sections 523 and 525 and Appendix 4
- Electrical Safety Council Technical Manual articles C5-14, C5-37, C5-55, C5-73,V33-1, V33-5, V33-9, V33-13 and V33-17
- IEE Guidance Note1

SECTIONS 523 & 525 FINAL REVISION EXERCISE

CALCULATION REVISION EXERCISES

Example 1. A lighting circuit is wired in 70 ^{O}C thermoplastic insulated and sheathed flat cable, direct in masonry (thermal resistivity not greater than 2K.m/W) with capping, and feeds a lighting load of 1.6 kW at 230 V. The cable is protected by a *BS EN 60898* circuit-breaker. The ambient temperature is 35 ^{O}C and the cable is grouped with two others similar sized circuits (all above 30% loaded). The cable does not pass through thermal insulation. The circuit length is 30 m and the maximum allowed voltage drop is to be in line with Table 12A. Find the minimum cross-sectional area to satisfy current-carrying and voltage drop requirements.

Example 2. A 6 kW 230V water heater is to be wired in a pavilion. The cables to be used are single-core 70 ^{O}C thermoplastic insulated (copper conductors) wired in conduit and the circuit runs for 27 metres.

The ambient temperature may reach 25 ^{O}C and the cable is grouped with 1 other circuit, both being loaded over 30% of their capacity. The maximum voltage drop is to be 4%. The overcurrent protective device is a *BS 1361* fuse. Find the minimum cross-sectional area to satisfy current-carrying and voltage drop requirements.

523.1 Current-carrying capacity and voltage drop values for cables and flexible cords can be found in which of the following?
- ☐ a. Appendix 3
- ☐ b. Appendix 4
- ☐ c. Appendix 5
- ☐ d. Appendix 12

523.2 Information relating to the maximum values allowed for voltage drop in consumers' installations can be found in which of the following?
- ☐ a. Appendix 3
- ☐ b. Appendix 4
- ☐ c. Appendix 5
- ☐ d. Appendix 12

523.3 The reference ambient temperature for cables buried direct in the soil or in ducts in the ground is which of the following?
- ☐ a. 20 ^{O}C
- ☐ b. 25 ^{O}C
- ☐ c. 30 ^{O}C
- ☐ d. 35 ^{O}C

523.4 The derating factor for a cable surrounded by thermal insulation over a length of more than 0.5 m is which of the following?
- ☐ a. 0.5
- ☐ b. 0.725
- ☐ c. 0.75
- ☐ d. 0.8

notes

523.5 The derating factor for a cable surrounded by thermal insulation for a length of 200 mm is which of the following?

☐ a. 0.5
☐ b. 0.63
☐ c. 0.725
☐ d. 0.78

523.6 The derating factor for a cable when a BS 3036 semi-enclosed fuse provides overcurrent protection is which of the following?

☐ a. 0.5
☐ b. 0.63
☐ c. 0.725
☐ d. 0.78

Things to do and find

1. What is the difference between a cable installation method and a cable reference method?

2. Up to what percentage of a cable's grouped current-carrying capacity can be ignored for grouping purposes?

3. What derating factor is applied to cables when a *BS 3036* semi-enclosed fuse is used as protective device?

4. What is the recommended maximum voltage drop for a lighting circuit from Appendix 12 for a circuit supplied directly from a public low voltage distribution system?

5. What do the symbols C_a, C_g, C_i and C_c represent?

6. What is the calculated voltage drop for a 1.5 mm^2 flat twin cable carrying 7 A with a length of 23 m?

7. What is the table that provides information relating to cables surrounded by thermal insulation?

8. What is the maximum operating temperature for a thermoplastic insulated cable?

9. What is the table that provides current-carrying capacities and voltage drop values for 70°C thermoplastic insulated and sheathed cables with protective conductors?

notes

1. Introduction

Section 524 provides information relating to the minimum cross-sectional area of conductors of cables generally and more specifically to the selection of neutral conductor cross-sectional area.

2. Minimum cross-sectional areas of conductors of cables

The cross-sectional area of each conductor in an a.c circuit or of a conductor in a d.c circuit must be not less than the value given in Table 52.3 of *BS 7671*. For information relating to the minimum cross-sectional area of conductors for extra-low voltage lighting installations see Regulation 559.11.5.2 of *BS 7671*.

> **Exercise 524.1**
>
> Refer to Table 52.3 (1). What is the minimum cross-sectional area for a sheathed cable with copper conductors supplying a lighting circuit in a fixed installation? (2) What is the minimum cross-sectional area for a flexible connection with non-sheathed and sheathed cables where it is not specified in a product standard.

3. Selection of neutral conductor cross-sectional area

Regulations 524.2 and 524.3 relate to the cross-sectional area of neutral conductors. The neutral conductor must have a cross-sectional area not less than that of the line conductor

• in single-phase, two-wire circuits whatever the cross-sectional area,

• in polyphase and single-phase three-wire circuits, where the size of the line conductors is less than or equal to 16 mm² for copper, or 25 mm² for aluminium.

• in circuits where it is required according to Regulation 523.6.3 of *BS 7671*.

For a polyphase circuit where each line conductor has a cross-sectional area greater that 16 mm² for copper or 25 mm² for aluminium, the neutral conductor is permitted to have a smaller cross-sectional area than that of the line conductors, providing the criteria required by Regulation 524.3 are met.

For more information relating to the effects of current carried by neutral conductors reference should be made to Regulation 523.6.3 and Appendix 11 of *BS 7671*.

> **Exercise 524.2**
>
> (1) What is the minimum cross-sectional area of a line conductor in a three-phase circuit with copper conductors such that consideration could be given to installing a neutral with a reduced cross-sectional area? (2) Why might Appendix 11 be consulted, when a reduced neutral cross-sectional area is being considered?

> Further information relating to Cross-sectional areas of conductors of cables can be found in:
> • *BS 7671* Section 524 (and Appendix 11)
> • Electrical Safety Council Technical Manual articles H5-1, L105-1 and S225-21

notes

SECTION 524 FINAL REVISION EXERCISE

524.1 The minimum cross-sectional area of a copper conductor for power and lighting circuits using non-sheathed cables is which of the following?
- a. 0.5 mm^2
- b. 0.75 mm^2
- c. 1.0 mm^2
- d. 1.5 mm^2

524.2 The minimum cross-sectional area of a copper conductor for signalling and control circuits using bare conductors is which of the following?
- a. 1.0 mm^2
- b. 2.5 mm^2
- c. 4.0 mm^2
- d. 6.0 mm^2

1. Introduction

Electrical connections (joints and terminations) are common within installations, both in live (line and neutral) conductors and in protective conductors. Although there are numerous references to connections in *BS 7671*, Section 526 outlines the main requirements for the integrity of electrical connections, to protect against the following dangers which could arise from a poorly constructed connection:

- Fire or other harmful thermal effects (due to excessive temperature developed in a high resistance connection when it carries current, or to arcs or high temperature particles emitted from a loose connection).

- Direct contact with a live part (due to contact of a person or livestock with a live conductor at a connection).

- Failure of fault protection measures (due, for example, to a high resistance or open-circuit connection in a protective conductor causing the earth fault loop impedance of a circuit to exceed the maximum value required for automatic disconnection of the supply in the event of an earth fault).

The overriding requirement is that every connection between conductors or between a conductor and other equipment should provide durable electrical continuity and adequate mechanical strength and protection. Further to this, the Regulations require that there should be no appreciable mechanical strain on the connections of conductors. Regulation Group 522.8 'Other mechanical stresses' should also be consulted in relation to installation requirements.

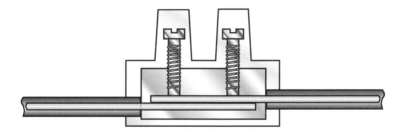

Fig 526.1 Connection providing durable electrical continuity and adequate mechanical strength

2. Selection of means of connection

When selecting the means of connection there are many aspects to be considered including; the cross-sectional area of the conductor, material of the conductor and its insulation, number and shape of wires and number of conductors to be connected together. It is also important to ensure the insulation is not impaired by the temperature attained in normal service and that where vibration or cyclic loading may be a problem adequate locking arrangements are provided.

Soldered connections may need special considerations such as the temperature rise under fault conditions, creep and mechanical stress.

In each case, the limitations of the equipment and its installation guidance, as specified in the manufacturers' instructions, must be observed.

notes

3. Accessibility of connections

With certain exemptions, electrical connections (joints and terminations) should be accessible
for inspection, testing and maintenance. This requirement includes protective conductors as
well as live conductors. Connections required to be accessible should be in a location where
they can be reasonably reached and where there is adequate working space. Where the
connections are housed in an enclosure it should include a detachable cover or other suitable
means for opening. Any obstructions within the enclosure, such as a barrier or the ends of
cables, should be readily moveable to give access to the connections.

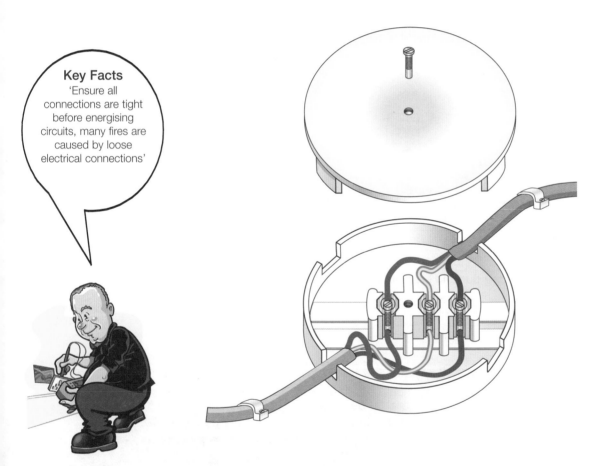

Key Facts
'Ensure all
connections are tight
before energising
circuits, many fires are
caused by loose
electrical connections'

**Fig 526.2 Joint box with screw terminals - an example of where connections must be
accessible**

The exemptions to accessibility of connections are:

• A joint designed to be buried in the ground

• A compound-filled or encapsulated joint

• A connection between a cold tail and a heating element as in a ceiling or floor heating system or a trace-heating system (see also Section 753 Floor and ceiling heating systems)

• A joint made by welding, soldering, brazing or appropriate compression tool. (For example, a joint using a crimped or soldered ferrule)

• A joint forming part of equipment complying with the appropriate product standard. (This provision applies for example to a joint between components within a manufactured item of equipment such as a circuit-breaker where the manufacturer intends the joint to be inaccessible. However, the provision does not apply to joints in site-assembled equipment where the manufacturer intends the connections to be checked periodically, such as in busbar trunking).

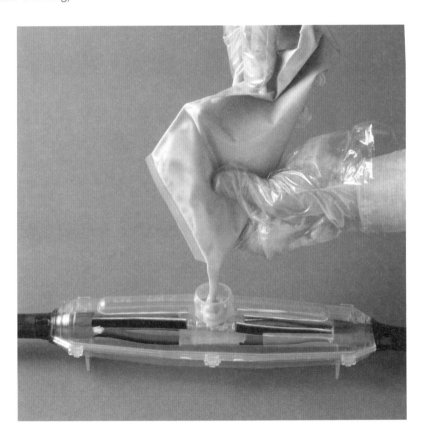

526.3 Resin-filled joint, often used underground - an example of where connections are not required to be accessible.

Where connections are made in roof spaces, inter-floor spaces and other non-readily accessible locations, the enclosures containing the connections should normally be fixed, and provision must be made for their access by providing, for example, removable access traps in the ceiling or floor (see Fig 526.4 below). Where such connection methods have had to be employed, it is good practice to record their specific location, for future use. This information should be appended to the Electrical Installation Certificate, or where applicable the Operation & Maintenance (O&M) manual.

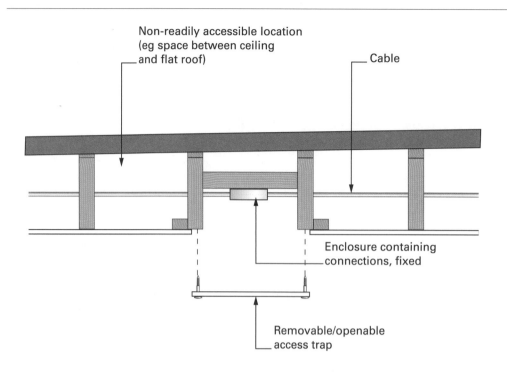

Fig 526.4 Connections in a non-readily accessible location

4. The effects of the temperature of connections on insulation

The temperature attained by a connection should not impair the effectiveness of the insulation of the conductors connected to it or any insulating material used to support the connection. An example of where a connection temperature may be in excess of the conductor insulation is at a busbar, where the busbar, for example, could be designed to operate at 90 $^{\circ}$C, but the cable insulation has a maximum rating of 70 $^{\circ}$C. One solution in this case is to replace the lower rated insulation with sleeving of a higher temperature rating, as illustrated below.

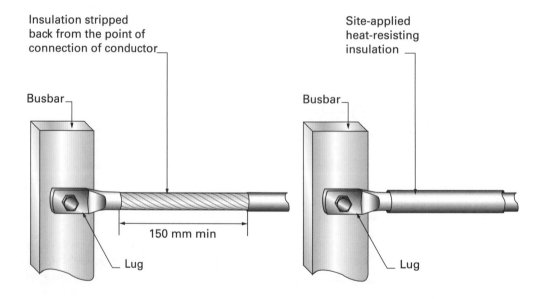

Fig 526.5 Removal and replacement of a section of conductor insulation, where necessary to withstand busbar normal operating temperature

A further consideration is the increased use of Steel Wire Armoured cables that utilize thermosetting insulation. Although the fully loaded cable is capable of operating at 90 $^{\circ}$C, it is often the case that terminations at both switchgear and connected equipment may not be able to withstand such high temperature use.

Manufacturers' data must therefore be sought, to verify such use and operation.

5. Requirements for terminations and joints to be enclosed

Regulation 526.5 calls for every electrical connection (joint or termination) in a live conductor or a PEN conductor to be made within one of the following types of enclosure, or a combination of them:

- A suitable accessory (such as a lighting switch or a socket-outlet) complying with the appropriate product standard (see Fig 526.6 below)

- An equipment enclosure (such as the enclosure of a luminaire, distribution board, item of switchgear, or a box forming part of a conduit system) complying with the appropriate product standard (see Fig 526.6 below)

- An enclosure partially formed or completed with building material which is non-combustible when tested to *BS 476-4.*

Enclosures for electrical connections must be selected and erected such that they provide adequate protection against mechanical damage (such as impact) and any other external influences (ambient temperature, presence of solid foreign objects, presence of water, etc) likely to be encountered.

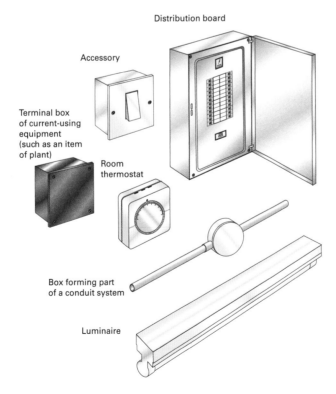

Fig 526.6 Accessories and enclosures of equipment complying with appropriate product standards - examples of permitted types of enclosure for electrical connections

notes

6. Requirements for sheathed and non-sheathed cable enclosure

The most basic form of acceptable mechanical protection is that afforded by PVC sheathed cables. At terminations this sheath must enter completely into the enclosure to ensure its mechanical integrity, as shown below. Standard non-sheathed cables run in conduit, trunking or ducting are also required to be enclosed.

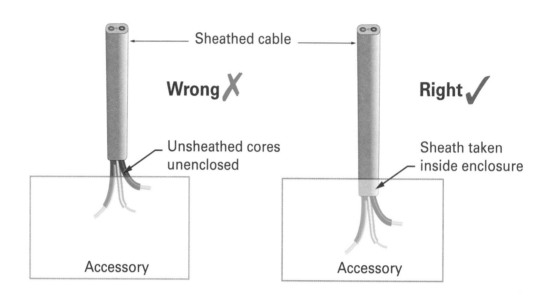

526.7 Correct enclosure of cable cores and non-sheathed cables

7. Connection of multi-wire, fine wire and very fine wire conductors

Connections with multiwire or fine wire conductors need particular care when they are being terminated to ensure individual strands do not separate. To avoid separation a suitable terminal or treatment of the termination may be required.

The use of soldered (tinned) whole conductor ends is restricted where screw terminals are used and/or where movement at the termination point is expected (for more information see Regulation Group 526.8 of BS 7671).

Further information relating to Electrical connections can be found in:
- *BS7671* Section 526 (and Section 522)
- Electrical Safety Council Technical Manual articles A5-1, C165-1, C165-3, E157-29, E157-45 and S309-1
- IEE Guidance Note 1
- NICEIC Snags and solutions Part 2 Wiring systems

notes

SECTION 526 FINAL REVISION EXERCISE

526.1 Which one of the following is not required to be considered in relation to the connection between conductors or between a conductor and other equipment?
☐ a. The material of the conductor and its insulation
☐ b. The number and shape of the wires forming the conductor
☐ c. The number of conductors to be connected together
☐ d. The type of overcurrent device protecting the cable

526.2 Which one of the following types of connection must be accessible?
☐ a. A joint designed to be buried in the ground
☐ b. A connection to a ceiling-rose
☐ c. A joint made by welding, soldering or brazing
☐ d. A connection between a cold tail and the heating element of a floor heating system

526.3 Which one of the following enclosures is unsuitable for a termination and joint?
☐ a. An accessory complying with the appropriate product standard
☐ b. An equipment enclosure complying with the appropriate product standard
☐ c. An enclosure formed or completed with building material which is non-combustible
☐ d. An enclosure formed or completed with building material which is combustible

526.4 Non-sheathed cables must be enclosed to provide which of the following?
☐ a. Protection against mechanical damage
☐ b. Protection against over-heating
☐ c. Protection against earth-leakage currents
☐ d. Protection against over-voltage

Things to do and find

1. List five items to be taken into account when selecting the means of connection.

2. What form of protection is required where the sheath of sheathed cables have been removed?

3. List three examples of an acceptable enclosure for a termination or joint in a live conductor.

4. List three types of connection that do not need to accessible.

Section 527
Selection and erection of wiring systems to minimize the
spread of fire

204

1. Introduction

Section 527 of *BS 7671* provides the requirements relating to the selection and erection of wiring systems such that the risk of spread of fire is kept to a minimum. Section 527 considers two aspects in relation to the risk of spread of fire:

* The precautions within a fire-segregated compartment (527.1) and
* The sealing of wiring system penetrations (527.2).

The objects of this section of the Learning Guide are to identify, in relation to the selection and erection of wiring systems to minimize the spread of fire, the requirements for:

* Wiring system selection and erection within a fire-segregated compartment
* Sealing of wiring system penetrations

2. Precautions within a fire-segregated compartment

a. General

Section 527.1 requires designers and installers to select appropriate materials and erection methods to minimize the risk of fire and that the general building structure performance and fire safety should not be reduced by the installed wiring system.   This section also provides information in relation to acceptable types of cable and wiring systems. The installation of wiring systems should follow the manufacturers' guidance and the requirements of other relevant sections of *BS 7671*, such as Chapter 42.

b. Cables

Cables that comply with *BS EN 60332-1-2 (Tests on electric and optical fibre cables under fire conditions. Test for vertical flame propagation for a single insulated wire or cable)* may be installed without special precautions. Most commonly used cables comply with *BS EN 60332-1-2*, including the following:

* Thermoplastic (PVC) to *BS 6004*
* Thermosetting (XLPE) to *BS 7211*
* Thermosetting to *BS 5467*
* Flexible cords to *BS 6500*

In installations of particular risk, such as those identified in Section 422 of *BS 7671*, further requirements in relation to cable selection may be required.

Cables that do not meet the requirements of *BS EN 60332-1-2* should be limited to short lengths for connection of appliances to the permanent wiring system and should not pass from one fire-segregated compartment to another.

Exercise 527.1

Refer to *BS 7671* Section 422 (Precautions where particular risk of fire exists) quickly review the additional requirements relating to cables & wiring systems in Regulations 422.2.1, 422.3.4, 422.4.5 and 422.4.6

notes

Where wiring systems utilizing conduit and trunking, are manufactured and installed in compliance with their appropriate product standard (*BS EN 61386* series for conduit, the appropriate part of *BS EN 50085* for cable trunking and cable ducting, *BS EN 60439-2* for busbar trunking, *BS EN 61534* series for power track trunking or *BS EN 61537* for tray and ladder systems), no further special precautions are required. Wiring systems that do not comply with the flame propagation requirements of the above product standards, but which do comply in all other respects with the requirements of their respective product standard should be completely enclosed in suitable non-combustible building materials.

3. Sealing of wiring penetrations

Where a wiring system passes through a building element that has a specific fire resistant property, the openings made are likely to compromise the ability of that element to resist the spread of fire. To ensure that the structure is able to continue to afford the original design fire resisting integrity of the compartment, wiring systems that pass through the element, will need to be sealed after their installation. Breaches in fire compartments such as floors, walls, roofs, ceilings, partitions or cavity barriers, will all require appropriate sealing to ensure that the element's fire resisting integrity has been comprehensively reinstated.

Temporary sealing arrangements are also required during the erection of wiring systems and any sealing which has been disturbed during alteration work must be reinstated as soon as practicable. The temporary sealing arrangement must afford the same level of fire resistance as the original structure that has been penetrated.

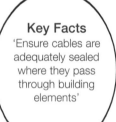

Key Facts
'Ensure cables are adequately sealed where they pass through building elements'

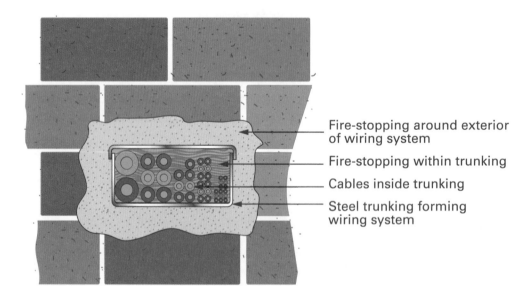

Fire-stopping around exterior of wiring system

Fire-stopping within trunking

Cables inside trunking

Steel trunking forming wiring system

Fig 527.1 Internal and external wiring system sealing

As well as the external sealing requirements, there is frequently the need to also seal the internal areas of trunking and larger conduit systems. However, where the system is classified as non-flame propagating (according to the relevant product standard) internal sealing is not required provided that it:

- Has a maximum internal cross-sectional area of **710 mm^2**
- The system provides a degree of protection to IP33
- Any termination of the system in one of the compartments, separated by the building construction being penetrated, provides a degree of protection to IP33.

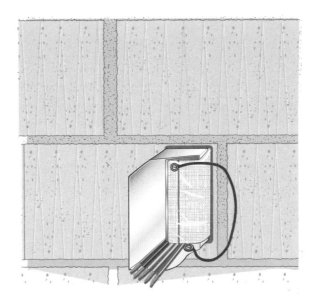

Fig 527.2 Internal sealing of a wiring system (trunking in this case)

Exercise 527.2

(1) What is the smallest size conduit (diameter) that requires internal sealing (ignoring the conduit wall) ?

The materials and methods used for sealing wiring systems must be selected carefully with consideration being given to the reinstatement of the existing building element. Knowledge of the building usage and which parts of the building structure have been designated as fire compartments will be necessary. Further information will also be required in relation to building construction and materials, the number of floors, escape routes, stairwells, lifts etc. Reference to Building Regulations Approved Documents, fire safety documentation and/or relevant personnel such as architects, fire prevention officers, licensing authorities or local building control department will be necessary.

In addition to providing effective fire resistance, *BS 7671* requires the sealing arrangement to resist external influences to the same degree as the wiring system with which they are used. Particularly consideration should be given to the effects on the sealing system of the compatibility of wiring system materials, thermal movement and mechanical stresses due to fire and dripping water.

Intumescent seals have the capacity to resist fire spread for between 1 and 4 hours, depending on their rating. Intumescent materials have the property of expanding as they are heated thus sealing an opening.

In some cases wiring system sealing will have to be carried out along with other services and careful liaison will be required to ensure all services are sealed appropriately. Comprehensive dialogue between both the electrical and mechanical services contractors and construction contactor is recommended at an early stage, to ensure that this area of the installation is appropriately coordinated.

notes

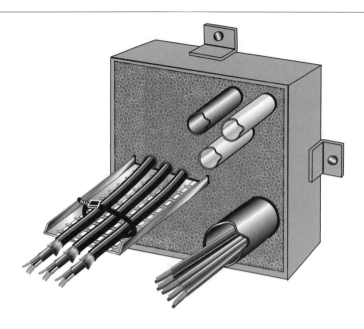

Fig 527.3 Multi-service barrier

Further to the above requirements for the sealing of cables and wiring systems, consideration may also be required in relation to reducing the risk of spread of fire where accessories and electrical equipment are fitted. One common issue that needs consideration is the fitting of recessed luminaires in ceilings. Depending upon the particular situation, an intumescent cover may be required to ensure the ceiling fire integrity is maintained. Another case for consideration is the situation where accessory boxes are fitted into thin-skinned walls and the walls form a part of a fire compartment. An intumescent gasket fitted behind the accessory may be required, in these cases.

Further information relating to Selection and erection of wiring systems to minimize the spread of fire can be found in:
• *BS 7671* Section 527
• IEE Guidance Note 4
• Electrical Safety Council Technical Manual articles C157-10, C157-13, F45-16, P115-21, P177-5 and W45-1

SECTION 527 FINAL REVISION EXERCISE

527.1 Which of the following conduit sizes (diameter, ignoring the tube wall) is the smallest one that requires internal sealing to prevent spread of fire?
☐ a. 22 mm
☐ b. 25 mm
☐ c. 32 mm
☐ d. 40 mm

527.2 Cables complying with the flame propagating requirements of which of the following standards do not require special precautions in relation to the risk of spread of fire?
☐ a. *BS EN 60332-1-2*
☐ b. *BS EN 61386*
☐ c. *BS EN 60529*
☐ d. *BS EN 60439-2*

Things to do and find

1. What are the considerations that need to be made when selecting a sealing arrangement?

2. What are the requirements to reduce the risk of spread of fire when erecting wiring systems?

3. What are the requirements to reduce the risk of spread of fire during alteration work?

Section 528 Proximity of wiring systems to other services *and*
Section 529 Selection and erection of wiring systems in relation to maintainability, including cleaning

210

1. Introduction

Section 528 of *BS 7671* sets out the requirements for precautionary measures to be taken where electrical equipment, including wiring systems, are in close proximity to other electrical services and to non-electrical services.

The two regulations of Section 529 relating to maintainability are outlined at the end of this section of the Learning Guide.

2. Proximity to electrical services (528.1)

Typical circuits covered by voltage Bands I and II circuits were covered in Part 2 (Definitions) of this Learning Guide. Voltage Bands I and II are used in Section 528 for the purposes of defining segregation. Fig 528.1 below illustrates the range of voltages in relation to Bands I and II.

Voltage Band I and Band II circuits must not be contained in the same wiring system as a circuit of nominal voltage exceeding that of low voltage and a Band I circuit must not be contained in the same wiring system as a Band II circuit except where one of the six requirements of Regulation 528.1 is met.

Exercise 528.1

Refer to Regulation 528 of *BS 7671* to review the options for segregation.

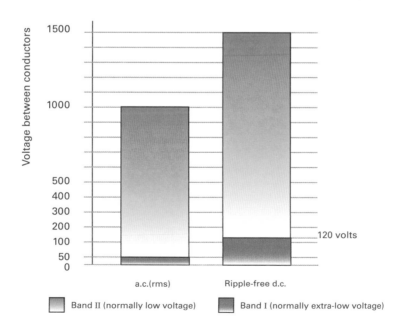

Fig 528.1 Voltage Bands I and II

For SELV and PELV systems the requirements of Regulation Group 414.4 must be met. Where wiring systems and lightning protection systems may be in close proximity the requirements of *BS EN 62305* should be considered. In relation to separation and segregation of safety services such as emergency lighting and fire alarm circuits the requirements of *BS 5266* and *BS 5839* should be consulted.

Section 528 **Proximity of wiring systems to other services *and***
Section 529 **Selection and erection of wiring systems in relation to maintainability, including cleaning**

The following diagrams provide examples of the above segregation requirements:

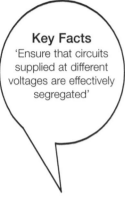

Key Facts
'Ensure that circuits supplied at different voltages are effectively segregated'

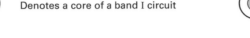

Ⓘ Denotes a core of a band I circuit

Ⓗ Denotes a core of a circuit of nominal voltage in excess of low voltage

ⒾⒾ Denotes a core of a band II circuit

⏚ Denotes earthed (connected to the main earthing terminal of the installation)

Fig 528.2 Key to symbols used in the following diagrams

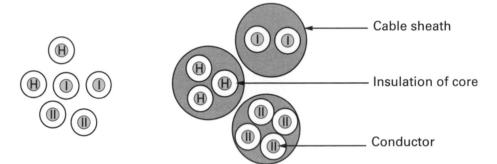

Single-core cables

Multi-core cables

Cable sheath

Insulation of core

Conductor

Fig 528.3 Segregation by insulating for the highest voltage present i.e. for the highest circuit voltage in excess of low voltage (Regulation 528.1 (i) above)

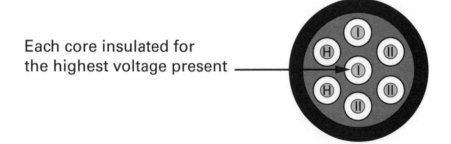

Each core insulated for the highest voltage present

Fig 528.4 Segregation by insulating for the highest voltage present in the cable (Regulation 528.1 (2 (ii) above))

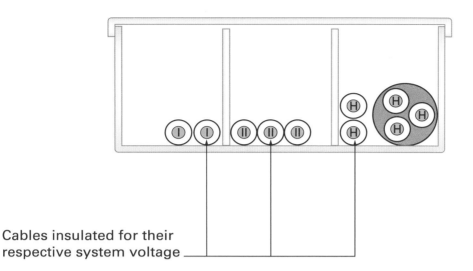

Cables insulated for their
respective system voltage

Fig 528.5 Segregation by installation in a separate compartment (Regulation 528.1 (2 (iii) above))

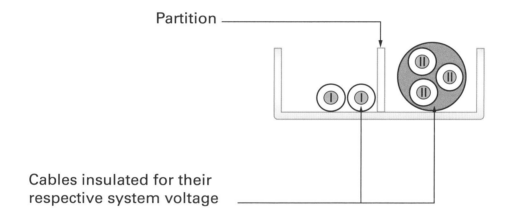

Partition

Cables insulated for their
respective system voltage

Fig 528.6 Segregation by partition on tray or ladder (Regulation 528.1 (2 (v) above))

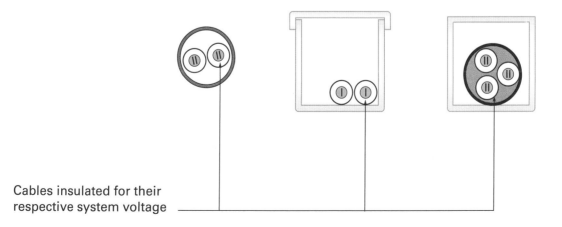

Cables insulated for their
respective system voltage

Fig 528.7 Segregation by installation in separate conduit, trunking or ducting
(Regulation 528.1 (2 (v) above))

213

Section 528 Proximity of wiring systems to other services *and*
Section 529 Selection and erection of wiring systems in relation to
maintainability, including cleaning

notes

The cores of the Band I circuit shall be separated
from the cores of the Band II circuit by an earthed
metal screen of equivalent current-carrying capacity
to the largest core of a Band II circuit

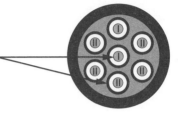

Fig 528.8 Segregation by earthed metal screen within a multicore cable (Regulation
528.1 (2 (vi) above))

> **Exercise 528.2**
>
> What is the difference between the requirements of 528.1 (i) and 528.1 (ii) (as illustrated by figures
> 528.3 and 528.4 above)?

3. Proximity of communication cables (528.2)

Where underground power cable and telecommunications cables cross or are in close
proximity a minimum clearance of 100 mm is to be maintained between services, or the
following requirements must be fulfilled:

- A fire retardant partition such as brick, clay protection caps, concrete blocks, cable
  troughs of fire-retardant material, shaped concrete blocks etc, should be provided
  between cables *or*,
- For cable crossings, mechanical protection between cables to be provided such as cable
  conduit, concrete cable protection caps, or shaped blocks.

It should be noted that special consideration in relation to electrical interference may apply to
data and telecommunication circuits. The requirements for segregation in relation to
communications are provided in *BS 6701* and *BS EN 50174* series.

4. Proximity to non-electrical services (528.3)

A wiring system should preferably be located away from non-electrical services. However,
where a wiring system is located in close proximity to a non-electrical service the following
conditions should be met:

(i) the wiring system is to be suitably protected against the hazards likely to arise from the
presence of the non-electrical service in normal use, and

(ii) fault protection is to be afforded in accordance with the requirements of Section 413, non
electrical metallic services being considered as extraneous-conductive-parts.

In relation to (i) above, wiring systems should not be installed in the vicinity of a service which
produces heat, smoke or fumes likely to be detrimental to the wiring, unless the wiring is
protected against such harmful effects by shielding. The shielding should be positioned such
that it does not affect the dissipation of heat from the wiring.

The illustration below shows an example of a wiring system being protected against heat
which is considered to be detrimental to the cable. The high pressure hot water pipes are
lagged with thermal insulation which limits the heat loss from the pipes and shields the wiring
from the source of heat. The arrangement has the advantage that it does not restrict the
dissipation of the heat generated in the wiring due to the passage of current.

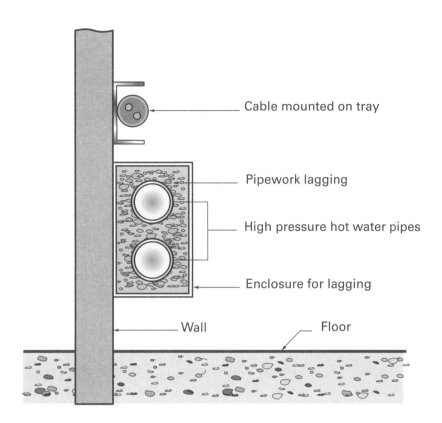

Cable mounted on tray

Pipework lagging

High pressure hot water pipes

Enclosure for lagging

Wall   Floor

Fig 528.9 Example of protection of an electrical installation against heat from a non-electrical installation

The reason for condition 4 (ii) (in the above text) being included in Regulation 528.3.4 requires further explanation. It could be decided that the possibility of an additional risk of electric shock due to a fault was envisaged in a location where a wiring system is in close proximity to a non-electrical service. For example, this may be the case where a person needs to squeeze between (say) a pipe and a cable tray, for some reason. If there is such an increased electric shock risk, provisions such as protective bonding should be considered.

In areas not specifically designed for the installation of cables, e.g. service shafts and cavities, the cables should be laid so they are not exposed to any harmful influence by the normal operation of the adjacent non-electrical services (e.g. gas, water or steam lines).

Consideration may also be required in relation to any foreseeable operation that may need to be carried out on non-electrical services where they are in proximity to electrical services to ensure the operation will not cause damage to the electrical services or the converse.

Where a non-electrical service is liable to cause condensation (for example a water, steam or gas service), precautions have to be taken to protect any wiring system that is routed near to such a service from any deleterious effects.

The illustration below (Fig 528.10) shows an example of precautions (the provision of a drip tray) to protect an electrical switchboard and its wiring systems from condensation that may form on chilled water pipework. The electrical equipment in the switchroom is also protected against potential water leaks from the joints of the chilled water pipe by locating the pipe joints in plantrooms 1 and 2, i.e., outside the switchroom. Where practicable, non-electrical services likely to introduce water into a location should not be installed in a switchroom.

215

Section 528 **Proximity of wiring systems to other services** *and*
Section 529 **Selection and erection of wiring systems in relation to maintainability, including cleaning**

notes

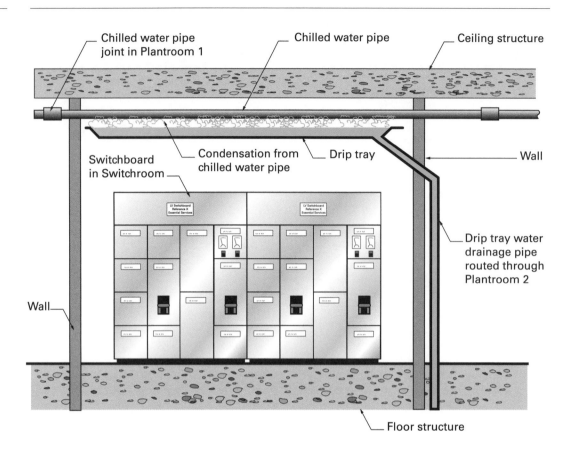

Chilled water pipe joint in Plantroom 1

Chilled water pipe

Ceiling structure

Switchboard in Switchroom

Condensation from chilled water pipe

Drip tray

Wall

Drip tray water drainage pipe routed through Plantroom 2

Wall

Floor structure

Fig 528.10 Example of protection of an electrical installation against condensation and potential water leaks from a non-electrical installation

5. Lift shafts (528.3.5)

In buildings where there is a lift shaft or a shaft for a hoist, the only cables that may be run in the lift or hoist shaft are those that form part of the lift installation as defined in *BS EN 81-1* series.

6. Section 529 Selection and erection of wiring systems in relation to maintainability, including cleaning.

All electrical installations and electrical equipment will tend to deteriorate over time due to accidental or deliberate damage, corrosion, electrical overloading and from environmental factors. It is important, therefore, that the installation can be maintained without undue difficulty and kept in a safe condition throughout its life. The likely requirements for future maintenance should be assessed in the early stages of the electrical installation design, and taken into account in the design.

Where it is necessary to remove any protective measure in order to carry out maintenance, the protective measure must be reinstated in a way that the original protection is not reduced. This could be for example the lid of a trunking or conduit box or internal and external covers of switchgear and controlgear.

Provision should also be made for safe and adequate access to all parts of the wiring system which requires maintenance. The provision of permanent walkways may be required as a result of a risk assessment.

Further information relating to Sections 528 & 529 Proximity of wiring systems to other services and Selection and erection of wiring systems in relation to maintainability, including cleaning, can be found in:

- *BS 7671* Sections 528 & 529
- Electrical Safety Council Technical Manual articles: A5-1, C5-77, M29-1, P177-5, S61-5, T113-9 and V29-1
- IEE Guidance Note 1

SECTION 528 FINAL REVISION EXERCISE

528.1 Which of the following would not be classed as voltage band I?
- ☐ a. A domestic bell circuit
- ☐ b. A domestic lighting circuit
- ☐ c. Data cabling
- ☐ d. Signalling circuitry

528.2 Voltage Band II relates to which of the following?
- ☐ a. SELV
- ☐ b. PELV
- ☐ c. ELV
- ☐ d. LV

528.3 Where circuits of Voltage Bands I and II are to be run together in a trunking which of the following is not permitted?
- ☐ a. All cables are insulated to Band I
- ☐ b. All cables are insulated to Band II
- ☐ c. All cables are insulated as for a low voltage circuit
- ☐ d. The cables are installed in a separate compartment within the trunking

528.4 Where an underground power cable crosses or is in close proximity to an underground telecommunications cable, which of the following is the required minimum clearance?
- ☐ a. 50 mm
- ☐ b. 100 mm
- ☐ c. 150 mm
- ☐ d. 450 mm

Section 528 Proximity of wiring systems to other services *and*
Section 529 Selection and erection of wiring systems in relation to maintainability, including cleaning

notes

Things to do and find

1. What are the problems that could occur where a cable is strapped to a pipework?

2. What type of circuits can be run in a lift or hoist shaft?

3. What types of hazard might need to be considered when electrical services are run in close proximity to non-electrical services?

1. Introduction

This section of the Learning Guide covers Sections 530, 531, 532, 533, 535 and 536 and 538 of *BS 7671*. Section 537 Isolation and switching is covered separately. Section 530 is an introduction to Chapter 53, Sections 530–535 contain the requirements relating to the selection and erection of the devices for:

- Fault protection by automatic disconnection of supply (Section 531)
- Protection against the risk of fire (Section 532)
- Protection against overcurrent (Section 533)
- Protection against undervoltage (Section 535)

Section 536 outlines the requirements for co-ordination of protective devices and Section 538 provides the requirements relating to monitoring.

2. General and common requirements

The moving contacts of all poles of a multi-pole device, in multi-phase circuits, should make and break substantially together. The exceptions to this requirement are in relation to neutral switching or where Regulation 543.3.4 applies (protective conductor switching)

In single-phase circuits single-pole switching or protective devices (independently operated) must not be inserted in the neutral conductor alone. In multi-phase circuits an independently operated single-pole switching device or protective device should not be inserted in the neutral conductor except where Regulation 537.2.2.5, which relates to *adjacent* single pole devices, applies.

> **Exercise 53.1**
>
> Considering Regulation 530.3.2, what is the difference in the requirements between multi-phase and single-phase circuits and what is the significance of this different requirement?

For installations with a 230 V single-phase supply rated up to 100 A that is under the control of ordinary persons, switchgear and controlgear should either:

- comply with *BS EN 60439-3* and Regulation 432.1 of *BS 7671, or*
- be a consumer unit complying with *BS EN 60439-3*.

3. Fixing of equipment

When connecting equipment by flexible connections, the connections between the wiring and equipment should not be subjected to undue stress and strain and fixing of equipment should be according to manufacturers' instructions.

Unenclosed equipment must be mounted in an enclosure and accessories should be fitted into a mounting box.

notes

Exercise 53.2

Refer to Regulation Group 530.4. (1) Give practical examples of the types of mounting boxes for socket-outlets, plate switches etc

4. Devices for fault protection by automatic disconnection of supply (Section 531)

a. Overcurrent protective devices

Overcurrent protective devices where they are used for fault protection in TN and TT systems must be selected and erected to comply with Chapter 41 of *BS 7671*.

b. RCDs

Section 531.2 provides the requirements for RCDs. The following is only meant to provide a summary of these requirements; Section 531.2 of *BS 7671* should be reviewed for further information.

(i) General (TN, TT or IT systems)

An RCD should be capable of disconnecting all line conductors at substantially the same time. The requirements of Section 411, as appropriate to the type of system earthing, should be met in relation to the rated residual operating current. When an RCD is used for fault protection, with, but separate from, an overcurrent device, RCDs are to be capable of withstanding without damage the fault currents to which they are likely to be subjected on the load side at their point of installation. An RCD cannot be used for fault protection on its own, for example where a circuit does not contain a protective conductor.

(ii) Discrimination (TN, TT or IT systems)

Discrimination between circuit protective devices is achieved when, under fault conditions, the device electrically nearest to the fault operates, leaving other upstream protective devices still providing supplies to the remaining healthy circuits. An RCD is to be selected and the circuits divided such that any protective conductor current expected during normal operation of the connected load(s) is unlikely to cause unwanted tripping. Where two or more RCDs are in series, and where discrimination in their operation is necessary to prevent danger, the characteristics of the devices should be such that the intended discrimination is achieved. Unlike overcurrent protective devices, increasing the rated residual operating current of an RCD will not necessarily provide discrimination and a time-delay incorporated into the RCD will be required. In this case, the downstream RCD will have time to disconnect the fault before the delay of the upstream device has expired (see Fig 53.1). In such cases the downstream RCD may need to disconnect all live conductors.

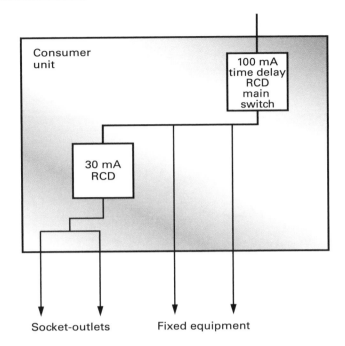

Fig 53.1 RCDs in series – use of time delay to provide discrimination

(iii) RCD installation and operation

The magnetic circuit of an RCD mechanism should enclose all live conductors of the protected circuit. The associated protective conductor is to be outside of the magnetic circuit. Where an RCD may be operated by a person other than a skilled or instructed person, it should be designed or installed so that any variable settings can only be adjusted by a key or a tool as a deliberate act.

> **Exercise 53.3**
>
> Refer to Regulations 531.2.6 and 531.2.7 to review the requirements relating to RCDs powered from auxiliary sources and potential impairment by magnetic fields caused by other equipment.

(iv) RCDs in a TN system.

In a TN system, RCDs may be required where the requirements of Regulation 411.4.5 for automatic disconnection cannot be fulfilled by an overcurrent protective device, such as where the value of earth fault loop impedance (Zs) of a circuit is too high. Where this is the case exposed-conductive-parts must be connected to the TN earthing protective conductor or to a separate earth electrode which affords an impedance low enough to operate the RCD. Where a separate earth electrode is used the requirements relating to TT systems (Regulation Group 41.5) should be followed).

(v) RCDs in a TT system

Where an installation forming part of a TT system is protected by a RCD, then either:

• the RCD should be located at the origin of the installation, or
• the part of the installation between the origin and the RCD should comply with the requirements for protection by the use of Class II equipment or equivalent insulation.

Where there is more than one origin, the above requirement applies to each origin.

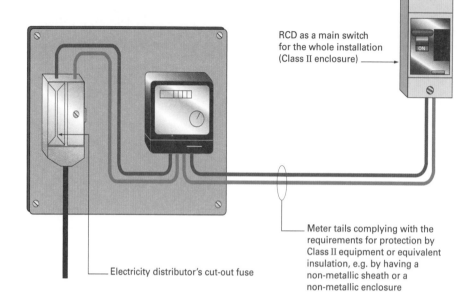

Key Facts
'Careful consideration should be given to the positioning of RCDs as well as their rated residual operating current. To ensure effective discrimination where more than one RCD is fitted in series, time delay devices will be required

RCD as a main switch for the whole installation (Class II enclosure)

Meter tails complying with the requirements for protection by Class II equipment or equivalent insulation, e.g. by having a non-metallic sheath or a non-metallic enclosure

Electricity distributor's cut-out fuse

Fig 53.2 An RCD supplied direct from the origin of an installation forming part of a TT system

5. Devices for protection against the risk of fire (Section 532)

The requirements relating the use of RCDs and the limitation of fault currents with respect to the risk of fire can be found in Regulation 532.1.

Exercise 53.4

Refer to Regulation 532.1 (1) What is the maximum rated residual operating current of an RCD used to limit the consequences of fault currents with respect to fire? (2) Where in the installation should the RCD be fitted? (3) What is the alternative (in Regulation 532.1) to the use of RCDs for limiting the risk of fire.

6. Devices for protection against overcurrent (Section 533)

A device for the protection against overcurrent must comply with one of the following:

Table 53.1 (Learning Guide Table) Overcurrent protection devices

Product standard	Type of device
BS 88-2.2	Low voltage fuse
BS 88-6	
BS 646	
BS 1361	
BS 1362	
BS 3036	
BS EN 60898-1 and -2	Circuit-breakers
BS EN 60947-2 and -3	Circuit-breakers and fuse combination units
BS EN 60947-4-1, -6-1 and –6-2	Contactors and motor starters, transfer switching equipment and control and protective switching devices
BS EN 61009-1	Residual current operated circuit-breakers with integral overcurrent protection

a. Overcurrent protective devices – installation and maintenance

When selecting overcurrent protective devices consideration should be given, in addition to the technical characteristics of the device, to the person responsible for the maintenance of the electrical system.

Where fuses are installed, particular attention needs to be given to the requirements of Regulation Group 533.1.1 (fuses). Where fuses are used with fuse-links that are likely to be removed or replaced by persons other than instructed persons or skilled persons, they should be of a type which complies with the safety requirements of *BS 88* and include markings to indicate the type of fuse link or be of a type such that there is no possibility of inadvertent replacement by a fuse link having the intended rated current but a higher fusing factor.

Fig 53.3 Different size fuses for different current ratings - one method to avoid inadvertent replacement.

Every fuse or circuit-breaker requires on or adjacent to it an indication of its intended nominal current and, where the fuse or circuit-breaker is likely to be replaced by a person other than a skilled or instructed person, it should be of a type that cannot be replaced inadvertently by one having a higher nominal current.

Chapter 53
Protection, isolation, switching, control and monitoring

A circuit-breaker that may be operated by persons other than instructed persons or skilled persons should be designed and installed such that access to overcurrent characteristic settings can only be accessible by the use of a key or a tool.

Where fuses are used preference should be given to cartridge type devices. Where a semi-enclosed (rewireable) fuse is selected manufacturers' instructions should be followed. Table 53.1 of *BS 7671* should be used for selection of tinned copper wire elements where manufacturers' instructions aren't available.

Exercise 53.5

Refer to Table 53.1 of *BS 7671*. What is the nominal diameter of a copper wire that should be selected for a semi-enclosed fuse with a nominal current rating of 20 A? (2) What are the requirements relating to unintentional contact with live parts where fuse-links are likely to be removed or replaced by instructed or skilled persons.

b. Selection of devices for overload protection of wiring systems

The rated current (or current setting) of the protective device should be chosen in accordance with Regulation 433.1 (see Chapter 43 Protection against overload of BS 7671 or this Learning Guide).

When selecting overcurrent protective devices peak current values should be considered to avoid unintentional operation. Where cyclic loading is a consideration the thermally equivalent constant load should be used for design and cable selection purposes.

c. Additional requirements against overload when harmonic currents are present.

When selecting an overload protective device account must be taken of harmonic currents (for further information relating to harmonics see Appendix 11 of *BS 7671* or this Learning Guide).

d. Selection of devices for protection of wiring systems against short circuit

A device may be selected on the basis of the rated ultimate short-circuit breaking capacity for the maximum fault circuit conditions. However, operational circumstances may make it desirable to select the protective device on the service short-circuit breaking capacity, for example where a protective device is placed at the origin of the installation.

Where the short-circuit breaking capacity of the protective device is lower than the short-circuit current that is expected at its point of installation, it will be necessary to ensure 'back-up' protection is provided.

7. Devices for protection against undervoltage (Section 535)

The requirements of Section 445 (see Chapter 44 of *BS 7671* or this Learning Guide) provide information relating to devices for protection against undervoltage.

8. Co-ordination of protective devices (Section 536)

a. General

Section 536 provides the requirements for the co-ordination of protective devices. Where devices (overcurrent protective or RCDs) are installed in series their selection should be carefully considered to ensure safety and proper functioning of the installation.

Details relating to the breaking capacity of devices can be found in Chapter 43 of *BS 7671* and this Learning Guide.

9. Monitoring (Section 538)

a. Introduction

Section 538 of *BS 7671* provides the requirements relating to monitoring. Within Section 538 there are two types of monitoring:

• Insulation monitoring devices (IMDs) for IT systems (Regulation Group 538.1) and
• Residual current monitor (RCM) (Regulation Group 538.4)

Because IT systems are uncommon and require specialist knowledge, the following text is only meant to provide a general overview of the subject. For further information relating to monitoring, Section 538 of *BS 7671* and/or The Electrical Safety Council articles M141-1 and M141-5 should be reviewed.

b. Insulation monitoring devices (IMDs) for IT systems

Regulation Groups 538.1 to 538.3 relate to monitoring of circuit insulation resistance to earth of IT installations. In an IT system the risk of losing continuity of supply is reduced because, in the event of a single earth fault, unlike in a TN or TT system, there is no requirement for automatic disconnection of supply. There is, however, a requirement for automatic disconnection of the supply in the event of two earth faults existing simultaneously. It is therefore important, if full advantage is to be taken of the reduced risk of losing continuity of supply, that the occurrence of a single earth fault is indicated so that remedial work may be carried out prior to the occurrence of a second earth fault. Hence there is a requirement for the provision of insulation monitoring in an IT system.

c. Residual current monitoring (RCM)

A residual current monitor permanently monitors any leakage current in the downstream installation or part of it; they are not intended to provide protection against electric shock.

In supply systems, RCMs may be installed to reduce the risk of operation of the protective device in the event of excessive leakage current of the installation or the connected appliances. A loop circuit is employed which consists of the protective conductor, a part of the protected equipment's metallic casing and the pilot conductor; the impedance of the loop is accurately monitored and any impedance changes cause disconnection and/or an alarm. Normally the RCM will alert the user of the installation before the protective device is activated.

Where an RCD is installed upstream of the RCM, it is recommended that the RCM has a rated residual operating current not exceeding a third of that of the RCD.

notes

Further information relating to Protection, isolation, switching, control and monitoring can be found in:

- *BS 7671* Chapter 53
- Electrical Safety Council Technical Manual articles F133-17, I17-4, I17-15, M141-1, M141-5 and R101-19
- IEE Guidance Note 4

CHAPTER 53 FINAL REVISION EXERCISE

53.1 For installations with a 230 V single-phase supply rated up to 100 A that is under the control of ordinary persons, switchgear and controlgear should be provided with which of the following?

☐ a. Provided with a single-pole switch
☐ b. Provided with a switch in the neutral alone
☐ c. A consumer unit complying with *BS EN 60309-2*
☐ d. A consumer unit complying with *BS EN 60439-3*

53.2 Which of the following is not an acceptable standard for a mounting box for accessories?

☐ a. *BS 4662*
☐ b. *BS 5733*
☐ c. *BS EN 60598*
☐ d. *BS EN 60670-1*

53.3 Which of the following 'capability of persons' category could have access to circuit-breaker overcurrent characteristic settings without the use of a key or tool?

☐ a. BA1
☐ b. BA2
☐ c. BA3
☐ d. BA4

53.4 The maximum rated residual operating current of an RCM where an RCD with a rated residual operating current of 30 mA is fitted upstream should be which of the following?

☐ a. 10 mA
☐ b. 30 mA
☐ c. 40 mA
☐ d. 90 mA

Things to do and find

1. What are the installation requirements at the origin of a TT installation protected by a single RCD?

2. Describe a method to ensure discrimination would work for RCDs in series.

3. List three requirements relating to RCDs where it is necessary to limit the consequences of fault currents in a wiring system from the point of view of fire risk?

4. What are the two options to reduce the risk of incorrect protective device replacement by a person other than an instructed or skilled person?

5. What is the rated current of a fuse element of nominal diameter of 1.53 mm?

6. What is back-up protection?

7. The 'line' terminal(s) of an IMD should be connected as close as practicable to the origin of the system. What are the three options in relation to the point on the circuit where the IMD can be connected?

1. Introduction

This section provides requirements for non-automatic local and remote isolation and switching measures for the prevention or removal of dangers associated with electrical installations or electrically powered equipment and machines as well as functional switching and control.

The term 'isolation and switching', used in *BS 7671* refers to four distinct operating functions (all defined in Part 2 Definitions of *BS 7671*):

- General requirements (537.1)
- Isolation (537.2)
- Switching off for mechanical maintenance (537.3)
- Emergency switching (537.4)
- Functional switching (537.5)

Firefighter's switches (537.6) are also covered in this section.

2. General

Where more than one of the above functions is performed by a common device, the arrangement of the device should ensure that all the requirements relating to the relevant sections are met. A single device is permitted to perform more than one of the four functions mentioned above, where the arrangement and characteristics of the device satisfies all the relevant requirements of *BS 7671*. For example, a functional switching device may be used for isolation purposes, provided all the applicable requirements for both functions are met.

Table 53.2 of *BS 7671* provides guidance on the selection of protective, isolation and switching devices.

Regulation Group 537.1 covers the general requirements for isolation and switching some of which are covered in the following text.

Switching or isolating devices are prohibited in combined protective and neutral (PEN) conductors and protective conductors except as permitted by Regulations 543.3.4 and as required by Regulation 537.1.5

Each installation should be provided with a device to disconnect the supply and every installation should be provided with a main linked switch or main-linked circuit-breaker fitted as near as practicable to the origin as a means of switching the supply on load and as a means of isolation.

Where a main switch is intended for operation by ordinary persons (for example household or similar installations) the switch must interrupt both live conductors (line and neutral).

Section 537
Isolation and switching

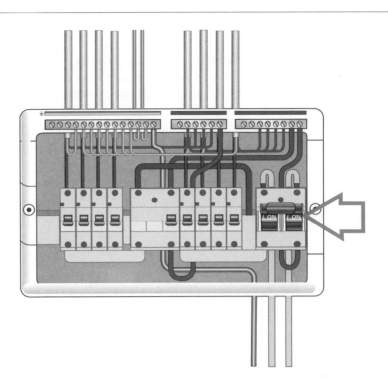

Fig 537.1 Consumer unit double-pole main switch

Exercise 537.1

(1) Why would it be potentially dangerous to have a switching device in a PEN conductor?
(2) What are the requirements where an installation is supplied from more than one source?

---

3. Isolation

a. General

Isolation is the function that allows operatives to work safely on electrical equipment, and is defined as:

'A function intended to cut off for reasons of safety the supply from all, or a discrete section, of the installation by separating the installation or section from every source of electrical energy.'

Every circuit must be capable of being isolated from each of the live supply conductors. Isolation of the neutral conductor of a circuit in TN-S or TN-C-S systems is not generally required where that conductor can be reliably regarded as being at earth potential. Isolation of the neutral, however, may be required (e.g. see above comments relating to household or similar installations). See also Figs 537.4 to 537.9 below.

A group of circuits may be isolated by a common means. However, before installing a device for the isolation and switching of a group of circuits, the installation designer should consider any inconvenience that may result. An example of the valid use of a single device to isolate a group of circuits is a main switch in a domestic dwelling.

In installations containing items of equipment or enclosures contains live parts connected to more than one supply, a durable warning notice must be permanently fixed in such a position as to warn any person before gaining access to live parts of the need to operate the isolation and switching device for each source of supply. Alternatively, a suitable interlock system may be provided.

WARNING
Before opening cover, isolation is required
at more than one location

Fig 537.2 Warning notice indicating that isolation is required from more than one position

Section 537.2 also contains specific requirements for the discharge of stored electrical energy and isolation of electric discharge lighting supplies (where the discharge lighting circuitry open circuit voltage exceeds low voltage).

Exercise 537.2

What are the requirements of Regulation Group 537.2 in relation to disconnection the neutral conductor?

b. Devices for isolation

When selecting and installing isolation devices careful consideration must be given to their intended use. It is essential that circuits intended to be isolated remain isolated and that inadvertent or unauthorised closure of devices is avoided. To ensure ongoing safety, isolation devices should be fitted with a provision for securing the device in the isolated position.

Exercise 537.3

Review Regulation Group 537.2.2 in relation to the requirements for (1) identification, (2) Remote isolation (3) Visibility and/or indication of the position of contacts (4) links inserted in the neutral.

Fig 537.3 A circuit-breaker secured in the open position

c. Conductor isolation requirements

The number of conductors to be isolated depends upon the type of earthing arrangement and whether the installation is controlled by skilled or unskilled persons. The means of isolation should preferably be provided by a multi-pole device which disconnects all applicable poles of the relevant supply simultaneously. However single-pole devices situated adjacent to each other, having appropriate labeling, are not excluded.

The following diagrams (Figs 537.4 to 537.9) illustrate the requirements for isolation at **the origin for all persons** (skilled or unskilled).

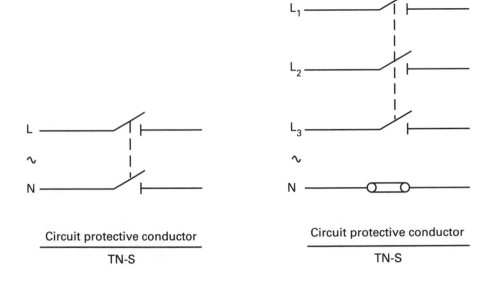

Fig 537.4 Single-phase TN-S system

Fig 537.5 Three-phase TN-S system

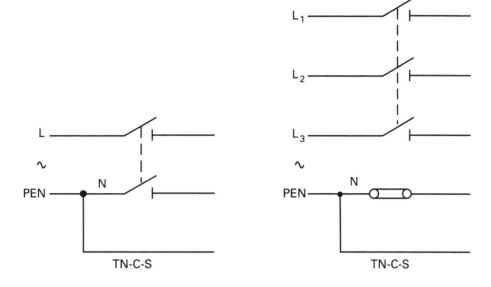

Fig 537.6 Single-phase TN-C-S system   Fig 537.7 Three-phase TN-C-S system

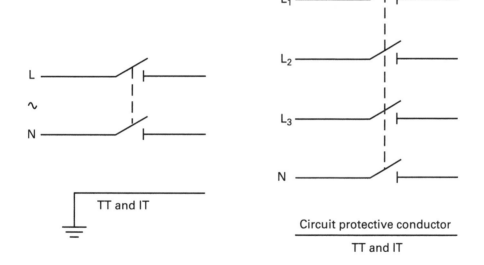

Fig 537.8 Single-phase TT & IT system   Fig 537.9 Three-phase TT & IT system

4. Switching off for mechanical maintenance

a. General

Switching off for mechanical maintenance is not necessarily intended to provide protection against electric shock. Switching off for mechanical maintenance is to enable non-electrical maintenance to be performed safely without the risk of burns or injury from mechanical movement. The demands of safety are such that in most cases the same means of preventing unintentional or inadvertent reclosing of the switch must be provided as are required for isolation. The enclosures of electrical parts of equipment are intended to remain in place during mechanical maintenance.

Section 537
Isolation and switching

Mechanical maintenance is defined as:

> 'The replacement, refurbishment or cleaning of lamps and non-electrical parts of equipment, plant and machinery.'

Injury could result from burns from heating elements or some types of lamps or from mechanical movement such as might be caused by electrically-actuated machinery. A typical situation where this may arise would be the replacement of a belt between an electric motor and a machine. This should be possible after switching off for mechanical maintenance.

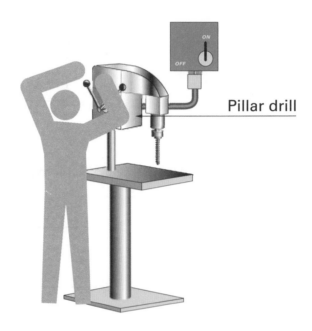

Pillar drill

Fig 537.10 The replacement of a belt from an electric motor to a machine may be able to be undertaken after switch off for mechanical maintenance

For example, consider where mechanical maintenance is required on an electric motor-driven circular saw to replace the saw blade and drive belt. As no live parts would be made accessible when completing this task isolation is not a requirement. However, this operation will require the electric motor that drives the circular saw to be switched off for mechanical maintenance and thus prevent unexpected operation of the saw, due to inadvertent energization of the motor. In many cases, the motor will be switched off by operating, and locking off, a locally-provided isolating device.

b. Devices for switching off for mechanical maintenance

Devices for switching for mechanical maintenance should be manually operated. They should be inserted, where practicable, in the supply main circuit and be capable of cutting off the full load current of the relevant part of the installation. The requirements relating to isolation devices (mentioned previously) in relation to visibility of contacts, prevention of inadvertent or unintentional switching of contacts and identification apply equally to devices for switching for mechanical maintenance.

A shower or cooker switch can perform the function of switching off for mechanical maintenance, providing the applicable requirements are met. This would include consideration for the location of the switch, to ensure it was continuously under the control of the person performing the maintenance task.

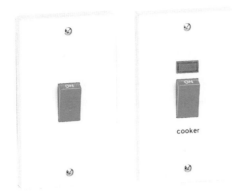

Fig 537.11 A shower or cooker switch may perform the function of switching off for mechanical maintenance

---

Exercise 537.4

(1) Give two examples of where switching off for mechanical maintenance could be employed. (2) What precaution should be taken where the device used for switching off for mechanical maintenance is not continuously under the control of the person(s) performing the maintenance task?

---

5. Emergency Switching

a. General

Where, in case of danger, there is necessity for immediate interruption of supply, an interrupting device must be installed in such a way that it can be easily recognized and effectively and rapidly operated.

Emergency switching is defined as:

'An operation intended to remove, as quickly as possible, danger, which may have occurred unexpectedly.'

A particular class of emergency switching, known as 'emergency stopping', is defined in Part 2 as:

'Emergency switching intended to stop an operation.'

The purpose of emergency switching is largely explained by its definition, although it should be added that the purpose is not only to remove danger, but also to prevent danger that is perceived to be imminent.

Exercise 537.5

The definition of 'danger' should now be referred to in Part 2 of *BS 7671*.

Section 537
Isolation and switching

It can be seen that the purpose of emergency switching expressed more fully, is to prevent or remove the risk of injury arising from (i) fire, electric shock and burns arising from the use of electrical energy, and (ii) mechanical movement of electrically controlled equipment, in so far as such danger is intended to be prevented by electrical emergency switching or by electrical switching for mechanical maintenance of non-electrical parts of such equipment.

Emergency stopping has the additional function of stopping the operation (normally the mechanical movement) of electrically actuated equipment.

b. Devices for Emergency Switching

The means for emergency switching must consist of either a single switching device or a combination of equipment operated by a single action resulting in the removal of the hazard by cutting off the appropriate supply.

An example of the latter system is the commonly-encountered circuit design consisting of a push-operated 'emergency stop switch' connected in the control circuit of a contactor which switches the supply to an electric motor. The contactor would not need to be situated adjacent to the machine. Devices such as circuit-breakers and contactors that are operated by remote control, must open upon de-energization of the coil, or utilize another technique of equivalent reliability.

The means of operating a device for emergency switching is to have a latching type mechanism or be capable of being restrained in the OFF or STOP position. Devices which have an operating means which automatically reset are precluded for emergency switching, unless both the operating means for emergency switching and the means of re-energizing are under the control of one and the same person.

Key Facts
'It is important to understand the different types of isolation and switching devices and where they can and can't be used'

Fig 537.12 An example of a device that may meet the requirements for emergency switching

There are many requirements relating to emergency switching devices, the following table provides a summary.

Table 537.1 (Learning Guide Table) Requirements for emergency switching devices

Must be capable of breaking the full load current of the relevant part of the installation.
Hand-held devices for direct interruption of the main circuit to be selected where applicable.
The means of operating devices (handles, push-buttons etc) for emergency switching to be clearly identifiable, preferably by colour.
The means of operating should be readily accessible at places of danger and, where appropriate, at any additional remote position from which that danger can be removed.
Devices should be so placed and marked as to be readily identifiable and convenient for their intended use.
The arrangement for emergency switching should be such that its operation does not introduce a further danger or interfere with the complete operation necessary to remove the danger.

7. Functional switching

a. General

Functional switching is provided for the users of electrical installations for normal operating purposes to control items of current-using electrical equipment. The equipment may be controlled either individually or in groups and via a manual or automatic operation. Examples of functional switching devices are wall-mounted plate switches provided to switch on a luminaire or group of luminaires and a wall-mounted dimmer switch used to control lighting levels. A time-switch used to control an external floodlight is an example of an automatically-operated functional switch.

Functional switching is defined as:

> 'An operation intended to switch 'on' or 'off' or vary the supply of electrical energy to all or part of an installation for normal operating purposes.'

Further examples of functional switching devices include:

- A switch in a socket-outlet
- A contactor switching the supply to start and stop an electric motor
- Push buttons used to control a contactor or relay
- A thermostat used to switch an immersion heater on and off
- A pressure switch or level switch used to switch a pump on and off
- A microswitch used to limit movement on a machine.

Section 537
Isolation and switching

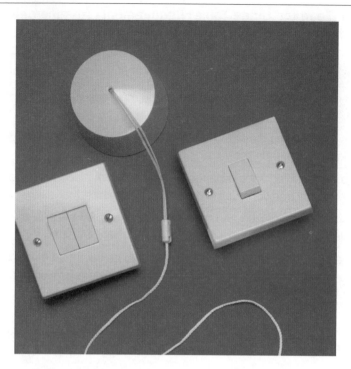

Fig 537.13 Familiar functional switching devices

b. Circuit requirements for functional switching

A functional switching device must be provided for each part of a circuit that requires the function to be controlled independently of other parts of the installation. However, a single functional switching device may be used to control two or more items of equipment where those items are intended to operate simultaneously, such as one plate switch configured to control a number of luminaires in a corridor.

Regulation 537.5.1.3 requires that all items of current-using equipment should have adequate control by an appropriate functional switching device. In the case of appliances, the device for functional switching can be, and often is, an integral part of the appliance.

A functional switching device does not necessarily have to control all the live conductors of a circuit. For example, a switch in a lighting circuit is usually a single-pole device acting in the line conductor only. It is, however, a requirement that a single-pole functional switching device *is not* connected in the neutral conductor only.

As with all other items of switchgear and controlgear, the purpose of a functional switching device is required to be identified by a label or other suitable means of identification, unless there is no possibility of confusion.

c. Devices for functional switching

Functional switching devices, due to their operational requirements, are devices capable of switching loads 'on' and 'off'. They are all required to be suitable for the most onerous duty intended, and should be selected to have a utilization category appropriate to the type of load being switched. Disconnectors (off-load isolators), fuses and links are not considered to be suitable devices for functional switching.

A plug and socket-outlet is not permitted to be used for functional switching of d.c. circuits but may be used for functional switching in a.c. circuits, providing the equipment has a rating of not more than 16 A.

Due consideration should be given to the prospective 'user' of this type of system. However, this would not be suitable for either elderly, the young or infirm.

Functional switching devices do not necessarily have contacts that open and close. Rheostats, potentiometers, and semiconductor devices that control current electronically may be used as functional switching devices. For example, a wall-mounted dimmer switch used to control the lighting level or a variable speed drive, arranged to control the speed of an a.c. motor-driven pump.

Exercise 537.6

(1) Provide an example of an automatically operated functional switch. (2) Can a socket-outlet be used as a functional switch? (3) Can a luminaire support coupler be used as a functional switch?

8. Firefighter's switches

a. General

A firefighter's switch, as the name suggests, is a device intended for use by the fire service, although not exclusively so. A firefighter's switch is used by the fire service to de-energize designated parts of an installation that operate at a voltage in excess of low voltage.

Fig 537.14 A typical example of a firefighter's switch

A Firefighter's switch is required in low voltage circuits supplying:

- Exterior electrical installations operating at a voltage exceeding low voltage, and
- Interior discharge lighting installations operating at a voltage exceeding low voltage.

For the purposes of Regulation 537.6.1, an installation in a covered market, arcade or shopping mall is considered to be an exterior installation, however a temporary installation in a permanent building used for exhibitions is considered to be an interior installation.

Exercise 537.7

(1) Review the definition of 'low voltage' (2) Provide examples of the type of installations/ equipment where a firefighter's switch would be required.

Section 537
Isolation and switching

b. Location of a firefighter's switch

For an exterior installation, the switch should be located outside the building and adjacent to the equipment. Otherwise, a notice should indicate its position with a further notice close to the switch to clearly identify its operation.

For interior installations, the switch should be in the main entrance to the building or in a position agreed with the local fire authority.

It should be conspicuous, reasonably accessible to firemen and not more than 2.75 m from the ground (except where otherwise agreed with the local fire authority).

When more than one such switch is used, each switch must be clearly labeled to indicate the installation it controls.

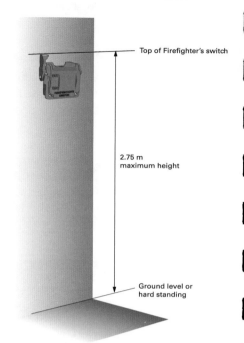

Fig 537.15 Height to a firefighter's switch

c. Firefighter's switch other requirements

Every firefighter's switch should be coloured red and have fixed to it (or adjacent to it) a label with the words '**FIREFIGHTER'S SWITCH**' clearly indicated, the label must be a minimum size of 150 mm x 100 mm with the letters not less than 36 point and easily legible from a distance appropriate to the site.

The ON and OFF positions must be clearly indicated by lettering which can easily be read by someone standing on the ground. The switch must have its OFF position at the top and be fitted with a lock or catch to prevent it being inadvertently returned to the ON position.

Most importantly, the switch must be installed so as to be accessible for operation by a firefighter.

Exercise 537.8

Refer to Table 53.2 of *BS 7671* (1). Give examples of devices used for isolation, switching for mechanical maintenance, emergency switching and functional switching. (2). Refer to Table 53.2; Can a plug and socket-outlet be used as an isolator? Can a fuse be used for functional switching?

Further information relating to Isolation and switching can be found in:
- *BS7671* Section 537
- Electrical Safety Council Technical Manual articles: I1-9, I93-13, I93-17, I93-21, I93-25, I93-45, I93-49, I93-53, I93-77, I93-89, I93-93, I93-97
- IEE Guidance Note 2

notes

SECTION 537 FINAL REVISION EXERCISE

537.1 The definition 'An operation intended to switch 'on' or 'off' or vary the supply of electrical energy to all or part of an installation for normal operating purpose' describes which of the following?
- ☐ a. Switching off for mechanical maintenance
- ☐ b. Emergency switching
- ☐ c. Isolation
- ☐ d. Functional switching

537.2 The definition 'An operation intended to remove, as quickly as possible, danger, which may have occurred unexpectedly' describes which of the following?
- ☐ a. Switching off for mechanical maintenance
- ☐ b. Emergency switching
- ☐ c. Emergency stopping
- ☐ d. Functional switching

537.3 The definition 'The replacement, refurbishment or cleaning of lamps and non-electrical parts of equipment, plant and machinery' describes which of the following?
- ☐ a. Switching off for mechanical maintenance
- ☐ b. Mechanical maintenance
- ☐ c. Emergency stopping
- ☐ d. Functional switching

Things to do and find

1. Use Table 53.2 to find out which isolation and switching functions can be carried out by use of a fuse.

2. Use Table 53.2 to find out which isolation and switching functions can be carried out by use of a semi-conductor device.

3. What is the maximum height of a firefighter's switch?

4. What is the definition of isolation?

1. Introduction.

Chapter 54 covers the requirements relating to earthing arrangements (Section 542) and protective conductors (Section 543). The protective measure automatic disconnection of supply (Section 411) is closely connected to Chapter 54.

The different types of earthing arrangements (earthing systems) were covered previously in Part 2 of this Learning Guide; therefore earthing arrangements will only be covered briefly in this section of the Learning Guide relating to Chapter 54. Earth electrodes which are part of the earthing arrangement will, however, be covered more fully in this section.

The term protective conductor covered in this section relates to all the conductors used for protective earthing and protective bonding.

Earthing can be divided into two parts:

• Supply system earthing arrangement.
• Electrical installation earthing.

The supply system earthing, is the provision of a connection between the source of energy - normally the distribution transformer secondary winding or generator winding - and the general mass of earth (Earth), via a source earth electrode. The provision and maintenance of source earthing is normally the responsibility of the owner of the source of energy.

Electrical installation earthing is the connection of the exposed-conductive-parts of an installation to an appropriate means of earthing (main earthing terminal) at the origin of the installation.

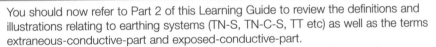

Exercise 54.1

You should now refer to Part 2 of this Learning Guide to review the definitions and illustrations relating to earthing systems (TN-S, TN-C-S, TT etc) as well as the terms extraneous-conductive-part and exposed-conductive-part.

2. Earthing arrangements

a. General requirements

The main earthing terminal (MET) of an installation must be connected with Earth by one of the following:

TN-S, to the earthed point of the source of energy (part of the connection may be formed by the distributor's lines and equipment),

TN-C-S, where protective multiple earthing is provided, to the neutral of the source of energy,

TT and IT, via an earthing conductor to an earth electrode.

Chapter 54
Earthing Arrangements and Protective conductors

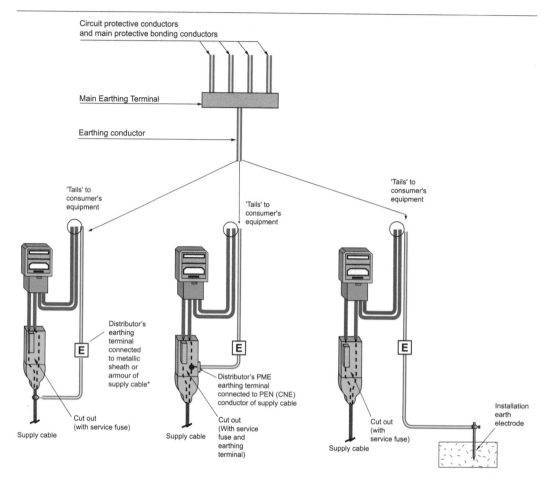

Fig 54.1 Earthing supply arrangements and installation earthing (Note: the incoming earthing arrangement can be by an underground supply as shown or overhead).

b. Earth electrodes

Seven distinct types of earth electrode are recognized in *BS 7671*. It is should be noted that further information in relation to earth electrodes (and earthing generally) can be found in *BS 7430 Code of practice for earthing.*

The local conditions regarding the type of soil, its composition and any regional soil freezing concerns will affect the appropriate choice and installation method of the earth electrode. The design and construction of an electrode may also be determined by concerns relating to damage and increase in resistance, due to corrosion.

Table 54.A (Learning Guide Table) Recognized types of earth electrodes

Earth rods or pipes
Earth tapes or wires
Earth plates
Underground structural metalwork
Welded metal reinforcement of concrete (except pre-stressed concrete) embedded in the earth
Lead sheaths and other metal coverings of cables (where not precluded by 542.2.5)
Other suitable underground metalwork

(i) Earth rods and pipes

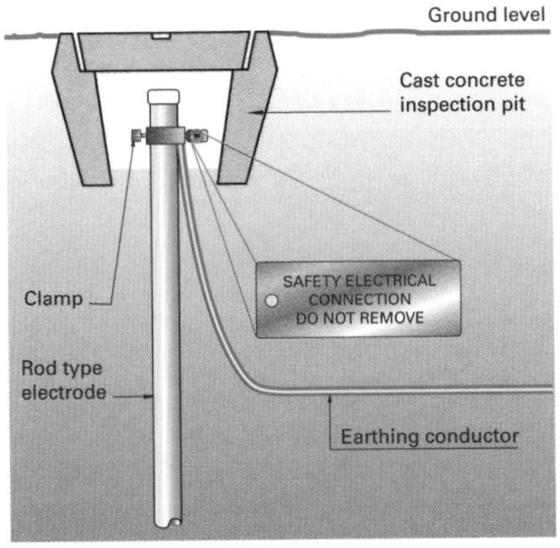

Solid rod or pipe earth electrodes are suitable for many, if not most, earthing applications, although they are not particularly well suited to situations where rock or other hard strata prevent deep driving.

Proprietary driven earth rods should be selected from those which are specifically manufactured to meet the requirements of *BS 7430*. Such rods are generally of solid circular cross-section, and are made of copper, copper-clad steel (bonded steel-cored), stainless steel, or galvanized steel of various diameters. A number of standard lengths of rod are available, which can be coupled together where necessary for deeper driving.

Fig 54.2 Earth rod

It should be noted that metallic pipes for gas or flammable liquids or a metallic pipe of a water utility supply are not permitted to be used as an earth electrode. Other metallic water supply pipework can be used, provided precautions are taken against its removal and it has been considered for such use.

(ii) Earth tapes or wire

Earth tapes and wires are usually of bare, untinned copper in strip or round cross-section. *BS 7430* provides further details and requirements. Earth tapes and wires are particularly suitable where hard, high-resistivity ground underlies shallow layers of low resistivity soil.

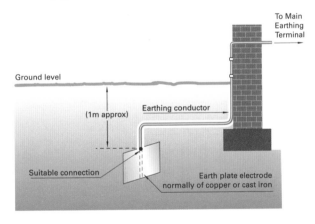

Fig 54.3 Earth plate electrode

(iii) Earth Plates

Earth plates are usually of copper or cast iron, and are normally of no more than 1.2 metres square. They are generally well suited to the types of ground condition described above for earth tapes and wires, and should be set vertically. Particular care needs be taken in relation to the earth plate connection when the earthing conductor and earth plate are of dissimilar metals.

(iv) Underground structural metalwork embedded in foundations.

Underground metalwork embedded in foundations includes, for example, steel stanchions encased in concrete. It may be necessary to connect to the metalwork of a number of foundation arrangements, possibly by partial or total use of the common structural metal frame (such as that of a building) which links them together, in order to obtain a sufficiently low resistance to Earth.

(v) Welded metal reinforcement of concrete (except pre-stressed concrete) embedded in the earth.

The welded metal reinforcing of concrete may be considered for utilization as an earth electrode, but its use for such a purpose must have the prior agreement of the structural engineer in charge.

(vi) Lead sheaths and other metal coverings of cables

The use of a lead sheath or other metal covering of a cable as an electrode is subject to certain conditions given in *BS 7671*.

Exercise 54.2

You should now refer to Regulation 542.2.5 to review the conditions required to be met when a lead sheath or other metal covering of a cable is being considered for use as an earth electrode.

c. Earthing conductors

The earthing conductor of an electrical installation is the protective conductor connecting the Main Earthing Terminal (MET) of the installation with the means of earthing (the external earthing system).

The requirements of section 543 must be met in relation to earthing conductors. Where PME conditions apply, the requirements of Regulation 544.1.1 relating to the cross-sectional area of the main protective bonding conductor also applies. In addition to the above requirements, where buried in the ground, the earthing conductor should have a cross-sectional area not less than that stated in Table 54.1 of *BS 7671*.

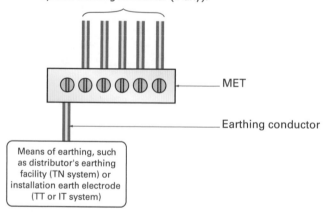

Circuit protective conductors, protective bonding conductors, functional earthing conductors (if required) and lightning protection system bonding conductor (if any).

MET

Earthing conductor

Means of earthing, such as distributor's earthing facility (TN system) or installation earth electrode (TT or IT system)

Fig 54.4 Earthing conductor and MET

Where tape or strip conductor is used, its composition should be such as to withstand mechanical damage and corrosion.

Whether determined by calculation or selection, the cross-sectional area of an earthing conductor must not be less than the lower limits given in Regulation 543.1.1 (covered in 3b of this section of the Learning Guide).

Where a copper earthing conductor is not an integral part of a cable (such as a core of a cable) and is not contained within an enclosure formed by a wiring system (such as conduit), the csa must be no less than 2.5 mm^2 if mechanically protected, or 4 mm^2 where such protection is not provided.

(i) Cross-sectional area of a buried earthing conductor

Where earthing conductors are to be buried, Table 54.1 outlines the minimum cross-sectional areas relating to the materials used and the particular installation method employed.

Exercise 54.3

Refer to Table 54.1 of *BS 7671*. (1) What is the minimum cross-sectional area of a copper conductor that is protected against corrosion by a sheath but not protected against mechanical damage?

d. Main earthing terminals (METs) or bars

A Main Earthing Terminal (MET) is required in every installation for connection to the means of earthing and the installation protective conductors (listed below):

- Circuit protective conductors, and
- The protective bonding conductors, and
- Functional earthing conductors (if required), and
- Lightning protection system bonding conductor (if any).

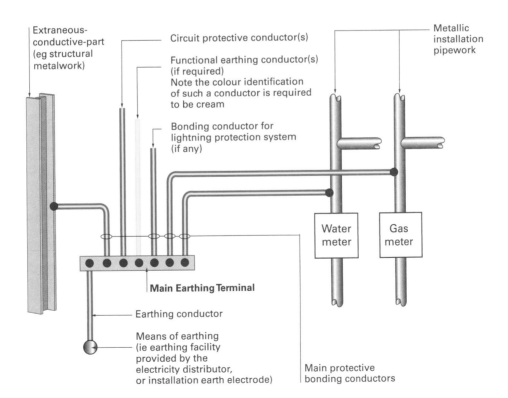

Fig 54.5 MET connecting the earthing conductor to installation protective conductors

Chapter 54
Earthing Arrangements and Protective conductors

To facilitate measurement of the resistance of the earthing arrangements a means of disconnecting the installation earthing conductor will be required. This provision may be combined with the main earthing terminal as shown below.

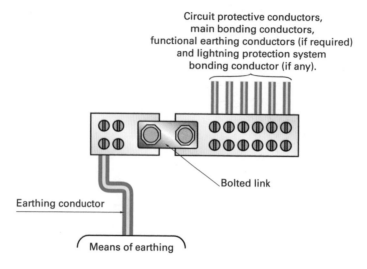

Fig 54.6 MET with disconnecting link

3. Protective Conductors

a. Introduction

Regulation Group 543 provides information on the selection of both, type and cross-sectional area of protective conductors. Protective conductors are conductors provided for the purposes of safety, for example protection against electric shock. The term protective conductor is a generic term relating to earthing conductors, circuit protective conductors, main protective bonding conductors and supplementary protective bonding conductors. It is not always appreciated that *BS 7671* permits not only cables, but also various other types of conductor to be used as protective conductors, provided that all of the relevant requirements are met.

b. Cross-sectional areas of protective conductors

There are two methods that may be employed when choosing a protective conductor, Regulation 543.1.1 requires that:

The cross sectional area (csa) of every protective conductor (other than protective bonding conductors, which are discussed later) must either be:

• Selected (in accordance with Regulation 543.1.4) *or*
• Calculated (in accordance with Regulation 543.1.3)

By far the simplest method of evaluating an appropriate protective conductor is via "selection" in accordance with the requirements of 543.1.4. However, it should be borne in mind that this will often lead to larger csa cables than those that would have been required when utilizing the calculation method. It should also be noted that the calculation method will be required if the choice of cross-sectional areas of line conductors have been determined by considerations of short-circuit current and if the earth fault current is expected to be less than the short-circuit current.

If the protective conductor is not one of the following:

- An integral part of a cable
- Formed by conduit, ducting or trunking
- Contained in an enclosure formed by a wiring system,

the csa of the conductor is to be not less than **2.5 mm²** copper equivalent, if **protected against mechanical damage** (e.g. by a sheath or other form of mechanical protection, as the situation demands), and not less than **4 mm²** copper equivalent, if protection against **mechanical damage is not provided**.

Where a protective conductor is common to two or more circuits, the csa must be calculated for the highest values of fault current and operating time of disconnecting device of the circuits, or to correspond to the csa of the largest line conductor of the circuits.

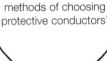

Key Facts
'It is important to be able to use the two methods of choosing protective conductors'

(i) Selection of protective conductor (from Table 54.7)

Where the csa of the protective conductor is to be selected, Table 54.7 should be consulted. This table provides the minimum cross-sectional area of the protective conductor in relation to the csa of the associated line conductor.

Table 54.7 (Reproduced from *BS 7671*) Minimum cross-sectional area of protective conductor in relation to the cross-sectional area of associated line conductor

Cross-sectional area of line conductor S	Minimum cross-sectional area of the corresponding protective conductor	
	If the protective conductor is of the same material as the line conductor	If the protective conductor is not the same material as the line conductor
$S \leq 16$	S	$\dfrac{K_1}{K_2} \times S$
$16 < S \leq 35$	16	$\dfrac{K_1}{K_2} \times 16$
$S > 35$	$\dfrac{S}{2}$	$\dfrac{K_1}{K_2} \times \dfrac{S}{2}$

Where,

k_1 is the value of k for the line conductor, selected from Table 43.1 in Chapter 43 according to the materials of both conductor and insulation.

k_2 is the value of k for the protective conductor, selected from Tables 54.2, 54.3, 54.4, 54.5 or 54.6, as applicable.

Exercise 54.4

Given the following line conductor cross-sectional areas, determine the minimum corresponding size of protective conductors (protective and line conductors are the same material) from Table 54.7:- 6 mm², 35 mm², 50 mm² and 150 mm².

Chapter 54
Earthing Arrangements and Protective conductors

When using PVC/PVC (Twin and Earth) cables, the designer must give serious consideration to the evaluation of the incorporated protective conductor. In almost all cases the csa of the protective conductor is of a reduced size and as such, **will not** meet the above requirements of Table 54.7.

This will therefore necessitate the use of the alternative "calculation method", to evaluate its suitability, as detailed below.

(ii) Calculation of protective conductors (adiabatic equation)

Where the above "selection" method has not been utilized for the sizing process, every protective conductor, other than a protective bonding conductor, will need to be verified by use of the calculation method.

The formula to be used for the calculation is:

$$S = \frac{\sqrt{I^2 t}}{k} \qquad \textbf{This is called the adiabatic equation}$$

Where,

S - is the nominal cross-sectional area of the conductor in mm^2

I - is the value in amperes (rms for a.c.) of the fault current for a fault of negligible impedance, which can flow through the associated protective device (due account being taken of the current limiting effects of the circuit impedances and the limiting capacity (I^{2}t) of that protective device).

t - is the operating time of the disconnecting device in seconds corresponding to the fault current I in amperes

k - is a factor taking account of the resistivity, temperature coefficient and heat capacity of the conductor material, and the appropriate initial and final temperatures of the conductors. (Tables 54.2 to 52.6 provide values of K for a range of cables and conductor types).

The adiabatic equation is based on the assumption that the duration of the earth fault current is so short that none of the heat energy produced in the protective conductor escapes before the protective device operates. This assumption is never true, but is reasonably accurate providing the operating time of the disconnecting device does not exceed 5 s, as is normally required by *BS 7671*.

Example: Calculate the minimum csa for a circuit protective conductor for a circuit protected by a 40 A *BS 88* fuse (assume maximum Z s and 5 s disconnection time). The cable is 70 ^{o}C thermoplastic single insulated with copper conductors, bunched with cables. The nominal voltage is 230 V.

$$S = \frac{\sqrt{I^2 t}}{k}$$

I (current) = 230/1.35 = 170 A. (1.35 = maximum earth fault loop impedance from Table 41.4 of *BS 7671*

t (disconnection time) for a 40 A *BS 88* fuse with 170 A flowing is 5 seconds (check this by referring to Appendix 3 Table 3.3B).

k (from Table 54.3) 115 (cable assumed to be less than 300 mm^2, with a 40 A device).

$$\therefore S \ \frac{\sqrt{28,900 \times 5}}{k} = \frac{380}{115} = 3.3 \text{ mm}^2. \quad \textbf{A 4 mm}^2 \textbf{ cable will be required.}$$

Exercise 54.5

Calculate the minimum size protective conductor for a 60 A *BS 1361* fuse. The cable is a steel-wire armoured thermosetting 90 °C cable; the armouring is to be used as the protective conductor. Assume maximum Z s and 5 s disconnection time. Nominal voltage is 230 V

c. Types of protective conductor

As stated previously, there are many options when protective conductors are being selected, provided that all of the relevant requirements are met. It should be noted that the term protective conductor includes bonding conductors.

The most commonly installed protective conductors are single-core cables (with green and yellow insulation), conductors within a cable, insulated or bare conductors within a common enclosure (such as conduit or trunking, alongside live insulated conductors), metal coverings (such as armoured cables or metal wiring systems such as conduits or trunking.

There are, however, other alternatives including the use of an extraneous-conductive-part providing they meet the requirements of Regulation 543.2.6.

Apart from metallic protective conductors such as cable armouring, metallic conduit etc protective conductors less than 10 mm^2 must be of copper.

Gas pipes, oil pipes, flexible or pliable conduit, support wires or other flexible metallic parts, or constructional parts subject to mechanical stress in normal service, must not be used as protective conductors.

Exercise 54.6

Refer to Regulation Group 543.2 and review the requirements for an extraneous-conductive-part when used as a protective conductor. (1) Name three types of extraneous-conductive-parts that cannot be used as a protective conductor

Where a metal enclosure or frame of low voltage switchgear or controlgear is used as a protective conductor, its electrical continuity must be assured, either by construction or by suitable connection. Also, the cross-sectional area (csa) of the enclosure or frame must be not less than that required by Regulation 543.1.3 (adiabatic equation) or Regulation 543.1.4 (Table 54.7), or verified by test in accordance with *BS EN 60439-1*.

Where a protective conductor is formed by conduit, trunking, ducting or the metal sheath and/or armour of a cable, the earthing terminal of each accessory (e.g. a socket-outlet or light switch) is required to be connected by a separate protective conductor to the earthing terminal incorporated in the associated box or other enclosure (as illustrated below).

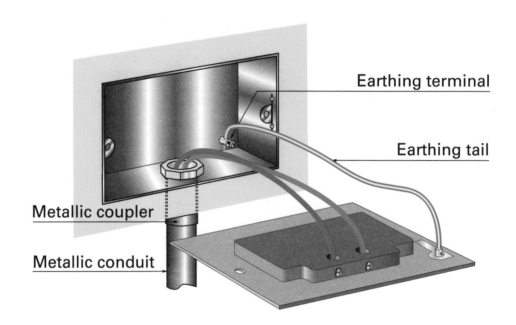

Earthing terminal

Earthing tail

Metallic coupler

Metallic conduit

Fig 54.6 Separate protective conductor from conduit accessory box.

d. Ring Final Circuits

Where the circuit protective conductors of a ring final circuit are not formed by the metal covering or enclosure of a cable, they must be installed in the form of a ring with both ends connected to the earth terminal at the origin of the circuit. This will normally be the distribution board or consumer unit.

e. Preservation of electrical continuity of protective conductors

Where protective conductors up to and including 6 mm^2 csa, run outside an enclosure, such as part of a multicore cable or cable trunking, they must be insulated. Where insulation is removed, for example from a sheathed cable and the protective conductor is below 6 mm^2 csa sleeving must be applied.

Protective conductors must be protected against any external influences that could cause deterioration (for example by mechanical damage or chemical corrosion) and where metallic conduits are utilized as a protective conductor they must be mechanically and electrically continuous (normally by use of screwed conduit).

Exercise 54.7

Refer to Regulation 543.3.3 to review the exceptions for joint and termination accessibility relating to protective conductors.

It is important to note that a switch must not be inserted in a protective conductor, except when it forms part of a multiple-pole linked plug-in device in which the protective conductor circuit must not be disconnected before the live conductors, and must be re-connected no later than the live conductors.

Where overcurrent protective devices are used for protection against electric shock, the protective conductor should be incorporated in the same wiring system as the live conductors or in their immediate proximity.

4. Combined protective and neutral (PEN) conductors

As there is limited application of PEN conductors limited reference will be made to them in this section of the Learning Guide (for further information see Regulation Group 543-4).

It should be noted that Regulation 8.4 of the *ESQCR 2002* prohibits the use of Combined protective and neutral (PEN) conductors in consumers' installations except for the three exemptions in Regulation 543.4.2.

Exercise 54.8

Review the three cases where the use of PEN conductors may be permitted.

---

5. Earthing arrangements for combined protective and functional purposes

As the title suggests earthing arrangements for combined protective and functional purposes provides two separate functions:

• a protective purpose (for reasons of electrical safety) *and*,

• a functional purpose (to facilitate the proper functioning of electrical equipment).

Examples of the use of conductors for combined protective and functional purposes are:

• The protective conductor of a circuit in an installation supplying equipment having a high protective conductor current

• A combined protective and neutral (PEN) conductor in a TN-C system or a TN-C-S system.

• A protective conductor that is used for both protective earthing and low-noise earthing in an installation.

It is important to recognize that, where earthing is provided for combined protective and functional purposes, the requirements for protective measures must take precedence.

Where a conductor is used for "functional earthing conductor" purposes only, the outer sheath should be coloured cream (Table 51).

---

6. Earthing requirements for the installation of equipment having high protective conductor currents

a. General

When energized and in normal use, some electrical equipment can cause current to flow in the circuit protective conductors. This process is referred to as functional earthing as the equipment concerned requires the current to flow in the protective conductor to function or operate normally.

Chapter 54
Earthing Arrangements and Protective conductors

Such 'protective conductor current' is often associated with filters and suppressors in items such as computers, and telecommunications equipment.

Any equipment or circuits having a protective conductor current greater than 3.5 mA may increase the risk of electric shock. There are therefore, additional requirements stipulated for these circuits.

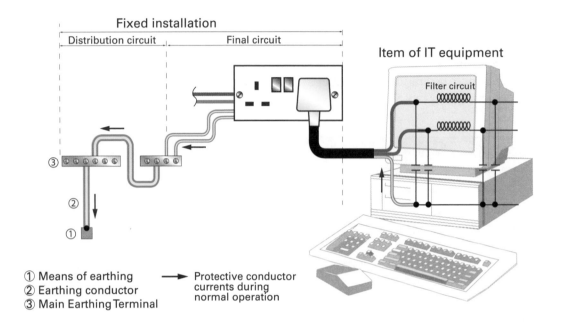

① Means of earthing
② Earthing conductor
③ Main Earthing Terminal

→ Protective conductor currents during normal operation

Fig 54.7 Typical equipment and circuit arrangement illustrating high protective conductor currents

b. Equipment having a protective conductor current exceeding 3.5 mA, but less than 10 mA.

Equipment which in normal service, will have a protective conductor current exceeding 3.5 mA, but less than 10 mA must be either:

• permanently connected to the fixed wiring of the installation without the use of a plug and socket-outlet, *or*

• connected by means of a connector complying with *BS EN 60309-2* (that is, an industrial-type connector as shown below).

Fig 54.8 Connector complying with *BS EN 60309-2*

c. Equipment having a protective conductor current exceeding 10 mA

Where an item of equipment having a protective conductor current exceeding 10 mA is to be supplied, there are several requirements and these can be met in three different ways. The following aspects of the installation must be considered:

• the means of connection of the equipment.

• the final circuits and distribution circuits supplying the equipment.

• the termination of protective conductors.

Equipment shall be connected to the supply by either:

(1) permanently connecting to the fixed wiring of the installation, the protective conductor being selected in accordance with Regulation 543.7.1.3.

(2) where a plug and socket-outlet arrangement is used they must comply with *BS EN 60309-2*. In addition, one of the following requirements must be met:

   • the csa of the associated flexible cable should not be less than 2.5 mm^2 for plugs rated at 16 A and not less than 4 mm^2 for plugs rated above 16 A *or*,

   • the protective conductor of the associated flexible cable should have a csa not less than the line conductor.

(3) an earth monitoring system to *BS 4444* may be used provided that, in the event of a continuity fault in the protective conductor, automatic disconnection of the supply to the equipment occurs.

d. Final circuits and distribution circuits where the total protective conductor current is liable to exceed 10 mA.

Every final circuit and distribution circuit intended to supply an item (or items) of equipment, where the total protective conductor current is likely to exceed 10 mA, must meet requirements of a high integrity protective connection. Five options are provided in Regulation 543.7.1.3; the following text provides a brief overview of the options:

• A single protective conductor having a csa of not less than 10 mm^2.

• A single copper protective conductor having a csa of not less than 4 mm^2, the protective conductor being enclosed to provide additional mechanical protection.

• Two individual protective conductors, each one complying with the requirements of Section 543. It is permitted for the two protective conductors to be of different types for example see Fig 54.9. (for further information see 543.7.1.3 (iii)).

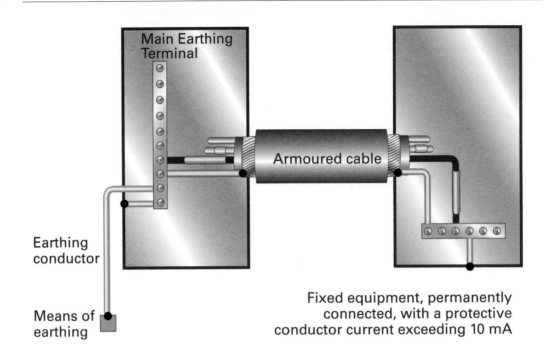

Main Earthing Terminal

Armoured cable

Earthing conductor

Means of earthing

Fixed equipment, permanently connected, with a protective conductor current exceeding 10 mA

Fig 54.9 Armouring of cable used in conjunction with internal protective conductor

- An earth monitoring system to *BS 4444* configured to automatically disconnect the supply to the equipment in the event of a continuity fault in the protective conductor.

- A double-wound transformer or equivalent in which the input and output circuits are electrically separate (for further information see Regulation 543.7.1.3 (v)).

e. Socket-outlet final circuits

A final circuit supplying socket-outlets or connection units where it is expected that the total protective conductor current in normal service will exceed 10 mA, must comply with Regulation Group 543.7.2. Where this is the case, the final circuit must be provided with high integrity protective conductor connections, such as two individual protective conductors or a single protective conductor having a csa of not less than 10 mm^2.

Where two separate protective conductors are used, Regulation 543.7.1.4 requires the socket-outlets and other accessories in the circuit to have two separate earth terminals (as shown in Fig 54.10 below), to enable the ends of the protective conductors to be terminated independently of each other at all connection points.

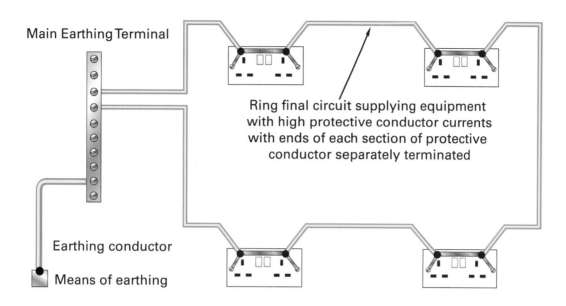

Fig 54.10 Separate protective conductor connections at all connection points

A ring final circuit, by its particular configuration, provides duplication of the protective conductor and, provided the requirements of Section 543 of *BS 7671* are met, a high integrity protective conductor connection exists. Where a cable branch (spur) is provided, this requires a high integrity protective conductor connection and separate termination of the protective conductors as described above.

Where a radial final circuit is utilized it must be provided with a high integrity protective conductor connection. Where duplicate protective conductors are employed, separate termination of the protective conductor ends is required. The duplicate protective conductor can be provided by any of the following options:

a) the protective conductor being connected as a ring, *or*

b) a separate protective conductor being provided at the final socket-outlet by connection to metal conduit or ducting, *or*

c) the protective conductor of an adjacent radial circuit can also be employed (providing certain requirements are met).

Where any of the above situations exist, the protective conductor connection arrangements at the distribution board will, in many cases, be affected. For example, there will in some cases be duplicate protective conductors separately terminated. At the distribution board, information, such as the label shown in Fig 54.11, should be provided indicating those circuits having a high protective conductor current, and such information must be so positioned as to be visible to a person modifying or extending the circuit.

Fig 54.11 Label for distribution board identifying circuits having a high protective
conductor current

7. Protective bonding conductors

a. Main protective bonding conductors, general.

Main protective bonding is an indispensable part of the most commonly used protective
measure, Automatic Disconnection of Supply (ADS). Such bonding is therefore required in
virtually every electrical installation.

Section 411 outlined the requirements for the arrangement of protective equipotential bonding
and it is worth reviewing Regulation 411.3.1.2 before continuing.

The increased use of plastic pipework for incoming services, and within buildings in recent
years has led to some confusion, resulting in either insufficient bonding, or over bonding.
Generally, if the incoming pipes are plastic and the pipes within the installation are plastic then
they do not require main bonding.

b. Cross-sectional area of main protective bonding conductors

The requirements for the minimum cross-sectional area (csa) of a main protective bonding
conductor are given in Regulation 544.1.1 and (for PME conditions) Table 54.8. Main
protective bonding conductors buried in the ground are additionally subject to the
requirements of Regulation 542.3.1 for earthing conductors.

(i) Where Protective Multiple Earthing (PME) conditions do NOT apply

Where PME conditions do not apply, a main bonding conductor should have a csa of not less
than half that required for the earthing conductor of the installation, and not less than 6 mm^2.
The bonding conductor in this case need not exceed 25 mm^2 if made of copper, or, if of other
metals, a csa affording equivalent conductance.

Note, when sizing the main bonding conductor, it should be referred to the size of the "required earthing conductor", and not necessarily the size of the installed earthing conductor, which may be larger than that actually required.

(ii) Where Protective Multiple Earthing (PME) conditions apply

Where PME conditions apply, the main bonding conductors should be selected in accordance with the neutral conductor of the incoming supply and Table 54.8 of *BS 7671*.

The requirement for protective bonding conductors also applies to the earthing conductor of the installation, as it also performs the function of a main bonding conductor (see also Regulation 542.3.1).

Where an installation has more than one source of supply to which PME conditions apply, a main protective bonding conductor must be selected according to the largest neutral conductor of the supply.

> **Exercise 54.9**
>
> Refer to Table 54.8 of *BS 7671*. (1) What is the minimum cross-sectional area of a copper main protective bonding conductor where the supply neutral conductor is 70 mm^2.

The note in Table 54.8 of *BS 7671*, that local electricity distribution network conditions may require a larger conductor, means that the data in the table should be used as a guide only, and that the specific requirements of the electricity distributor should always be obtained.

It is important to note that the 'supply neutral conductor' referred to in Table 54.8 is the neutral conductor of the electricity distributor's low voltage network (otherwise known as the combined protective and neutral (PEN) conductor). It is **not** the neutral conductor on the consumer's side of the supply terminals, which may have a smaller csa.

c. Connections to extraneous-conductive-parts

The main bonding connection to any gas, water or other service must be made as near as practicable to the point of entry of that service into the premises.

Where there is an insulating section or insert at that point, or there is a meter, the connection should be made to the consumer's hard metal pipework (not to a lead pipe or a flexible pipe for example) and before any branch pipework.

Where practicable, the connection is required to be made within 600 mm of the meter outlet union or at the point of entry of the service to the building if the meter is external.

Where an electrical installation serves more than one building, *these requirements are to be applied at each building.*

Main bonding connections to metal pipework should normally be made using bonding clamps complying with *BS 951: Specification for clamps for earthing and bonding purposes*. Clamps should be selected to suit both the pipe diameter and bonding conductor size. Other suitable means of connection may be required when connecting to extraneous- conductive-parts other than pipes, such as structural steelwork.

The clamp selected must be suitable for the environmental conditions at the point of connection. This is typically identified by the colour of the clamp body or a coloured stripe on the warning label.

Fig 54.12 *BS 951* clamp

Fig 54.13 Clamps for different environmental conditions.

A red stripe on the label indicates it is only suitable where conditions are non-corrosive, clean and dry (e.g. hot pipes indoors). A blue or green stripe on the label indicates that the clamp is suitable for all (including corrosive and humid) conditions.

d. Supplementary bonding conductors

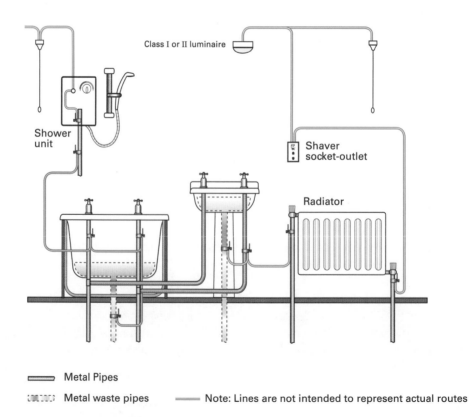

Class I or II luminaire

Shower unit

Shaver socket-outlet

Radiator

▭ Metal Pipes

▨ Metal waste pipes   ── Note: Lines are not intended to represent actual routes

Fig 54.14 Typical supplementary bonding connections

(i). Introduction

Supplementary bonding is an additional protective provision that is used to enhance the protective measures outlined in Chapter 41. It may be required where disconnection times cannot be met or where required due to the special nature of the installation. Part 7 of the Regulations gives further details on the requirements of supplementary bonding in certain special installations or locations.

Supplementary bonding involves connecting together the conductive parts of all electrical items (exposed-conductive-parts) and non-electrical items (extraneous conductive-parts), to prevent the occurrence of a dangerous voltage between them under earth fault conditions. Supplementary bonding should be provided by either a separate supplementary conductor, a conductive part of a permanent and reliable nature (including a circuit protective conductor or an extraneous-conductive-part) or a combination of both. Where doubt exists in relation to the effectiveness of supplementary bonding an assessment should be made by using the calculation contained within Regulation 415.2.2

The exception to the above requirement for supplementary bonding is where a fixed appliance is connected by a short length of flexible cord from an adjacent connection unit or other accessory in which case the protective conductor also provides the function of a supplementary bonding conductor for the short section.

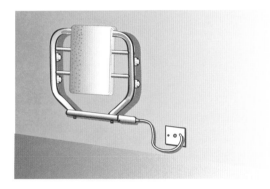

Fig 54.15 Protective conductor in a flexible cord providing both circuit protective conductor and supplementary bonding conductor functions

(ii) Supplementary bonding sizing

The table below sets out the basic requirements of Regulations 544.2.1, 544.2.2 & 544.2.3 relating to the size of supplementary bonding conductors:

Table 544.1 (Learning Guide Table) Minimum CSA of copper conductors required for supplementary bonding

| Regulations | Bonding conductor connecting | | | |
	Sheathed or mechanically protected	Two exposed-conductive-parts	An exposed-conductive-part and an extraneous-conductive-part	Two extraneous-conductive-parts
544.2.1, 544.2.2 & 544.2.3	Yes	CSA ≥ CSA of smaller cpc	CSA ≥ CSA of cpc	CSA ≥ 2.5 mm²
	No	CSA ≥ 4.0 mm²	CSA ≥ 4.0 mm²	CSA ≥ 4.0 mm²

notes

Further information relating to earthing arrangements and protective conductors can be found in:
- *BS7671* Chapter 54, Part 2, Chapter 41
- *BS 7430* Code of practice for earthing
- Electrical Safety Council Technical Manual articles A57-21, B37(-5, 21, 25, 29, 31, 33, 41, 47, 49, 61 & 65), C225-7, E1-1, E5(-1, 5, 9), E45-5, E49-1, P157-7, S205-29
- IEE Guidance Note 5 & 8
- Snags and solutions Part 1 Earthing and bonding

CHAPTER 54 FINAL REVISION EXERCISE

54.1 Which of the following must not be used as an earth electrode?
- ☐ a. An earth rod
- ☐ b. A gas service pipe
- ☐ c. underground structural metalwork
- ☐ d. Earth plates

54.2 Which of the following is the minimum cross-sectional area where a protective conductor is run separately (not an integral part of a cable or formed by a conduit) and does not have mechanical protection?
- ☐ a. 1.5 mm^2
- ☐ b. 2.5 mm^2
- ☐ c. 4.0 mm^2
- ☐ d. 6.0 mm^2

54.3 In the formula S = $\frac{\sqrt{I^2t}}{k}$, a factor taking account of the resistivity, temperature coefficient and heat capacity of the conductor material is symbolized by which of the following?
- ☐ a. S
- ☐ b. I
- ☐ c. t
- ☐ d. k

54.4 What is the k factor of a 90 $^\circ$C thermosetting (rubber) copper cable where the protective conductor is incorporated in a cable or bunched with cables?
- ☐ a. 85
- ☐ b. 94
- ☐ c. 143
- ☐ d. 176

54.5 Where a final circuit is intended to supply one or more items of equipment, such that the total protective conductor current is likely to exceed 10 mA and the protective conductor is mechanically protected, the minimum csa for a single copper conductor should be which of the following?
- ☐ a. 2.5 mm^2
- ☐ b. 4.0 mm^2
- ☐ c. 6.0 mm^2
- ☐ d. 10 mm^2

54.6 The minimum size for a supplementary bonding conductor connecting two extraneous-conductive-parts where mechanical protection is provided should be which of the following?

☐ a. 2.5 mm^2
☐ b. 4.0 mm^2
☐ c. 6.0 mm^2
☐ d. 10 mm^2

Chapter 54
Earthing Arrangements and Protective conductors

Things to do and find

1. List the systems or services that will typically require main protective bonding.

2. List five different types of protective conductor.

3. What are the three conditions that have to be met where a metal enclosure is used as a protective conductor?

4. What type of socket-outlet should be used for the installation of equipment having high protective conductor currents?

5. What special installation requirements should be adhered to when installing a ring circuit that may supply equipment having high protective conductor currents?

6. List five different types of earth electrode.

7. Give three examples of buried metalwork that cannot be used as an earth electrode.

8. What do Tables 54.7 and 54.8 relate to?

9. What is the minimum cross-sectional area of a buried steel earthing conductor where it is not protected against corrosion and not protected against mechanical damage?

1. Introduction

BS 7671 mainly addresses the protection and installation requirements relating to the fixed electrical installation. Although it may at first appear that Chapter 55 (*Other equipment*) is different from the other sections of *BS 7671* as it relates to equipment, it should be noted that the equipment in question is part of the fixed installation and not portable.

The sections in Chapter 55 relate to a wide range of equipment as outlined below:

• Low voltage generating sets (Section 551)
• Rotating machines (Section 552)
• Accessories (Section 553)
• Current-using equipment (Section 554)
• Transformers (Section 555)
• Luminaires and lighting installations (Section 559)

It should be noted that Section 559 Luminaires and lighting is covered in a separate section in this Learning Guide (immediately following this section).

2. Low voltage generating sets (Section 551)

Section 551 of the *BS 7671* applies to both low voltage and extra-low voltage installations incorporating generating sets intended to supply all or part of an installation continuously or occasionally. Requirements are included for the supply to an installation which is not connected to a system for distribution of electricity to the public, supply to an installation as an alternative to a system for distribution of electricity to the public, supply to an installation in parallel with a system for distribution of electricity to the public or an appropriate combination of the above.

Key Facts
'The installation of or alterations to generators requires specialized knowledge and may require additional advice from manufacturers'

Fig 55.1 Standby generator

Regulation Group 551.1 provides details of the types of power sources, generating sets and installations that are covered by the requirements of Section 551.

Chapter 55
Other equipment

Exercise 55.1

Refer to Section 551 and consider whether the following power sources, generating sets and installations are within the remit of *BS 7671*: (1) An electrical supply from a photovoltaic cell (2) a turbine (3) a mains-excited and separately excited synchronous generator (4) the use of a generator to supply permanent installations.

a. General requirements

Section 551.2.1 provides the general requirements relating to the selection and installation of generating sets. It is important that the characteristics of the generator do not impair the safety and proper functioning of other sources. Where a generator is operating independently or in combination the prospective short-circuit current and prospective earth fault current must be assessed for each source of supply and the short-circuit rating of the protective devices within the installation must not be exceeded.

Regulation 551.2.3 of *BS 7671* provides the requirements in relation to potential dangers when connecting or disconnecting loads for generating sets used to provide a supply not connected to a distribution system or as a switched alternative. Where a generating set is intended to provide a supply not connected to a distribution system,or as a switched alternative, the capacity and operating characteristics of the generating set should be such that danger or damage to equipment does not arise after connection or disconnection of any intended load. Further guidance is given in the Notes to Regulation 551.2.3 of *BS 7671*.

Exercise 55.2

Refer to Section 551. If a generator, with a diesel engine prime mover was installed within an existing building, what additional external influences might require consideration?

For additional requirements for SELV and PELV, where the installation is supplied from more than one source, see Regulation Group 551.3.

b. Fault protection

Fault protection must be provided for the installation in respect of each source of supply or combination of supplies. Fault protection should be selected so that no influence should occur or conditions arise that impairs the effectiveness of the fault protective provision. The generating set connections should be connected so that any RCD provisions within the installation remain effective for every intended combination of sources of supply. When the source of supply changes either to an alternative source or a combination of sources the characteristics of the supply will also change. These changes will include values of earth fault loop impedance, impedances between lines or line to neutral and the related currents that will flow should a fault occur.

Regulation 551.4.3.1 requires automatic disconnection of supply to be provided for low voltage generating sets in accordance with Section 411 of *BS 7671*. However, the requirements of Section 411 may need to be modified in cases where either the generating set provides a switched alternative to the system for distribution of electricity to the public, for installations incorporating static convertors or for protection by automatic disconnection where the installation and generating sets are not permanently fixed. (see Regulation Group 551.4 for further information).

Where the installation and generating set are not permanently fixed an RCD with a rated residual operating current of not more than 30 mA should be installed in accordance with Regulation 415.1 to protect every circuit.

c. Protection against overcurrent

Overcurrent protection of the generating set (when required) should be located as near as practicable to the generator terminals.

Where a generating set is intended to operate in parallel with a system for distribution of electricity to the public, or where two or more generating sets may operate in parallel, circulating harmonic currents may occur due to the different characteristics of the systems. The effects of the circulating harmonic currents should be limited so that the thermal rating of conductors is not exceeded. Further information can be found in *BS 7430 Code of practice for earthing* or from generator manufacturers' guidance.

> **Exercise 55.3**
>
> State two ways in which the effects of circulating harmonic currents may be limited (refer to Chapter 55).

d. Additional requirements for installations where the generating set provides a supply as a *switched alternative to the system for distribution of electricity to the public (standby system)*

Regulation Group 551.6 provides the additional requirements relating to where a generating set provides a supply as a switched alternative to a public distribution system (standby system). Precautions complying with the relevant requirements of Section 537 for isolation must be taken so that the generator cannot operate in parallel. Regulation 551.6.1 provides five alternatives that may be utilized to ensure safe isolation.

> **Exercise 55.4**
>
> Refer to Regulation Group 551.6. (1) List three suitable methods for isolation where a generating set provides a supply as a switched alternative to the system for distribution of electricity to the public (standby system)

e. Additional requirements for installations where the generating set may *operate in parallel with systems for distribution of electricity to the public*

The requirements of Chapter 42 (protection against thermal effects) and Chapter 43 (protection against overcurrent) of *BS 7671* and this Learning Guide must remain effective when a generator set is operating in parallel with other sources. Regulation 551.7.2 provides the requirements for positioning, installation methods and protection for generators operating in parallel with other sources.

When selecting and using generating sets that may operate in parallel with the system for distribution of electricity to the public, care should be taken to avoid adverse effects to that system and to other installations in respect of power factor, voltage changes, harmonic distortion, unbalance, starting, synchronising or voltage fluctuation effects. Where synchronisation is necessary, the use of automatic synchronising systems which considers frequency, phase and voltage are preferred. Further guidance from generator manufacturers is recommended.

Chapter 55
Other equipment

A means of automatic switching must be provided to disconnect the generating set from the public system in the event of loss of that supply or deviation of the voltage or frequency at the supply terminals from declared values.

For a generating set with an output exceeding 16 A, the type of protection and settings will depend on the public supply protection system and the number of generating sets connected and must be agreed with the distributor. For a generating set with an output not exceeding 16 A, the settings should comply with *BS EN 50438**.

A means must be provided to prevent the connection of a generating set to the public supply system in the event of loss of that supply (or a deviation in the voltage or frequency at the supply terminals from the declared values for normal supply). **BS EN 50438* provides requirements for generating sets not exceeding 16 A relating to disconnection when the public supply fails. (See * below)

A suitable means of isolating the generating set from the distribution of electricity to the public should be provided. For generating sets with an output exceeding 16 A the accessibility of the isolating device must comply with national rules and distribution system operator requirements. For generators with an output not exceeding 16 A the accessibility for the isolation device must comply with *BS EN 50438*. (* Further information can be found in the *Electrical Safety Council Best practice Guide – Connecting a microgenerator system to a domestic or similar electrical installation (in parallel with the mains supply)*.

Exercise 55.5

(1) Name three methods that could be employed to ensure a generator providing a supply as a switched alternative cannot operate in parallel with the system for distribution of electricity to the public. (2) What do the Regulations say about the connection of a generating set to the system for distribution of electricity to the public in the event of loss of that supply? (3) When operating a generator in parallel with the system for distribution of electricity to the public aspects of the supply need to be considered to avoid adverse effects on the public supply. Name four aspects to be considered.

f. Requirements for installations incorporating stationary batteries

Stationary batteries must be installed in a secure location with adequate ventilation. Access to the batteries should only be available to skilled or instructed persons.

Exercise 55.6

Refer to Regulation Group 551.8 of *BS 7671*. (1) Describe the precautions necessary to avoid an electric shock from an installation incorporating stationary batteries.

3. Rotating machines (Section 552)

Motors require additional consideration in relation to their starting currents and control equipment. The starting, accelerating and load currents of a motor must be considered when assessing the suitability of the equipment and cables carrying these currents. Account should also be taken of any cumulative effects of the starting or braking currents which may produce a temperature rise in the equipment of the circuit (Regulation 552.1.1 refers).

Every electric motor having a rating in excess of 0.37 kW should be provided with control equipment incorporating means of protection against overload of the motor. Overload devices are designed so that they do not trip out as a result of the high starting current but will trip out as a result of a small but prolonged overload (Regulation 552.1.2 refers).

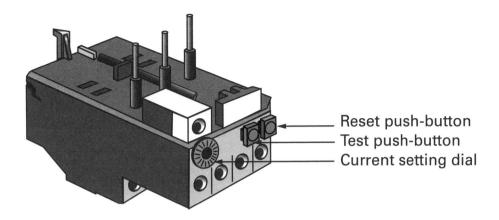

Reset push-button
Test push-button
Current setting dial

Fig 55.2 Typical current monitoring thermally-operated overload relay

Every motor should be fitted with means to prevent automatic restarting after a stoppage due to a drop in voltage or failure of supply, where unexpected restarting of the motor might cause danger.

Exercise 55.7

Consider the requirements of Regulation 552.1.3 and provide a practical example of where this would be applicable (see also Section 445 in Chapter 44 of this Learning Guide for further information).

---

4. Accessories (Section 553)

Section 553 of *BS 7671* is concerned with plugs, sockets and cable couplers and incorporates Table 55.1 which identifies the rating and applicable British Standard of the various plug and socket outlet types. Section 553 also clarifies the requirements relating to the exposure of plug pins, the shuttering of socket-outlets and, apart for SELV or a special circuit (see Regulation 553.1.5) every plug and socket-outlet must be of the non-reversible type, with a provision for the connection of a protective conductor.

Socket-outlets mounted on a wall or similar structure should be mounted at a height above the floor or any working surface to minimise the risk of mechanical damage. This includes damage that may occur to the flexible cord caused during insertion or withdrawal of the plug.

Where portable equipment is likely to be used, provision should be made so that the equipment can be fed from an adjacent and conveniently accessible socket-outlet, taking into account the length of flexible cord normally fitted to appliances and luminaires. The consequence of this requirement is that an adequate number of socket-outlets should be provided to supply equipment likely to be used.

Exercise 55.8

(1) Where does Regulation 553.2.2 require the connector of a coupler to be fitted to a cable and why? (2) Referring to Table 55.1 what is the applicable British Standard for a 13 ampere fuse (for use in a *BS 1363* plug)

Chapter 55
Other equipment

5. Current-using equipment (Section 554)

a. Electrode water heaters and boilers

(i) Principle of operation

Electrode water heaters or boilers are used to heat water or raise steam in certain domestic, commercial and industrial applications. Typical applications include saunas, central heating, humidifying, cleaning and sterilizing. Electrode boilers can be low voltage, high voltage, single-phase or three-phase.

In an electrode boiler, two or three electrodes are immersed in the boiler water and a single-phase or three-phase supply is connected to them.

Electric current always flows through the path of least resistance from a high potential to a low potential. In an electrode boiler, the current carrying medium is the boiler water itself and the power supply contacts are the electrodes. Since the electrodes are always positioned nearer to each other than any other part of the boiler, the path of least resistance is a straight line from electrode to electrode so that most of the current will flow between electrodes. Some current, however, will flow to the metal shell of the boiler if it is earthed or connected to the neutral of the supply, which could cause electrolytic erosion of the boiler shell. In practice, the risk of current flowing from a line electrode to boiler shell is minimized by manufacturing the neutral electrode such that it surrounds the line electrode(s), thereby creating a neutral shield which confines the current path within the shield.

Electrode boilers can be classified as insulated or uninsulated, depending upon their construction. The requirements of *BS 7671* differ in some respects for these two types of construction as outlined below.

(ii) General requirements

Every electrode boiler **must** be fed only from an a.c. supply. A d.c. supply would cause electrolysis to occur, causing the boiler water to break down into its elements of hydrogen and oxygen, thereby creating an explosion hazard.

The supply to an electrode boiler should be controlled by a linked circuit-breaker which provides overcurrent protection in each live (line and neutral) conductor feeding an electrode and which is arranged to disconnect the supply to all electrodes simultaneously. The circuit-breaker may also be used as an isolating device where it is designed to perform this function; otherwise a separate linked isolating device will need to be provided.

Electrode boilers must be earthed in accordance with the requirements of Chapter 54 of *BS 7671*. The cross-sectional area (csa) of the circuit protective conductor (cpc) is to comply with requirements of Regulation 543.1.1 and the conductor must be connected to the outer shell of the boiler. Additionally, the boiler shell should be bonded to the metallic sheath or armour, if any, of the main incoming supply cable to the electrical installation. Where such a bond is required, the electrical installation designer can either install an additional bonding conductor sized in accordance with Regulation 543.1.1 or use the cpc to the boiler shell as permitted by Regulation 543.1.3; provided it meets the specific requirements of that Regulation.

The a.c. supply must be one with an earthed neutral that is, a TN or TT system, and the boiler shell must be connected to the neutral of the supply as well as to the circuit protective conductor (cpc) and/or metallic sheath or armour, if any, of the main incoming supply cable.

The purpose of this connection is to minimize the potential difference between the boiler electrode connected to the neutral conductor, and the boiler shell, which may otherwise result in stray leakage current from the boiler electrodes to the boiler shell. Fig 55.3 below outlines the requirements for a single-phase uninsulated electrode boiler.

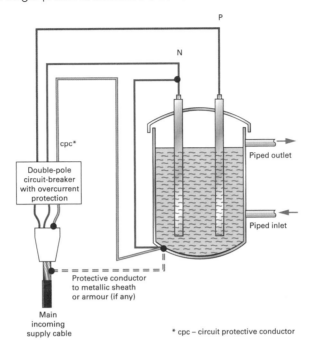

Fig 55.3 Single-phase uninsulated electrode boiler

(iii) Three-phase electrode boilers

The shell of a three-phase electrode water heater or electrode boiler acts as the star point of the boiler electrodes. Therefore, in addition to being connected to the cpc and/or metallic sheath or armour, if any, of the incoming supply cable, the shell must be connected to the neutral of the supply with a conductor of cross-sectional area at least equal to the largest line conductor supplying the boiler. Because the line electrodes will not be completely identical a small current imbalance is inevitable; this imbalance shows as a current in the neutral conductor and cpc in proportion to the impedance of each conductor.

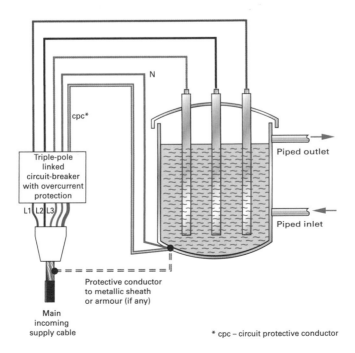

Fig 55.4 Three-phase uninsulated electrode boiler

Chapter 55
Other equipment

(iv) Insulated single-phase electrode boiler

When an electrode water heater or electrode boiler is not piped to a water supply or is in contact with any earthed metal, it is said to be 'insulated'. The electrodes and the water in contact with the electrodes must be insulated and shielded to prevent them from being touched while they are live. For insulated single-phase electrode boilers, overcurrent protection by means of a linked circuit-breaker as required by Regulation 554.1.2 may be substituted by a fuse in the line conductor. Additionally, the shell of the electrode boiler need not be connected to the neutral of the supply.

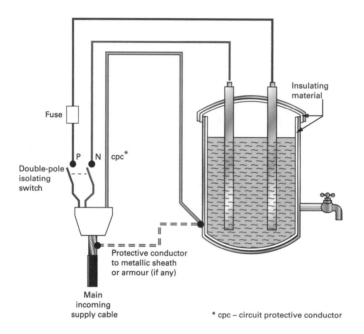

Fig 55.5 Insulated type single-phase electrode boiler

(v) Electrode boilers fed from a voltage exceeding low voltage

Where an electrode boiler is fed directly from an a.c. supply exceeding low voltage, that is, a voltage exceeding 1 000 V a.c., an RCD should be provided so that the supply from all electrodes is disconnected in the event of a sustained protective conductor current in excess of 10 % of the rated boiler supply current under normal conditions of operation. However, if setting the RCD tripping current to 10 % causes nuisance tripping, the tripping current setting may be increased to a maximum of 15 % to ensure the stability of operation of the boiler. Furthermore, a time-delay RCD may be fitted to prevent unnecessary operation of the RCD due to short duration current imbalance.

b. Water heaters having immersed and uninsulated heating elements (554.3)

A single-phase water boiler or heater having an uninsulated heating element immersed in water is deemed **not** to be an electrode water heater or electrode boiler. The difference in this case is that the resistive element between line and neutral is continuous and the current does not flow through the water. All metal parts of the heater or boiler which are in contact with water (other than the current carrying parts) must be solidly and mechanically connected to the metal water pipe which supplies the water boiler. The water pipe must then be connected to the installation main earthing terminal by means of a separate circuit protective conductor (cpc).

The heater or boiler must be controlled by a double-pole linked switch which is either separate from or within easy reach of the boiler and the wiring of the boiler must be connected directly to the switch without the use of a plug and socket. Prior to the water boiler or heater being used, confirmation is required, by the installer, that the following have not been connected in the neutral conductor:

- single pole switch,
- non-linked circuit-breaker
- fuse

Exercise 55.9

(1) What is the difference between a water heater/boiler having immersed elements and an electrode water heater/boiler? (2) What sort of supply must an electrode water heater/boiler never be connected to? (3) On an uninsulated electrode water heater/boiler where should the neutral be connected to in addition to one of the electrode terminals?

6. Heating conductors and cables (Regulation Group 554.4)

a. Introduction

Cables used for the distribution of electrical energy generally are designed to have a low resistance so that the passage of current causes minimum heating effect (I^2R losses). However, by employing conductors made of a suitable resistive alloy, the passage of current in a cable may be used to purposely generate heat to transfer to the surroundings. Such heating is commonly used for the following applications:

Fig 55.6 Typical Stadium heating system

- Underfloor electric heating in dwellings and other premises
- Heating of the playing area at open-air sports stadiums
- Heating roads and pavements to prevent icing
- Soil warming in agricultural and horticultural premises
- Industrial heating applications
- Trace heating of pipes and vessels

b. Requirements for selection and installation

Heating cables should be selected to ensure that where they pass through or are in close proximity to materials which presents a fire hazard they should be enclosed in materials of limited combustibility and be adequately protected from mechanical damage.

Heating cables intended to be laid directly in materials such as soil, concrete or cement must be able to withstand mechanical damage during installation. Damage may result from sharp stones, the movement of workmen, wheelbarrows and vehicles, and from impact from tools. Heating cables must also be constructed of material that will be resistant to damage from dampness and/or corrosion during normal operation.

Heating cables laid in the structure of a building, or soil or a road must be completely embedded in the substance that is to be heated and must not be subject to damage in the event of movement.

The loading of floor warming cables should be limited to a value such that its manufacturers' stated conductor temperature is not exceeded.

7. Transformers (Section 555) -Autotransformers and step-up transformers

An autotransformer is any transformer in which two or more of the windings have a common part. Where an autotransformer is connected to a circuit having a neutral conductor, the common terminal of the winding must be connected to the neutral conductor.

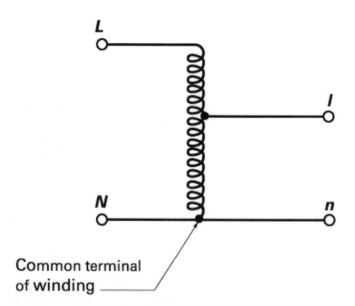

Fig 55.7 Connection of the common terminal of an autotransformer to the neutral of the supply

Where a step-up transformer is used, a linked switch must be provided for disconnecting the transformer from all live conductors of the supply.

Further information relating to Electrical equipment can be found in:
- Chapter 55 of *BS 7671*
- ESQCR 2002
- *BS EN 50438*
- Electrical Safety Council Technical Manual articles A77-1, E97-1, H33-1, I93-53, O69-1, S13-23 and S173-5
- Electrical Safety Council Best practice guide – Connecting a microgenerator system to a domestic or similar electrical installation (in parallel with the mains supply)
- *BS 7430* Code of practice for earthing

CHAPTER 55 FINAL REVISION EXERCISE

55.1 Which of the following could be fitted in the neutral conductor of a water heater having immersed and uninsulated heating elements?
- ☐ a. A double-pole switch
- ☐ b. A single-pole switch
- ☐ c. A non-linked circuit-breaker
- ☐ d. A fuse

55.2 Which of the following would not be an acceptable device to ensure a generator set, providing a supply as an alternative to the system for distribution of electricity to the public, cannot operate in parallel?
- ☐ a. A double-pole manual changeover switch
- ☐ b. A three-position break-before-make change-over switch
- ☐ c. A system of locks with a single transferable switch
- ☐ d. An automatic change-over switching device with a suitable interlock

55.3 Control equipment incorporating means of protection against overload should be provided for every motor in excess of which of the following?
- ☐ a. 0.25 kW
- ☐ b. 0.37 kW
- ☐ c. 0.5 kW
- ☐ d. 3.7 kW

55.4 Which of the following is not a British Standard relating to plugs and socket-outlets?
- ☐ a. *BS 196*
- ☐ b. *BS 546*
- ☐ c. *BS 1362*
- ☐ d. *BS 1363*

55.5 The common terminal of an autotransformer must be connected to which of the following?
- ☐ a. The neutral conductor
- ☐ b. The phase conductor
- ☐ c. The line conductor
- ☐ d. The protective conductor

notes

Things to do and find

1. What are the requirements relating to RCDs where an installation and generator set are not permanently fixed?

2. What does *BS 7671* say about the required height of socket-outlets?

3. Which type of electrode water heater/boiler requires the neutral to be connected to the shell of the heater/boiler?

4. What type of switch must be used in a step-up transformer?

1. Introduction and scope (559.1)

Section 559 of *BS 7671* and this section of the Learning Guide applies to the selection and erection of luminaires (lighting fittings) and lighting installations intended to be part of the fixed installation and to highway power supplies and street furniture.

An explanation is given of the Requirements of *BS 7671* for:

i) Fixed outdoor lighting installations

ii) Extra-low voltage installations supplied up to 50 V a.c. or 120 V d.c.

iii) Lighting for display stands.

Lighting installations within special locations are covered within Part 7 of *BS 7671*.

The requirements of Section 559 of *BS 7671* do not apply to high voltage signs and luminous discharge tube installations or high voltage signs supplied at low voltage. The requirements relating to outdoor lighting installations do not cover temporary festoon lighting or distributors' equipment

2. Outdoor lighting Installations (559.3)

The following outdoor lighting installations are included within *BS 7671*:

(i) Lighting installations for roads, car parks, parks, gardens, sporting areas, places open to the public, illumination of monuments and floodlighting.

Fig 559.1 Streetlighting   **Fig 559.2 Floodlighting**

(ii) lighting arrangements in telephone kiosks, bus shelters, advertising panels, and town plans

Fig 559.3 Bus shelter lighting

(iii) road signs and traffic signal systems

Fig 559.4 Street sign (bollard)

Fig 559.5 Traffic signal

3. General requirements for installations (559.4)

All luminaires must comply with the relevant standard for manufacture and test of that luminaire, and be installed in accordance with the manufacturers' instructions.

In this section of the Regulations, luminaires without transformers or convertors, but which are fitted with extra-low voltage lamps connected in series are considered as low voltage equipment and not extra-low voltage equipment.

Table 55.2 of *BS 7671* outlines the symbols used in luminaires, in control gear for luminaires and in the installation of luminaires. These symbols are also used throughout Section 559 of *BS 7671*. The table below provides a sample of the symbols used. To review the full range of symbols see Table 55.2 of BS 7671.

Table 55.2 *(Learning Guide Table a sample of Table 55.2 of BS 7671)*
Explanation of symbols used in luminaires, in controlgear for luminaires and in the installation of luminaires

Luminaire with limited surface temperature (*BS EN 60598*-series)	▽D	Minimum distance from lighted objects (m)	⌓—m │
Luminaire suitable for direct mounting on normally flammable surfaces	▽F	Luminaire for use with high pressure sodium lamps that require an external ignitor (to the lamp)	△E
Luminaire suitable for mounting on non-combustible surfaces only	▽F (crossed out)	Transformer – short-circuit proof (both inherently and non-inherently)	(transformer symbol)
Rated maximum ambient temperature	**ta.....°C**	Electronic convertor for an extra-low voltage lighting installation	▽110

4. Protection against fire (559.5)

When selecting and erecting luminaires consideration should be given to the effect of heat generated by luminaires with respect to the surroundings, including the maximum power dissipated by the lamp, the fire resistance of adjacent material and the minimum distance to the combustible materials, including those in the path of spotlight beams.

Exercise 559.1

(1) Which of the following is not covered by Section 559 of *BS 7671*: Temporary Festoon lighting; lighting for display stands; distributor's equipment; road signs. (2) In relation to voltage what type of equipment should luminaires fitted with extra-low voltage lamps but without transformers or converters be considered as?

---

5. Wiring systems (559.6)

a. Connection to the fixed wiring

In lighting circuits connections made to the fixed wiring must use a recognized device at each connection point. *BS 7671* lists nine different devices covered by relevant British or Harmonized standards.

> **Exercise 559.2**
>
> (1) List four devices suitable for connection to the fixed wiring of a lighting circuit.

Ceiling roses should only be used for one outgoing flexible cord unless they are designed for multiple pendants. Their use is also restricted to circuits not exceeding 250 V.

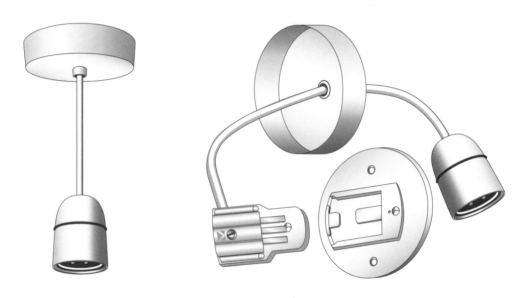

Fig. 559.6 Typical pendant arrangement   Fig. 559.7 Typical Luminaire support coupler (LSC)

b. Fixing of luminaires (559.6.1.5)

Luminaires must be fixed securely, and the means of fixing must be able to support the weight of the luminaire. Where the fixing is intended to support a pendant luminaire it must be able to carry a mass of not less than 5 kg. If the mass of the luminaire is greater than 5 kg, then the installer must ensure the fixing means can support the weight of the pendant luminaire. The ceiling structure must also be considered.

Further to the above requirements, any cable or cord between the fixing means and the luminaire should be installed to accommodate any expected stress in the conductors or terminals so as not to impair the safety or operation of the luminaire.

Lighting circuits incorporating B15 (SBC), B22 (BC), E14 (SES), E27 (ES), or E40 (GES) lampholders should be protected by an overcurrent device having a rating not exceeding 16 A.

Bayonet lampholders B15 (SBC) and B22 (BC) should comply with *BS EN 61184* and have the temperature rating T2 described in that standard (lamp cap temperatures up to and including 210 °C).

Except for E14 (SES) and E27 (ES) lampholders to *BS 60238*, circuits connected to TN or TT systems must have the outer contact of every ES or centre bayonet cap type lampholder connected to the neutral conductor. This requirement also applies to track mounted systems.

c. Through wiring (559.6.2)

The term 'through wiring' relates to the practice of passing cables through luminaires using the fitting as a wiring enclosure. Because of the possible hazards relating to mechanical damage and heat this practice is restricted as outlined in Regulation Group 559.6.2.

Through wiring is only permitted if the luminaire is designed for that purpose. For luminaires complying with *BS EN 60598*, but with no temperature markings, heat resistant cables are not required. Luminaires to this standard with temperature marking will require suitable heat resisting cables. Where no information is provided, heat resisting cable (or conductors insulated in accordance with Regulation 559.6.2.2) must be used.

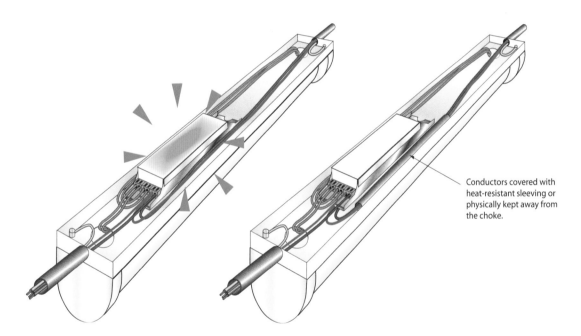

Conductors covered with heat-resistant sleeving or physically kept away from the choke.

Fig 559.8 & 559.9 Example of through wiring problem and solution

For groups of luminaires divided between three line conductors of a three-phase system with one common neutral, Regulation 559.6.2.3 requires at least one device such that all the line conductors can be simultaneously disconnected.

Exercise 559.3

(1). What do the terms SBC, BC, SES, ES and GES stand for in relation to lampholders? (2) What is the maximum voltage of a circuit for supply to a ceiling rose? (3) What is the minimum weight a pendant luminaire must be capable of carrying

notes

6. Independent lamp controlgear, e.g. ballasts (559.7)

Regulation 559.7 provides symbols for control gear which can be mounted external to a luminaire, and mounted on flammable surfaces. It is important to consider the temperature ratings of ballast and the type of surface they are to be mounted on when selecting independent lamp controlgear.

i) Symbol for a 'class P' thermally protected ballast/transformer:

ii) Symbol for a temperature declared thermally protected ballast/transformer. This symbol indicates a marked value equal to or below 130 °C

iii) The generally recognised symbol of an independent ballast of *BS 60417* is shown below:

7. Requirements for outdoor lighting installations, highway power supplies and street furniture (559.10)

a. General

Where the protective measure is Automatic Disconnection of Supply, the following requirements must be provided in relation to outdoor lighting installations.

- Doors in street furniture or street located equipment that provide access to electrical equipment and are located less than 2.5 m above ground level, must be lockable in the closed position or securable by means of a tool. However, such a door should not be relied upon as a means of complying with the requirements of Section 416 of *BS 7671* for the provision of basic protection by barriers or enclosures.

- An intermediate barrier, removable only by use of a tool and affording a degree of protection of at least IP2X or IPXXB, must be provided to prevent contact with live parts when any door providing access to electrical equipment is open.

- Where the lamp of a luminaire is located at less than 2.8 m above the ground, it should be accessible only after removing a barrier or opening an enclosure requiring the use of a tool.

- Where an outdoor lighting installation is located close to a metallic grid or fence, which does not form part of the outdoor lighting installation, there is no requirement to connect the grid or fence etc to the installation main earth terminal.

Fig 559.10 Street lighting column door

A maximum disconnection time of 5 seconds is permitted for all circuits feeding fixed equipment used within highway power supplies. The earthing conductor of a street lighting column or electrical fixture must have a cross-sectional area of not less than the copper equivalent of 6 mm^2, or that of the supply neutral, whichever is smaller (Regulation 559.10.3.4 refers).

b. Additional protection

Regulation 559.10.3.2 recommends that additional protection is provided to lighting installations within telephone kiosks, bus shelters etc. This additional protection will be in the form of an RCD having a residual operating current ($I_{\Delta n}$) not exceeding 30 mA and an operating time not exceeding 40 ms at a residual current of 5 $I_{\Delta n}$.

It should be noted that the following protective measures should not be used for outdoor lighting installations:

i) Placing out of reach and obstacles

ii) Non-conducting location and earth free local equipotential bonding

Where the outdoor lighting installation uses Class II equipment as its protective measure, no protective conductor should be provided and the conductive parts of the lighting column should not intentionally be connected to Earth.

c. Devices for isolation and switching

Where the isolation of street lights etc is to be carried out only by instructed persons, Regulation 559.10.6.1 permits the use of the fuse carrier within the column. However where the column can only be isolated by the distributors' cut-out, permission from the distributor must be obtained.

Section 559
Luminaires and Lighting Installations

d. Warning notices

Warning notices for periodic inspections and RCD testing need not be installed where the street/highway lighting installation is subject to a programmed test and inspection programme. Where installations are temporary, a durable label should be fixed externally to the supply unit stating the maximum current to be supplied from that unit.

e. External influences

The general recommendations for external influences are provided in Regulation Group 559.10.5. Information is provided in relation to ambient temperature, climatic conditions, presence of water and presence of foreign bodies.

The main requirement is that electrical equipment should have by construction or installation a degree of protection of at least IP 33

For further information on external influences see Appendix 5 of *BS 7671* or Part 2 of this Learning Guide.

> **Exercise 559.4**
>
> (1).What is the minimum height of a door in street furniture where access below that height can only be gained by the use of a key or a tool? (2) What additional protection is recommended for lighting arrangements in bus shelters? (3) What are required external influences for outdoor lighting in relation to ambient temperature and climatic conditions? (4) What are the requirements for earthing conductors of a street lighting fixture?

8. Extra-low voltage lighting installations (559.11)

a. Protective measures and supplies

FELV should not be used as a protective measure for supplying extra-low voltage lighting installations. Where extra-low voltage luminaires are installed without provision for the connection of a protective conductor they should only be installed as part of an SELV system.

In extra-low voltage installations where a safety isolating transformer is used the transformer must comply with *BS EN 61558-2-6* as well as the requirements of Regulation 559.11.3 for protection against fire risk due to short-circuit. One method of compliance is to use a safety isolating transformer marked with the following symbol (which indicates the transformer is short-circuit proof).

Where an electronic converter is used for an extra-low voltage lighting installation, it should comply with *BS EN 61347-2-2*, and be marked with the symbol shown below

b. Fire risks in extra-low voltage lighting installations (559.11.4)

Where both live conductors are uninsulated, either:

- they should be provided with a protective device complying with the requirements of Regulation 559.11.4.2 or
- the system should comply with *BS EN 60598-2-23*

> **Exercise 559.5**
>
> Review Regulation 559.11.4.2 for the requirements relating to devices providing protection against the risk of fire.

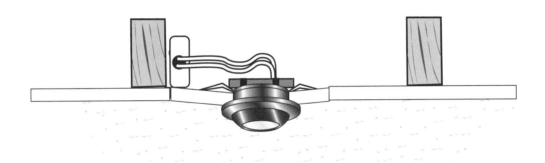

Fig 559.11 Extra-low voltage downlighter

Care should be taken when selecting and installing recessed luminaires into ceiling voids. The effects of thermal insulation on the luminaire and associated conductors must be considered. Also, the consequences of penetrating the existing fire compartment must be considered. Built-in intumescent seals or intumescent hoods may be required.

c. Wiring systems in ELV lighting systems

Table 559A (Learning Guide Table) Minimum cross-sectional area of extra-low voltage conductors (copper)

General	1.5 mm^2
Flexible cables with a maximum length of 3 m	1.0 mm^2
Suspended flexible cables or insulated conductors	4.0 mm^2
Composite cables consisting of braided tinned copper outer sheath, having a material of high tensile strength inner core	4.0 mm^2

If the nominal voltage does not exceed 25 V a.c. or 60 V d.c., bare conductors may be used provided the conductor csa is not less than 4 mm^2, and the conductors are not placed on combustible material.

At least one conductor and its terminal should be insulated between the transformer and the protective device in order to prevent a short-circuit.

notes

Key Facts
'Serious consideration needs to be given as to whether Intumescent fire hoods are required for recessed extra-low (or low) voltage downlighters'

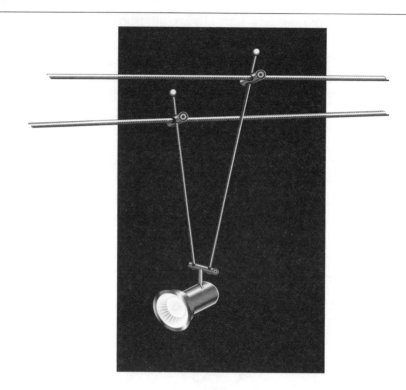

Fig 559.12 Suspended extra-low voltage luminaire with bare conductors

Where the ELV system is suspended, the suspension devices must be able to support five times the weight of the ELV luminaire and its lamp and not less than 5 kg. The installation should be accessible throughout its length. The use of insulation piercing type connectors is prohibited.

Exercise 559.6

(1). Name one of the requirements a safety isolation transformer must meet when used in an ELV installation. (2) State the minimum cross-sectional area of extra-low voltage conductors for a flexible cable which is 4 metres in length.

Further information relating to luminaires and lighting installations can be found in:
- Section 559 of *BS 7671*
- Electrical Safety Council Technical Manual articles: L105-1, L105-37, S205.33
- IEE Guidance Note 7

CHAPTER 559 FINAL REVISION EXERCISE

559.1 **Which of the following is not recognized as a suitable connection for use at a fixed lighting point?**
- a. Luminaire support coupling
- b. Batten lampholder
- c. Open connector block
- d. Connection unit to *BS 1363-4*

559.2 The use of a key or a tool is required for access to the lamp of an outdoor luminaire where the luminaire is located below which of the following?
- [ ] a. 1.5 m
- [ ] b. 2.5 m
- [ ] c. 2.8 m
- [ ] d. 3.5 m

559.3 Bayonet lampholders B15 and B22 should have a minimum temperature rating of which of the following?
- [ ] a. T1
- [ ] b. T2
- [ ] c. T3
- [ ] d. T4

559.4 The minimum cross-sectional area of an extra-low voltage lighting flexible copper cable with a maximum length of 3 m is which of the following?
- [ ] a. 1.0 mm^2
- [ ] b. 1.5 mm^2
- [ ] c. 2.5 mm^2
- [ ] d. 4.0 mm^2

559.5 An acceptable supply system for use with extra-low voltage lighting could be which of the following?
- [ ] a. SELV
- [ ] b. FELV
- [ ] c. RELV
- [ ] d. LV

559.6 For outdoor lighting installations the minimum degree of protection should be at least:
- [ ] a. IP2X
- [ ] b. IP22
- [ ] c. IP33
- [ ] d. IP4X

notes

Things to do and find

1. List three considerations in relation to protection against fire and the effects of heat generated by a luminaire

2. What are the required classes of external influence in relation to outdoor lighting installations, highway power supplies and street furniture in relation to ambient temperature and climatic conditions?

3. Review the types of installation that are included and excluded from Section 559. Is temporary festoon lighting included within Section 559? Is a bus shelter included within Section 559?

4. Where should the neutral connection be made on an E40 (Edison screw) lampholder?

5. Review the symbols used in luminaires etc (Table 55.2). Draw the symbols for a luminaire with limited surface temperature and a transformer-short-circuit proof.

6. The minimum copper cross-sectional area for an earthing conductor in a street electrical fixture should be not less than the supply neutral at that point or not less than what size?

1. Introduction

Chapters 56 and 35 of *BS7671* give guidance on the requirements for the specialised areas of Safety Services. This section of the Learning Guide covers both chapters. Further references to safety services can be found in other sections of *BS 7671* such as Regulations 132.4 and 313.2.

A Safety Service is defined as:

> 'An electrical system for electrical equipment provided to protect or warn persons in the event of a hazard, or essential to their evacuation from a location'

Such systems are commonly employed in buildings open to the public and in general commercial and industrial premises and would usually include Emergency lighting and Fire detection and alarm systems.

In more complex installations, additional specialist systems may also be encountered including Fire pumps, Fire rescue service lifts, Fire evacuation systems, smoke ventilation systems, fire services communication systems, CO detection and alarm systems, Industrial safety systems as well as essential medical systems. This list is not exhaustive.

Due to the nature of these life support systems it is normally the case that they have their own design and installation guidance via appropriate British or European Standards. Examples are Emergency lighting (*BS 5266/1*) and Fire detection and alarm systems (*BS 5839 (1 or 6)*) as appropriate. Reference to these standards is important where designers or installers are involved in these areas of work.

Photo Courtesy of Grundfos Pumps Ltd

Fig 56.1 Typical safety services

2. Scope

The requirements for the general characteristics relating to these systems are specified within Chapter 35.

Four distinct types of source are recognized as being suitable for use as the safety service:

(i) storage batteries
(ii) primary cells
(iii) generator sets independent of the normal supply

(iv) a separate feeder of the supply network effectively independent of the normal feeder.

Chapter 56 of *BS 7671* emphasizes that the requirement for a particular safety system is often determined by regulations formed in a statutory instrument. This is further clarified within Regulation 313.2, which demands that a separate assessment of the characteristics of each safety service be made.

3. Classifications (560.4)

There are two classes of electrical safety service supply detailed in 560.4:

(i) non-automatic
(ii) automatic

In most instances it is far safer and more efficient to employ an automatic safety system that will work independently of an operator, although those that are "manually operated" are also recognized.

Automatic systems are further classified by whether they offer a continuous "no-break" supply, or are based on their maximum change-over time duration. Six types of automatic system are recognized. Regulation 560.4.1 provides details of the classifications.

The response time relating to the safety service will need to meet the maximum time duration as set out in the particular British Standard. Where no specific British Standard exists, the limiting duration must be evaluated by an appropriate risk assessment.

Exercise 56.1

You should now refer to Chapters 35 & 56 to answer the following: (1) Name three sources that are recognized for use in safety service circuits. (2) What are the minimum and maximum change-over times for short break and medium break automatic supply systems?

4. General (560.5)

It is normally the case that safety service systems will be required to operate at times of "mains failure" and also continue their effective operation through the harsh environment of a fire condition.

The required performance criteria for the particular safety service is often set by either legislation or via appropriate guidance from a British or European Standard. It is imperative that these potential life saving installations have adequate consideration given for their design, installation and continued verification (via regular inspection and testing) to ensure that they have and maintain, the appropriate level of operational integrity.

Those involved in the design and installation of such systems will need to be well versed within these areas, and ensure that comprehensive consultation between all interested parties takes place. The relevant parties would include such representation as the fire authority, building control, the Health and Safety Executive and the local authority. Discussions with insurers of the properties concerned may also be required.

5. Electrical Sources for Safety Services (560.6)

a. General

The integrity of the electrical source is of paramount importance, and as such must be of appropriate capacity capable of supplying the total load and installed as fixed equipment, located in an area that is only accessible to appropriate personnel.

A further design consideration is to ensure that any gases, fumes or smoke that may be generated by the supply source are adequately ventilated, and cannot contaminate other areas in the general vicinity.

The majority of safety sources take the form of either a dedicated, constantly charged battery, or a combination of battery and generator set. However, the less common system of separate independent feeder supplies is also recognized, providing appropriate assurance is obtained from the supplying network or networks that these supplies are unlikely to fail concurrently.

Where the safety source is designed as a "back up" standby system, further requirements, given in Regulation Group 551.6 have to be met. These requirements generally deal with ensuring that the system cannot be inadvertently operated in parallel with the standard supply, by utilization of electrically operated or mechanically switched interlocks etc.

For safety sources that are to be utilized for parallel operation with the normal supply, Regulation Group 551.7 should be consulted regarding appropriate design criteria to ensure suitable compatibility exists between the two systems. Consultation with and authorization by the distributor will also be required.

b. Battery supplies

Batteries used as the supply for safety services are classified into two categories; "central power supply sources" and "low power supply sources", the low power source being limited to 1500 watt-hours. Batteries for central power supply sources must be of vented or valve-regulated type, whilst low power supply sources should be of gastight or valve-regulated type. All batteries must be capable of supplying the safety system for its required duration, due regard being taken for the battery's expected reduction in capacity, over its operational life.

The required minimum operational design life of batteries should be in accordance with *BS EN 50171*, with a minimum declared life of 10 years for central power supply sources and 5 years for low power supply sources. Further requirements for stationary battery systems can be found in Regulation Group 551.8.

c. Uninterruptible power supply sources (UPS)

Uninterruptible power supply sources (UPS) are devices which maintain a continuous supply to connected equipment by supplying power following the failure of the primary source. They can be either static (delivering an output voltage from a stored source through a convertor) or rotary (for example a diesel driven generator).

Static UPS sources offer a comprehensive arrangement as a power supply source. However, care must be taken to ensure that when the system is operating in the emergency condition (fed from the converter and supplied by the battery) it will be capable of starting all of the required safety devices, as well as allowing any circuit protective devices to function in the event of a fault. It must be borne in mind that the UPS's effective earth fault loop impedance, when fed via the converter and battery system, may offer differing values to those found when the circuits are functioning under normal conditions.

All generator supply sources will need to comply with *BS 7698-12*.

6. Circuits for safety services (560.7)

To ensure a high integrity supply and to minimize disruption (electrical faults, maintenance or modification to other systems) safety services should employ a dedicated independent circuit that is ideally run through areas of low fire risk. Where this is impracticable, the circuit must be run using a fire-resistant cable system. On no account should circuits of safety services be run through areas exposed to explosion risk.

Courtesy of Wrexham Mineral Cables Ltd

Fig 56.2 Fire-resistant cables

Unusually, protection against overload may be omitted in a safety circuit if the loss of the supply may cause a greater hazard. The system, however, must indicate when an overload has occurred. Fault protection, however, must still be provided. Serious design consideration must be given to the selection of all related overcurrent protective devices, as it is essential that a fault on one circuit should not affect the operation of another safety service.

All switchgear and controlgear should be located in areas accessible only to the appropriate personnel and will require clear, durable labeling.

Safety circuit cables must either have a minimum of a metallic screen and be fire-resistant, or will need to be appropriately separated from other circuits (including other safety services), by use of distance and / or barriers.

Lift shafts and other flue-like openings cannot be used to carry safety circuits, however, wiring specifically relating to a "fire rescue service lift", may be run within its shaft.

Safety services are in a number of cases a requirement of legislation in addition to being a potential life saving support system.

It is therefore imperative that all information regarding the wiring, operation, maintenance, and any alterations that may have been carried out on the system, are kept up to date and are available to all of the appropriate personnel. A copy of the drawings of the electrical safety installations should be displayed at the origin of the installation showing the exact location of:

- all electrical control equipment and distribution boards with equipment designation,
- safety equipment with final circuit designation and particulars and purpose of the equipment *and*
- any special switching and monitoring equipment for the safety power supply (e.g. area switches, visual or acoustic warning equipment)

Further to the above requirements, a list should be made available of all current-using equipment permanently connected to the safety power supply, providing details of rated and starting currents, as well as starting times.

Comprehensive operating instructions, written to take into account the specifics of the particular installation must also be made available.

notes

Key Facts
'When safety services are being provided, designers and installers need to consider the special requirements relating to sources, circuitry, wiring systems, overcurrent protection and documentation'

7. Wiring Systems for safety services (560.8)

The majority of wiring systems that are employed to serve as safety services, will be required to operate under fire conditions, and as such will need to utilize fire-resistant cables. These cables must comply with the relevant standards for tests of cables in emergency circuits and their resistance to fire. Cables used for fire detection and alarm systems should be in accordance with *BS 5839-1* clause 26. Alternatively, cables that have been evaluated to maintain the necessary fire and mechanical protection may be utilized.

It is vital that the installation and mounting system employed, ensures the cable's fire resisting integrity, and will therefore normally require metallic fixings at distances in accordance with the manufacturer's recommendations, and other guidance, such as the NHS Health Technical Memoranda.

Any other related control or bus system wiring that could have a detrimental effect on the safety service should utilize a wiring system that offers similar performance criteria to the wiring system of the safety system.

The wiring supplying the distribution board from its safety source will need to be erected in such a manner as to ensure risk of fault currents, fire or danger to persons is minimized.

Further information relating to safety services can be found in:
- *BS 7671* Chapters 35 and 56
- *BS 5839* (Parts 1 & 6) and *BS 5266*
- Electrical Safety Council Technical Manual articles S13-11, S13-14, S13-17, S13-20, S13-21 and S13-23
- IEE Guidance Notes 1 & 4

CHAPTER 56 FINAL REVISION EXERCISE

56.1 **The central power supply for a safety service should have a power source that provides which of the following?**
- ☐ a. Capacity over 1500 watt-hours and a minimum declared life of 5 years
- ☐ b. Capacity over 1500 watt-hours and a minimum declared life of 10 years
- ☐ c. Capacity under 1500 watt-hours and a minimum declared life of 5 years
- ☐ d. Capacity under 1500 watt-hours and a minimum declared life of 10 years

56.2 Which of the following is not recognized as a suitable source for a safety service?
☐ a. Independent generator set(s)
☐ b. Distributor's single supply
☐ c. Storage batteries
☐ d. Primary cells

56.3 An automatic supply that is available between 5 s and 15 s would be classified as which of the following?
☐ a. Short break
☐ b. Lighting break
☐ c. Medium break
☐ d. Long break

56.4 An automatic supply classified as lighting break would be available within which of the following?
☐ a. 0.15 s
☐ b. 0.15 s and 0.5 s
☐ c. 0.5 s and 5 s
☐ d. 5 s and 15 s

56.5 Which of the following would not normally be considered as an example of a safety service?
☐ a. Office unit
☐ b. Fire pump
☐ c. Emergency lighting
☐ d. Essential medical system

Things to do and find

1. What are the general classifications for electrical safety service supplies?

2. What is a UPS?

3. What type of circuit may be run in a fire rescue service lift?

4. List four items whose location should be identified on a drawing of the electrical safety installation provided at the origin of the installation.

Part 6
Inspection and testing

Part 6
Inspection and testing

1. Introduction

Part 6 of *BS 7671* contains the general requirements relating to Inspection and Testing of installations. Appendix 6 of *BS 7671* contains Model Forms for certification and reporting. *BS 7671* does not provide specific information or practical details of the tests outlined in Part 6. This Learning Guide in line with Part 6 of *BS 7671* only covers the general requirements for inspection and testing. Students requiring further information and/or knowledge relating to inspection and testing, such as practical details of the required tests or periodic inspection reporting procedures should consider attendance on the following courses or courses providing equivalent information.

- **City and Guilds Level 2 Certificate in Fundamental Inspection, Testing and Initial Verification – (2392-10)** - (for the initial verification of new work, alterations or additions) *and/or the*
- **City and Guilds Level 3 Certificate in Inspection, Testing and Certification of Electrical Installations – 2391-10** (for the inspection, testing and reporting procedures for existing properties (often referred to as Periodic Reporting).

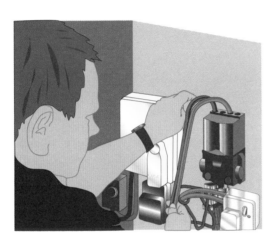

Fig 6.1 Inspection and testing

2. Persons carrying out inspection, testing and certification/reporting

It should be noted that there are several references in Part 6 of *BS 7671* to the competency of the people carrying out verification (inspection, testing and certification). Regulations 610.5 (initial verification) and 621.5 (periodic inspection and testing) confirms an important requirement in that persons carrying out these types of work should be classified as competent (as defined in Part 2 of *BS 7671*). Also Regulation 631.4 requires Electrical installation Certificates, Periodic Inspection Reports and Minor Electrical Installations Works Certificates to be compiled and signed (or otherwise authenticated) by a competent person or persons. It follows, therefore, that the person carrying out this type of work must have sufficient knowledge of *BS 7671* to determine whether an existing installation complies with the Regulations or not and if not what the implications of the departures mean. For new installation work the person carrying out verification must confirm the installed work complies with the Regulations. In addition, the person responsible for verification of both new and existing installations must be conversant with all the required tests and certification/reporting procedures.

3. Structure of Part 6

Part 6 is split into three Chapters.

Part 6
Inspection and testing

a. Chapter 61 covers *Initial* verification (inspection and testing for new electrical installation work). Chapter 61 includes the required inspections which precede testing and are normally carried out prior to the installation being energised. Some tests are required to be completed prior to the installation being energised, others immediately afterwards.

Fig 6.2 Inspecting a new installation

b. Chapter 62 covers Periodic inspection and testing (for existing electrical installations). A great deal of knowledge and experience is required by the people carrying out periodic inspection and testing. As well as an in-depth knowledge of *BS 7671* the inspector is required to be fully conversant with inspection and testing procedures as well as being able to communicate the outcome of his findings in the periodic inspection report.

Fig 6.3 Inspecting an existing electrical installation

Chapter 63 covers Certification and Reporting (Appendix 6 also provides model forms for certification and reporting). Chapter 63 provides the requirements relating to the correct issue of certificates and reports, including details of the persons responsible for design, construction and inspection and testing.

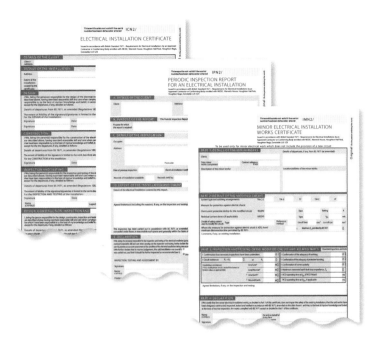

Fig 6.4 Electrical Installation Certificate, Minor Electrical Installation Works Certificate and Periodic Inspection Report

4. Initial verification (Chapter 61)

a. General (Section 610)

The term **'verification'** is defined as:

> *All measures by means of which compliance of the electrical installation with the relevant requirements of BS 7671 are checked, comprising of inspection, testing and certification.*

Even the most experienced electrical operative can sometimes make the occasional mistake when carrying out new electrical installation work, alterations or additions. This is one of the reasons why every electrical installation should be thoroughly inspected and tested before being put into service. In addition, where alterations and additions to an existing installation have been installed it must be verified that this work has not impaired the safety of the original installation.

The results of the inspection and testing should confirm that the requirements of all the relevant Regulations have been met. This will mean the electrical installation has been correctly designed and constructed and all equipment is suitable for its intended purpose.

To do this effectively, the verification process will need to include a comparison of the test results with relevant criteria as provided by the designer of the installation, and/or from manufacturer's data to ensure the requirements of *BS 7671* have been met.

b. Information required prior to verification

Before carrying out the inspection and testing, the person or persons carrying out this work will require specific information in relation to the electrical installation to allow him to make informed judgments in relation to compliance to the Regulations.

Part 6
Inspection and testing

This information includes the result of the assessment of:

- The Fundamental Principles, Section 131
- The General Characteristics required by Sections 311 and 313
- Information required by Regulation 514.9.1

Generally, details of the following will be required:

- methods used for basic and fault protection
- protective devices
- earthing arrangements
- required circuit impedances
- types of circuits
- number of installed electrical points
- number and size of conductors
- type of wiring system
- location of protective devices
- location of isolation and switching devices
- any circuit or equipment vulnerable to a typical test

Exercise 6.1

You should now refer to Regulation 514.9 to review the requirements relating to items required for a typical distribution board schedule.

c. Inspection (Section 611)

Before an electrical installation is put into service it is essential that the requirements of *BS 7671* have been met (so far as is reasonably practical) and that the installation is safe in all aspects. Every new installation, alteration or addition to an electrical installation should, therefore, be inspected during erection and on completion.

Some items can only be inspected at the installation stage (as they may be inaccessible later) for example inspecting cables that are to be concealed under floors or in walls are in the correct cable zones or adequately mechanically protected. For some items it is likely that they will only be available for inspection at or near the completion stage of the installation. Inspections will nearly always take place with the supply disconnected.

There are three general requirements that the initial inspection should ascertain in relation to installed electrical equipment*:

- Compliance with the requirements of Section 511 (relating to British Standard or Harmonized Standards etc)
- It has been correctly selected and erected
- It is not visibly damaged or defective so as to impair safety

* See Part 2 of *BS 7671* Definitions for *electrical equipment*

To ensure the above criteria are met the Regulations lists 17 main items that need to be visually checked, many of these having sub-sections within them that will require a visual inspection. These items form the basis of the inspection schedule, required by Chapter 63 Certification and reporting.

An example of an inspection schedule is provided in Appendix 6 of *BS 7671* and this schedule is required with every electrical installation certificate.

It is important that anyone carrying out electrical inspections understands the terminologies used in the inspection schedule and how this then relates to the specific electrical installation being inspected. The items listed in Regulation 611.3 (and in the associated inspection schedule) have all been covered in the Chapters/Sections related to Parts 1 to 5 and Part 7 of the Learning Guide. For further information and/or clarification in relation to any of the inspection items see the relevant Chapter/Section.

It is worth spending time reviewing the items listed in Regulation 611.3 as well as the inspection schedule in Appendix 6.

Exercise 6.2

You should now refer to Regulation 611.3 and go through each of the inspection items listed to ensure that you understand what each item refers to. A useful exercise is to find (and write down) the related Section, Regulation Group or Regulation after each inspection item.

---

d. Required tests and initial testing sequence

Testing carried out as part of the initial verification can be considered of two types, that is, the tests *before* the installation is energized and the tests *after* the installation is energized. The tests prescribed in Regulations 612.2 to 612.7 covering the tests prior to the installation being energized (where relevant) should be carried out in the sequence prescribed in Part 6 of *BS 7671*. Once the installation has been energized tests that require a supply, such as the earth fault loop impedance test, RCD test and prospective fault current test can be carried out. *All* test results must be compared with relevant criteria.

Table 6.A (Learning Guide Table) Tests for initial verification (where relevant)

Tests prior to the installation being energized
Continuity of protective conductors
Continuity of ring final circuit conductors
Insulation resistance
Protection by SELV, PELV or by electrical separation
Basic protection by a barrier or an enclosure provided during erection
Insulation resistance/impedance of floors and walls
Polarity
Earth electrode testing
Tests following the installation being energized
Protection by automatic disconnection of the supply
Earth fault loop impedance
Additional protection (RCDs)
Prospective fault current
Check of phase sequence (multi-phase circuits)
Functional testing
Verification of voltage drop

Where any test indicates a failure to comply, that test and any preceding test, the results of which may have been influenced by the fault indicated, must be repeated following rectification of the fault.

e. Continuity of protective conductors (612.2.1)

The test is applied to all protective conductors (circuit protective conductors, earthing conductors, and protective and supplementary bonding conductors) to ensure they are connected to each required point on the circuit and that their value compares with relevant criteria.

This test is made using a low-resistance ohmmeter with a no-load voltage between 4 V and 24 V, d.c or a.c and a short-circuit current of not less than 200 mA.

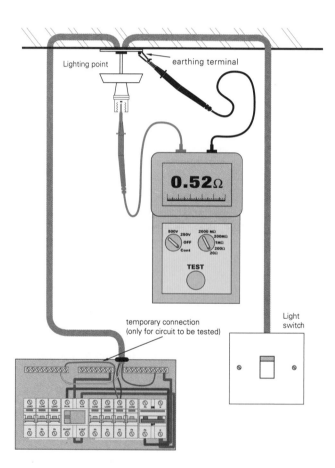

Fig 6.5 Continuity of protective conductors

f. Continuity of ring final circuit conductors

The continuity of each conductor (line, neutral and protective conductors) in a ring final circuit must be verified.

This test is made using a low-resistance ohmmeter with a no-load voltage between 4 V and 24 V, d.c. or a.c. and a short-circuit current of not less than 200 mA.

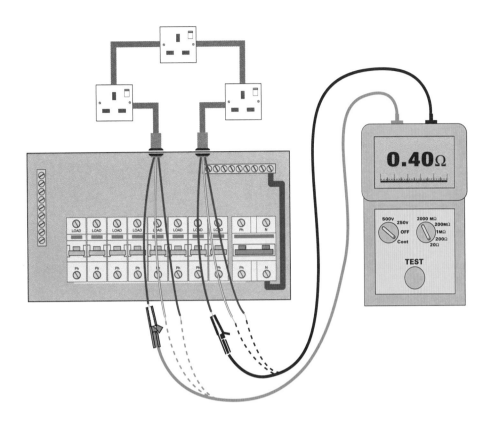

Fig 6.6 Continuity of ring final circuit conductors

g. Insulation resistance

The insulation resistance must be measured to ensure that the measured values exceed those given in Table 61 of *BS 7671*. The test voltages that must be applied when carrying out insulation tests are also given in Table 61.

Now refer to 'Things to do and find' and complete question 8 in line with Table 61 of *BS 7671*.

Part 6
Inspection and testing

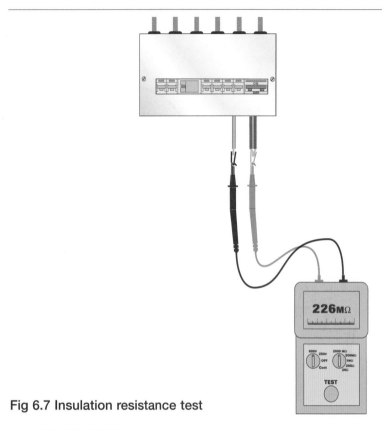

Fig 6.7 Insulation resistance test

POINTS TO NOTE:

- Insulation resistance measurements must be made between live conductors and between live conductors and the protective conductor connected to the earthing arrangement. The line and neutral conductors may be connected together where this is appropriate, for example when periodic testing is being carried out.
- Insulation testing will normally be applied to the main switchboard and each distribution circuit, with all final circuits connected but current-using equipment disconnected.
- Where electronic devices, which are likely to be damaged or influence the results, are connected to circuits to be tested, the test should only be measured between live conductors connected together and the earthing arrangement. In some cases, to avoid damage, electronic devices may require disconnection.
- Functional extra-low voltage circuits should be considered as low voltage circuits in relation to insulation testing requirements.

h. Protection by SELV, PELV or by electrical separation

Where insulation tests are being carried out in relation to circuits where SELV, PELV or electrical separation systems are part of the installation being tested, Regulation Group 612.4 should be followed.

i. Basic protection by a barrier or an enclosure provided during erection

This requirement is not required where the equipment complies with the relevant British or Harmonized Standard. Normally verification is carried out by inspection to ensure equipment is installed to manufacturers' recommendations.

j. Insulation resistance/impedance of floors and walls

These insulation tests relate to the requirements of Regulation 418.1. Because of their limited application no further information will be provided in this section of the Learning Guide. Appendix 13 of *BS 7671* provides further information.

k. Polarity

The requirement to ensure that single-pole fuses, switches or circuit-breakers are inserted in the line conductor only is prescribed in Chapter 13 (Fundamental Principles) which indicates the importance of this test. Incorrect polarity can give rise to danger in a number of ways, including:

- Parts of the installation remaining live, even when single-pole devices have been switched off and the installation appears to be 'dead'
- In the event of an overload, the fuse or circuit-breaker would disconnect the neutral but leave the load at full voltage
- An earth fault might remain undetected by overcurrent protective devices.

> **Exercise 6.3**
>
> Make a list of items in an installation that should be verified for correct polarity.

As mentioned previously the above tests (Regulations 612.2 to 612.6) should be carried out in the sequence prescribed and before the installation is energized. Although Regulation 612.1 indicates that earth electrode testing should be carried out prior to the installation being energized (by an earth resistance tester) an alternative is to use an earth fault loop impedance tester which requires the installation to be energized. However, care should be taken to follow the recommendations provided in IEE Guidance Note 3 or the NICEIC Inspection and Testing book.

l. Earth electrode resistance

BS 7671 states that where an earthing system incorporates an earth electrode as part of the installation, the electrode resistance to Earth must be measured. For the testing methods and details of the instruments to be used, further information should be sought in inspection and testing guidance documents.

For initial verification the following tests (Regulations 612.8 to 612.14) following the earth electrode resistance test require the installation to be energized.

m. Protection by automatic disconnection of the supply

For TN systems, Regulation 612.8.1 outlines the requirements to ensure verification to Regulation Group 411.4. The measurement of the earth fault loop impedance is required (see 'n' below) **and** the measurement must be verified in relation to the characteristics and/or effectiveness of the associated protective device(s). For overcurrent protective devices the characteristics should be visually inspected, for RCDs this requires a visual inspection **and** test.

For TT systems, Regulation 612.8.1 outlines the requirements to ensure verification to Regulation Group 411.5. In this case the reference to earth fault loop impedance above changes to the measurement of R_A of the earth electrode for exposed-conductive-parts of the installation. The requirements to verify measurements against the characteristics of the associated protective device are the same as for TN systems above.

n. Earth fault loop impedance

Where protective measures are being used and they require a knowledge of earth fault loop impedance the relevant impedances should be measured or determined by an alternative method.

One method is to use an earth fault loop impedance tester and this is the normal method for testing socket-outlets, distribution boards and the earth fault loop impedance at the origin (Z_e). The alternative method would be to utilize the $R_1 + R_2$ tests results obtained during the continuity testing and add these values to the earth fault loop impedance measured at the origin of the installation.

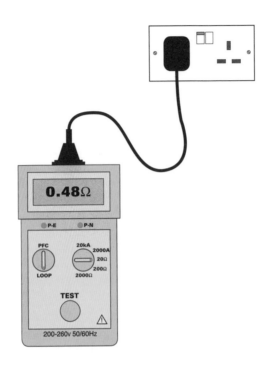

Fig 6.8 Earth fault loop test at a socket-outlet

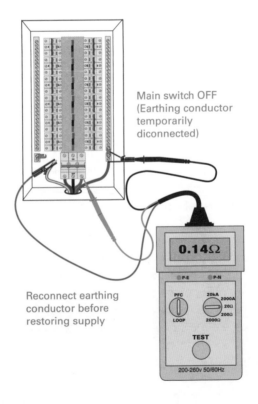

Main switch OFF
(Earthing conductor temporarily diconnected)

Reconnect earthing conductor before restoring supply

Fig 6.9 Earth fault loop test at the origin of the installation

o. Additional protection

The provision of additional protection is outlined in Section 415. This provision is in addition to the other requirements for basic and fault protection. Additional protection can be provided by RCD and/or supplementary bonding. Part 6 requires the effectiveness of these measures to be verified by visual inspection and test.

p. Prospective fault current

Prospective fault current is the maximum fault current likely to occur in the installation, on which value the design and selection of equipment have been based. It is required to verify the prospective fault current at the origin and other relevant points of the installation. The prospective fault current at the origin is one of the requirements outlined in General Characteristics (Section 313).

The instrument usually used is an earth fault impedance tester and this test would normally be carried out at the same time as the earth fault loop impedance measurement. It is important to note that it is the highest fault level that is required and this could be between line and neutral, line and earth or line to line (for multi-phase circuits)

The magnitude of prospective fault current may be obtained by measurement, calculation or determined by another method.

q. Check of phase sequence

In the case of multi-phase circuits it must be verified that the phase sequence is maintained throughout the installation. This could be an issue, for example where large supplies are being connected, particularly changes in service, transformer connections, main switch connections, motor circuitry or any parallel multi-phase connections.

The instrument used would normally be a phase sequence indicator.

r. Functional testing

This requirement relates to the testing of RCDs providing fault protection or additional protection to ensure any test facility incorporated into the device operates effectively.

Functional testing is also required for all other relevant electrical equipment to ensure they are installed and operate in accordance with the requirements of the Regulations. Control devices, interlocks, starters and sensors are examples of items that need to be checked to ensure they operate as intended.

s. Verification of voltage drop

The requirement relating to volt drop is dependent upon the lowest acceptable limit corresponding to the equipment being supplied and should ensure that the safe functioning of the equipment is not impaired. This requirement would normally be met by following manufacturers' recommendations.

Verification of voltage drop can be ascertained by:

• Calculation using the circuit impedance
• By use of calculations using established data.

Voltage drop calculations are usually carried out when cable current-carrying capacities are being assessed. Voltage drop is covered in more detail in Section 523/525 of this Learning Guide. Further to this, Appendix 12 of *BS 7671* provides more details in relation to recommended voltage drop limits.

Exercise 6.4

(1) Name 4 tests, in sequence, that are required to be carried out prior to circuits being energised.
(2) Name 4 tests that are required following circuits being energised. (3) What is the minimum insulation value for a 230 V circuit?

5. Periodic inspection and testing (Chapter 62)

a. General

Every electrical installation deteriorates with use and age. It is important, therefore, that the person responsible for the maintenance of electrical installations is sure that the safety of the users is not put at risk and that the installation continues to be in a safe and serviceable condition.

Where the initial certification, or for older properties reports from previous periodic inspection and testing are available, then the information in these documents should be taken into account. Where there are no previous certificates or reports an investigation should take place prior to carrying out the periodic inspection and testing to compile sufficient data to undertake the work safely and effectively.

The periodic inspection and testing procedure does not require all equipment to be inspected or all tests to be carried out. The emphasis should be to assess which areas require inspection or tests on a risk basis. Because some dismantling may create problems the Regulations recommend either no dismantling or partial dismantling, supplemented by appropriate tests. It is important that precautions are taken to ensure that the inspection and testing does not cause danger to persons or livestock or damage to property and equipment even if the circuit is defective.

The purpose of the periodic inspection and testing is to show that the requirements for disconnection times as required by Chapter 41 are complied with. Four key areas that must be provided for (or a relevant departure recorded) are given in Regulation 621.1 of *BS 7671*.

It is important that the extent and limitations of the report are recorded. The report should include all observed or identified departures from *BS 7671*. A schedule of inspections and schedule of test results should also accompany every periodic inspection report.

b. Frequency

The frequency of periodic inspection and testing of an installation will depend on many factors such as:

• Type of installation
• Its use and operation
• The frequency and quality of maintenance
• External influences

For new installations the designer completes the section on the Electrical Installation Certificate that recommends the time period until the next inspection and test.

6. Certification and reporting (Chapter 63)

a. General

Chapter 63 outlines the requirements for the issue of certificates and reports. Model Forms for Electrical Installation Certificates, Minor Electrical Installation Works Certificate, Periodic Inspection Reports, Schedule of Inspections and Schedule of Test Results are provided in Appendix 6 of *BS 7671*.

The requirements for issuing certificates and reports are illustrated in the table below:

Table 6B (Learning Guide Table) Types of work and related form (Certificate/Report)

TYPE OF WORK COMPLETED	TYPE OF FORM REQUIRED
New installation or change to existing installation	Electrical Installation Certificate
New installation work that does not include the provision of a new circuit	Electrical Installation Certificate or Minor Electrical Installation Works Certificate
Alterations or additions	Electrical Installation Certificate
Alterations or additions that does not include the provision of a new circuit	Electrical Installation Certificate or Minor Electrical Installation Works Certificate
Periodic Inspection and Testing	Periodic Inspection Report

Records of inspection and testing in the form of a schedule of inspections and a schedule of test results must be provided with the electrical installation certificate and periodic inspection report.

Information relating to the relevant inspection and tests should be provided as part of the Minor Electrical Installation Works Certificate.

All the above forms, complete with schedules of inspections and schedules of test results, must be compiled, signed or otherwise authenticated by a competent person or persons and given to the person ordering the work.

b. New work or alterations and additions

The person or persons responsible for design, construction and inspection and testing of the new installation work or alterations and additions must be identified on the certificate.

Defects or omissions revealed during the inspection and testing of new installation work must be made good before the certificate is issued. In the case of alterations or additions, where defects are identified in the existing installation (and this does not impact on the safety of the altered/additional work) then this should be recorded on the certificate.

notes

c. Periodic inspection and testing

Following the periodic inspection and testing a Periodic Inspection Report, together with a schedule of inspections and a schedule of test results must be given to the person ordering the inspection.

Any damage, deterioration, defects, dangerous conditions and non-compliance with the requirements of the Regulations, which may give rise to danger, together with any significant limitations of the inspection and testing, including their reasons, should be recorded on the report.

Further information relating to Inspection and testing can be found in:
- *BS 7671* Part 6 and Appendix 6
- Electrical Safety Council Technical Manual articles A13-1
- NICEIC Inspection, testing and certification (including periodic reporting). Practical advice and guidance
- IEE Guidance Note 3

PART 6 FINAL REVISION EXERCISE

6.1 Model Forms for certification and reporting are to be found in which of the following locations in *BS 7671*?
- ☐ a. Part 4
- ☐ b. Part 6
- ☐ c. Appendix 4
- ☐ d. Appendix 6

6.2 Which of the following types of electrical installation work would not be suitable for the issue of a Minor Electrical Installation Works Certificate?
- ☐ a. A socket-outlet added to an existing ring final circuit
- ☐ b. A socket-outlet added to an existing radial circuit
- ☐ c. A replacement socket-outlet
- ☐ d. A new lighting circuit

6.3 The minimum value of insulation for SELV and PELV circuits should be which of the following?
- ☐ a. Not more than 0.5 MΩ
- ☐ b. Not less than 0.5 MΩ
- ☐ c. Not more than 1.0 MΩ
- ☐ d. Not less than 1.0 MΩ

6.4 For initial testing, which of the following is part of the correct sequence?
- ☐ a. Continuity, polarity. Ring continuity, insulation
- ☐ b. Polarity, continuity, ring continuity, insulation
- ☐ c. Insulation, continuity, polarity, ring continuity
- ☐ d. Continuity, ring continuity, insulation, polarity

6.5 For a new installation which of the following persons completes the section on the Electrical Installation Certificate that recommends the time period until the next inspection and test?
- ☐ a. The designer
- ☐ b. The installer
- ☐ c. The inspector
- ☐ d. The owner

Things to do and find

1. List the titles of the three Chapters in Part 6 of *BS 7671*.

2. List three of the items in Regulation 131.1 that risk of injury may result from.

3. List three of the items in Regulation 313.1 that should be made available to the person carrying out verification of new work.

4. Regulation 514.9 requires a legible diagram, chart or table or equivalent information to be provided. List three items that should be provided within the diagrams, charts, tables, etc.

5. List three items that you would check during a polarity test

6. Review Appendix 6 and read the guidance relating to model forms of certificate and reporting.

7. What is the purpose of an RCD test button?

8. Complete the following chart::

Circuit nominal voltage (V)	Test voltage d.c. (V)	Minimum insulation resistance (MΩ)
SELV and PELV		
Up to and including 500 V with the exception of the above systems		
Above 500 V		

Part 7
Special installations or locations

1. Introduction

Part 7 of *BS 7671* contains the regulations relating to special installations or locations. These installations or locations are not special because they are unusual (bathrooms for example are very common), but because they require special consideration in relation to the design and construction of the electrical installation. Part 7, therefore, contains additional regulations that must be adhered to when installing electrical equipment in these locations.

Fig 700.1 Swimming pool

It is important to note that the regulations in Part 7 are intended to supplement or modify the general requirements contained in other parts of the Regulations. All the normal criteria must, therefore, be considered, as well as the additional requirements of Part 7.

Prior to considering the additional regulations required by Part 7 of *BS 7671* it is important that all other Parts of *BS 7671* have been covered. In particular it is important that students have a good understanding of protective measures (Part 4) and Section 522 (external influences, specifically IP Codes).

Fig 700.2 Milking parlour

2. Factors that make a special installation or location special

The additional requirements of Part 7 relate to installations or locations where, due to the nature of the installations or locations, there are considered to be additional risks of electrical shock. The most common factors that increase electric shock risk are:

- a reduction in body resistance caused either by bodily immersion or by wet skin,
- lower contact resistance of the body that is associated with, for example, wet hands, wet clothing and wet footwear
- likely contact of substantial areas of the body with earth potential

- arduous site conditions and increased risk of mechanical damage
- unusual supply and/or isolation arrangements
- special equipment considerations
- access to the installations or locations by the general public
- temporary installations and frequent reconnection of systems
- installations that are mobile and prone to vibration etc

Some or all of the above factors may need to be considered dependent upon the installation or location in question.

3. Special installations or locations covered by Part 7

The 16th edition of *BS 7671* had 10 special installations or locations. Two of these were moved into Part 5 when *BS 7671*: 2008 (17th edition) became current. However, another 6 new sections were added at that time to make a total of 14 special installations or locations. It should be noted that further additions to Part 7 are planned for the future.

Table 700A *(Learning Guide Table)* **Sections contained within Part 7**

Section in BS7671	Title of special installation or location
701	Locations containing a bath or shower
702	Swimming pools and other basins
703	Rooms and cabins containing sauna heaters
704	Construction and demolition site installations
705	Agricultural and horticultural premises
706	Conducting locations with restrictive movement
708	Electrical installations in caravan/camping parks and similar locations
709	Marinas and similar locations
711	Exhibitions, shows and stands
712	Solar photovoltaic (pv) power supply systems
717	Mobile or transportable units
721	Electrical installations in caravans and motor caravans
740	Temporary electrical installations for structures, amusement devices and booths at fairgrounds, amusement parks and circuses
753	Floor and ceiling systems

4. Protective measures

The protective measures that are permitted and any special requirements relating to each special installation or location are covered in the relevant section of this Learning Guide. Some particular protective measures may not be allowed or they may be allowed but only with additional measures or requirements. Apart from some very special exceptions the following protective provisions/measures are not permitted:

- Obstacles
- Placing out of reach

- Non-conducting locations
- Earth-free local equipotential bonding

Table 700B (below) illustrates the exclusions to the restricted measures/provisions.

Table 700B *(Learning Guide Table)* Prohibited protective measures

	PROTECTIVE MEASURES/PROVISIONS NOT PERMITTED			
Section	Obstacles	Placing out of reach	Non-Conducting location	Earth-free local equipotential bonding
701	X	X	X	X
702	X	X	X	X
703	X	X	X	X
704	X	X	X	X
705	X	X	X	X
706	X	X	X	X
708	X	X	X	X
709	X	X	X	X
711	X	X	X	X
712	4	4	X some restrictions	X some restrictions
717	X	X	X	X not recomended
721	X	X	X	X
740	X	X Except for dodgems at ELV	X	X
753	X	X	X	X

X Measure or provision prohibited.   **4** Measure or provision allowed.
Further to the above restrictions the following should be noted:

SELV and PELV (for further information relating to protection by SELV and PELV see Section 414 of this Learning Guide)

Normally, no further provisions are required for basic protection where the protective measure is SELV or PELV, provided specified conditions are met.

However, for many of the special locations listed in Part 7, basic protection is required in addition to the SELV or PELV system and in some cases the maximum voltage for these systems is limited. The requirements vary depending upon the section in question and the related section(s) need to be reviewed prior to commencing design or installation.

Electrical separation

There are several restrictions in relation to the protective measure electrical separation in special installations or locations.   This is particularly the case where more than one item of equipment or socket-outlet is being supplied by this protective measure as these circuits can only be installed in installations that are controlled or under the supervision of a skilled or instructed person, even when they are not special installations or locations.

Automatic disconnection of supply

Each section of Part 7 should be reviewed carefully. Additional protection in the form of RCDs or supplementary bonding may be required and in some cases there are voltage limitations.

> Further information relating to Part 7 Special installations or locations particular requirements can be found in:
> * *BS 7671* Part 7
> * Electrical Safety Council Technical Manual articles S205-1 to S205-53
> * IEE Guidance Note 7

SECTION 700 FINAL REVISION EXERCISE

700.1 Which of the following installations or locations is not covered by a separate section in Part 7 Special Installation or locations?
☐ a. Agricultural and horticultural premises
☐ b. Commercial units
☐ c. Mobile or transportable units
☐ d. Marinas and similar installations

700.2 Which of the following installations or locations is specifically covered in Part 7 Special Installation or locations?
☐ a. Locations containing a kitchen
☐ b. Locations containing electrical machinery
☐ c. Locations containing a bath or shower
☐ d. Locations containing office equipment

700.3 Which of the following protective measures is not permitted in the vast majority of special locations?
☐ a. Non-conducting location
☐ b. SELV or PELV
☐ c. Automatic disconnection of supply
☐ d. Double or reinforced insulation

700.4 Which of the following protective measures, when used in special installations or locations, is commonly restricted to the supply of a single piece of equipment or single socket-outlet?
☐ a. SELV
☐ b. Automatic disconnection of supply
☐ c. PELV
☐ d. Electrical separation

notes

Things to do and find

1. What are the voltage restrictions relating to dodgems?

2. Why are special installations or locations classified as 'special'?

3. List the typical factors that could increase the risk of shock for a swimming pool.

4. List the typical factors that could increase the risk of shock on a construction site.

5. What is the number of the section relating to marinas and similar locations?

6. What does Section 704 relate to?

7. What is the difference between Section 708 and Section 721?

1. Introduction

Locations containing baths, showers and cabinets containing a shower and/or bath and the surrounding areas are considered to be locations where there is an increased risk of electric shock due to:

• a reduction in body resistance caused either by bodily immersion or by wet skin, and

• likely contact of substantial areas of the body with earth potential.

Consequently, such locations are covered by Part 7 (Special installations or locations) of *BS 7671*, the applicable section being Section 701 (Locations containing a bath or shower).

Fig 701.1 Location containing a bath and shower

2. Scope

The requirements of Section 701, covered in this topic, apply to locations containing baths, showers and cabinets containing a shower and/or a bath, and the surrounding zones.

The requirements of Section 701 do not apply to showers and similar decontamination facilities for emergencies in industrial areas and laboratories, and special requirements beyond those of *BS 7671* may apply to locations containing baths and showers for medical treatment or for disabled people. The requirements for such installations must be determined by the designer of the installation by consultation with the customer and/or the manufacturer of the equipment concerned.

3. Zonal concept

The requirements for safety for locations containing a bath or shower are based on the application of the particular requirements for each zone and beyond being based on the perceived degree of risk of electric shock.

Section 701
Locations containing a bath or shower

Regulation Group 701.32 and Figures 701.1 and 701.2 of *BS 7671* provides the information relating to the zones in locations containing baths, showers or cabinets containing a shower and/or bath. The zones are determined taking account of walls, doors, fixed partitions, ceilings and floors, where these effectively limit the extent of a zone (see the diagrams and descriptions below)

It is important to understand the prescribed zones, as section 701 gives information in relation to which protective measures, switchgear, controlgear, accessories and current using equipment can be used in each of the prescribed zones.

To fully understand the prescribed zones and their related dimensions the following text, diagrams and the related regulations in Section 701 of *BS 7671* need to be studied carefully.

ZONE 0 is the interior of the bath tub or shower basin. Where a shower is not fitted with a basin the height of zone 0 is 0.10 m and this requirement extends horizontally to the limit of zone 1.

ZONE 1 is
(i) the three dimensional space immediately above the bath or shower basin up to a height of 2.25 m. For showers without a basin and for showers without a basin, but with a fixed partition, there are specific dimensions (see Figs 701.1 and 701.2 of *BS 7671*).

(ii) the space under the bath or shower, unless it is only accessible by a key or a tool in which case it is considered to be outside the zones

(iii) the vertical surface at a distance 1.20 m from the centre point of the fixed water outlet on the wall or ceiling for showers without a basin

ZONE 2 is: the area that extends to a point horizontally 0.6 m starting from the boundary of zone 1. Zone 2 extends 2.25 m vertically from finished floor level (or to the highest fixed shower head or water outlet)
Note: for showers without a basin there is no Zone 2 but Zone 1 is extended horizontally a further 0.6 m.

The following diagrams illustrate the required dimensions relating to zones in a location containing a bath. For diagrams relating to bath tubs with a permanent fixed partition and a location containing a shower refer to Fig 701.1 and 701.2 of *BS 7671*.

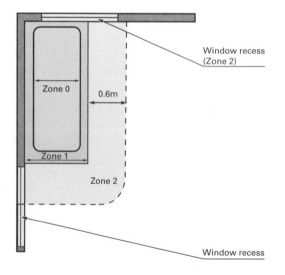

Fig 701.2 Zone dimensions. Bath tub (plan view)

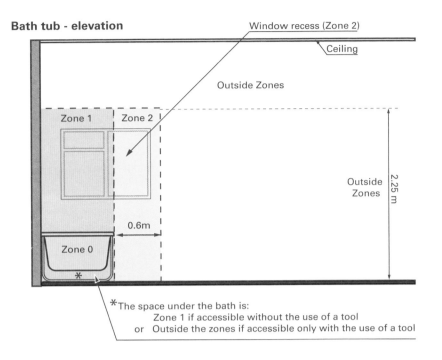

*The space under the bath is:
    Zone 1 if accessible without the use of a tool
or Outside the zones if accessible only with the use of a tool

Fig 701.3 Zone dimensions. Bath tub (elevation view)

Exercise 701.1

Refer to Figs 701.1 and 701.2 of *BS 7671*. (1) What is the maximum height of Zone 2? (2) To what distance from a fixed water outlet in a shower does Zone 1 extend to? (3) How far does Zone 2 extend from Zone 1 in a bathroom?

---

4. Protective measures against electric shock

a. Protective measures not permitted

See Section 700 of this Learning Guide

b. Acceptable protective measures

Normally the protective measures used in locations containing a bath or shower would be automatic disconnection of supply, extra-low voltage provided by SELV or PELV or electrical separation particularly in the case of shaver supply units. However, specific requirements may be required depending upon the type of equipment and the zone into which the equipment is being installed.

(i). Automatic disconnection of supply

Where the protective measure automatic disconnection of supply is being used, additional protection by residual current devices (provided by **one or more RCDs,** with a rated residual operating current not exceeding 30 mA) **are required for all circuits in locations containing a bath or shower.**

Whilst in the 16th edition of *BS 7671* supplementary equipotential bonding was required for the vast majority of locations containing a bath or shower, the changes in the 17th edition means that supplementary bonding will no longer be required for new installations or additions/alterations relating to final circuits in locations containing a bath or shower bathroom supplementary bonding if:

• The disconnection times prescribed in Section 411 of *BS 7671* are met and
• All circuits are protected by RCDs having the characteristics specified in Regulation 415.1.1 *and*
• The building has protective equipotential bonding in accordance with 411.3.1.2 *and*
• All extraneous-conductive-parts of the location are effectively connected to the protective bonding *

* An assessment of whether the extraneous-conductive-parts are effectively connected to the protective bonding can be made by following the requirements of Regulation 415.2.2. In Regulation 415.2.2, for a.c. systems, effectiveness of the protective bonding would be assured by applying the equation: $R \leq 50 \text{ V}/I_a$. As an RCD (in compliance with Regulation 415.1.1) is required for all circuits in a location containing a bath or shower, this equation becomes: 50 V/30 mA which equates to a maximum resistance of 1667 Ω.

It should be noted that as RCDs are now required for all circuitry within a location containing a bath or shower the requirement for supplementary bonding is very unlikely, although the above criteria needs to be applied in each case.

Where supplementary bonding is required, Regulation 701.415.2 of *BS 7671* requires the protective conductor terminals of each circuit supplying Class I and Class II electrical equipment and extraneous-conductive-parts within the location containing a bath or shower to be connected together by local supplementary bonding conductors (complying with Regulation 415.2 and Regulation Group 544.2 This is to prevent the occurrence of voltages between any such parts of such magnitude as could cause danger of electric shock.

Examples of parts that may commonly be found in a bathroom that may come within the definition of an extraneous-conductive-part include:

• metallic pipes supplying services, and metallic waste pipes (e.g. water, gas),
• metallic central heating pipes and air conditioning systems,
• accessible metallic structural parts of the building; (metallic door architraves, window frames and similar parts are not considered to be extraneous-conductive-parts unless they are connected to metallic structural parts of the building).

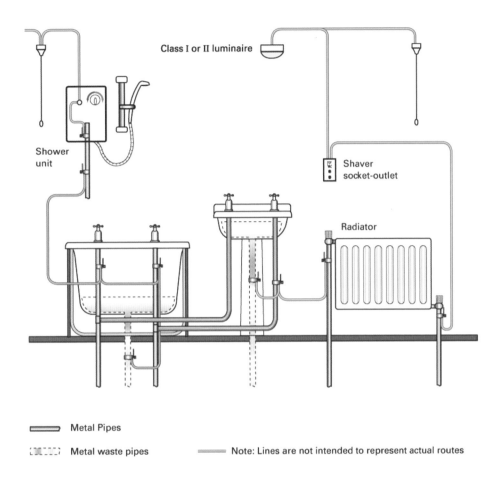

Class I or II luminaire

Shower unit

Shaver socket-outlet

Radiator

Metal Pipes

Metal waste pipes

Note: Lines are not intended to represent actual routes

Fig 701.4 Supplementary equipotential bonding

(ii) SELV and PELV (for further information relating to protection by SELV and PELV see Section 414 of this Learning Guide and *BS 7671*)

Normally, where the protective measure is SELV or PELV, no further devices are required for basic protection, provided specified conditions are met. However, in locations containing a bath or shower, basic protection is required in addition to the SELV or PELV system by either:

• barriers or enclosures affording a degree of protection of at least IPXXB or IP2X (for further information relating to IP codes see Part 2 of this Learning Guide) *or*
• Basic insulation of live parts

(iii) Electrical separation

In a location containing a bath or shower the protective measure electrical separation can only be used to supply one item of current-using equipment or one single socket-outlet. Shaver supply units to *BS EN 61558-2-5* for use in locations containing a bath or shower utilize the protection measure electrical separation. With this measure the electrical system must be completely separated from Earth and from every other system. This means even where an item of equipment has a fault to earth there is no path through which shock current can flow (see the diagram below)

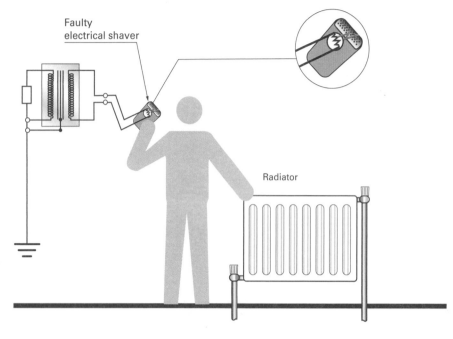

> **Key Facts**
> Before continuing,
> check out IP codes in
> Part 2 of this Learning
> Guide and External
> Influences in Appendix 5
> of *BS 7671*

Fig 701.6 Shaver with an electrical fault

5. Selection and erection of electrical equipment

a. External influences

The types of electrical equipment to be installed must be selected to ensure that water or moisture is not detrimental to the safe working of the installed systems. The IP rating system needs to be considered generally when selecting electrical equipment. However, there are specific requirements for locations containing a bath or shower:

- **Zone 0**   IPX7 (or ●● if the equipment is not IP coded)
- **Zone 1**   IPX4 (or ◭ if the equipment is not IP coded)
- **Zone 2**   IPX4 (or ◭ if the equipment is not IP coded)

- **Electrical equipment exposed to water jets** (e.g. for cleaning purposes)
          IPX5 (or ◭◭ if the equipment is not IP coded)

Note 1: The above requirements do not apply to shaver supply units complying with *BS EN 61558-2-5* (when installed in Zone 2 and located where direct spray from showers is unlikely).

Note 2: The water droplet (or drip) symbols (●● and ◭) have been superseded and are no longer specified in *BS 7671* as an alternative to the IP code on equipment. It should be further noted that the two systems are not directly comparable. However, as installers may still come across these symbols the above references have been retained.

Photograph courtesy of Redring Electric Ltd

Fig 701.7 Shower units, as with all equipment, must be suitable both for the zone and the conditions likely to occur

b. Erection of switchgear, controlgear and accessories

Strict restrictions apply to the type of switchgear, controlgear and accessories that can be used in locations containing a bath or shower as indicated below:

- **Zone 0**   no switchgear or accessories to be installed

- **Zone 1**   only switches of SELV circuits (supplied at a nominal voltage not exceeding 12 V a.c. rms or 30 V ripple-free d.c. The safety source must be installed outside zones 0, 1 and 2)

- **Zone 2**   Generally no switchgear or accessories incorporating switches or socket-outlets must be installed apart from:
  (i) switches and sockets-outlets of SELV circuits (the safety source being outside zones 0, 1 and 2)
  (ii) shaver supply units complying with *BS EN 61558-2-5*

Socket-outlets* may be installed in a room containing a bath or shower. However they can only be installed in locations which are at least 3 m horizontally from the boundary of Zone 1. * SELV sockets-outlets complying with Section 414 and shaver supply units to *BS EN 61588-2-5* are exceptions to the above as they can be installed within Zone 2. Although switches are not permitted in Zone 1 or zone 2 the insulated pull cords of cord operated switches (complying with *BS EN 60669-1*) are permitted in zones 1 and 2.

c. Current-using equipment

In zone 0 only fixed current-using equipment that meets the following requirements must be installed:

- suitable for zone 0, according to the manufacturer's instructions for use and mounting and comply with the relevant standard *and*
- fixed and permanently connected *and*
- protected by SELV with a rated voltage not exceeding 12 V a.c. or 30 V d.c.

In zone 1 only fixed and permanently connected current-using equipment must be installed. The manufacturer's instructions for use and mounting must always be followed. The following list indicates the type of equipment that would normally be expected to be installed:

- whirlpool units
- electric showers
- shower pumps
- equipment protected by SELV or PELV (maximum rated voltage 25 V a.c. or 60 V d.c.)
- ventilation equipment
- towel rails
- water heating appliances
- luminaires

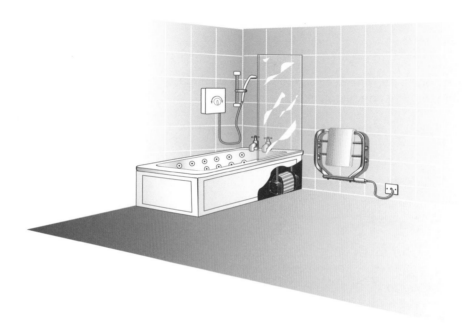

Fig 701.8 Typical equipment for use in Zone 1

d. Electric floor heating systems

For more general information relating to floor heating systems see Section 753 of *BS 7671* or this Learning Guide. When these systems are installed in locations containing a bath or shower all heating cables must be of the type incorporating one of the following:

- a metal sheath,
- metal enclosure *or*
- fine mesh metallic grid.

In all the above cases, the metallic sheath, enclosure or grid must be connected to the protective conductor of the supply circuit (unless the supply is SELV).

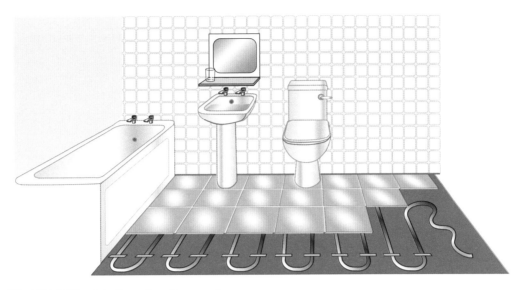

Fig 701.9 Electric floor heating system

Further information relating to Section 701 Locations containing a bath or shower can be found in:

- *BS7671* Section 701
- Electrical Safety Council Technical Manual articles S205-45
- IEE Guidance Note 7

SECTION 701 FINAL REVISION EXERCISE

701.1 The interior of a bath tub or shower basin would by described as which of the following?

☐ a. Zone 0
☐ b. Zone 1
☐ c. Zone 2
☐ d. Outside the zones

701.2 For installed electrical equipment in Zone 0, the degree of protection must be at least which of the following?

☐ a. IPX0
☐ b. IPX4
☐ c. IPX5
☐ d. IPX7

701.3 Which of the following is correct? Sockets-outlets other than SELV socket-outlets

☐ a. may be installed in zone 1
☐ b. may be installed in zone 2
☐ c. may be installed in locations 3 m beyond the zone 1 boundary
☐ d. may not be installed in a location containing a bath or shower

701.4 A shaver unit to *BS EN 61558-2-5* for use in a location containing a bath or shower uses which of the following protective measures?
- ☐ a. automatic disconnection of supply
- ☐ b. electrical separation
- ☐ c. non-conducting location
- ☐ d. earth-free local equipotential bonding

701.5 Which of the following protective measures/provisions is allowed in a location containing a bath or a shower?
- ☐ a. non-conducting location
- ☐ b. placing out of reach
- ☐ c. automatic disconnection of supply
- ☐ d. earth-free local equipotential bonding

701.6 Which of the following voltages for use with a SELV switch may be used in zone 1?
- ☐ a. 12 V a.c. rms
- ☐ b. 30 V a.c. rms
- ☐ c. 60 V ripple-free d.c.
- ☐ d. 120 V ripple-free d.c.

Things to do and find

1. Make a list of current-using equipment that you would expect to find in a location containing a bath or shower (then check against Regulation 701.55)

2. What does the reference to IPX5 in Section 701 refer to? Electrical equipment exposed to .... (e.g. for .... purposes)

3. Give four examples of items that may require supplementary equipotential bonding

4. What vertical height does Zone 1 extend to?

5. For a shower without a basin how high does zone 0 extend to?

1. Introduction

Swimming pools, the basins of fountains, paddling pools and their surroundings are locations of increased electric shock risk due to:

• a reduction in body resistance caused either by bodily immersion or by wet skin, and

• likely contact of substantial areas of the body with earth potential.

Consequently, such locations are covered by Part 7 (Special installations or locations) of *BS 7671*, the applicable section being Section 702 (Swimming pools and other basins).

Fig 702.1 Picture of a typical swimming pool

2. Scope

The requirements of Section 702, covered in this topic, apply to the basins of swimming pools, the basins of fountains and the basins of paddling pools as well the surrounding zones of all these basins.

The requirements of Section 702 do not apply to natural waters, lakes in gravel pits, coastal areas or similar except for areas especially designed as swimming pools.

3. Zonal concept

The requirements for safety for swimming pools and other basins are based on the application of a zonal concept similar to that used for locations containing a bath or shower; the particular requirements for each zone and beyond being based on the perceived degree of risk of electric shock.

Regulation 702.32 provides the information relating to the zones in swimming pools and other basins. The zones consider recessed pools as well as pools above ground and are determined taking account of fixed partitions where these effectively limit the extent of a zone. Section 702 of *BS 7671* also provides diagrams illustrating the dimensions of zones.

notes

- Fig 702.1 of *BS 7671* provides the zone dimensions for a swimming pool and paddling pool where the pool is recessed below ground or fixed floor level. A version of Fig 702.1 from *BS 7671* is provided below (Fig 702.2)
- Fig 702.2 of *BS 7671* provides the zone dimensions for basins which are constructed above ground level
- Fig 702.3 of *BS 7671* provides an example of zone dimensions (as a plan view) where fixed partitions are installed. To affect zone dimensions partitions need to be at least 2.5 m high.
- Fig 702.4 of *BS 7671* provides information relating to the zones of fountains. Because of the diverse nature of fountains Fig 702.4 is given as an example of how to determine zones in these locations.

It is important to understand the prescribed zones as section 702 gives information in relation to which protective measures, switchgear, controlgear, accessories and current using equipment can be used in each of the prescribed zones.

To fully understand the prescribed zones and their related dimensions the following text needs to be studied in conjunction with Regulation 702.32 and Figs 702.1 to 702.4 of *BS 7671*.

Zone 0 is the interior of the basin of a swimming pool or fountain and includes any recesses within the pool or fountain as well as any other basins that could be considered as part of the pool. For a full description of Zone 0 see Regulation 702.32. In zone 0 the use of electrical equipment is extremely restricted. Pool lights in zone 0 are common and there may be other equipment specifically intended for use within the pool or fountain.

Zone 1 is limited by zone 0 and an area immediately outside zone 0 extending horizontally and vertically. The exact dimensions are best understood by referring to Fig 702.1 of *BS 7671* (reproduced as Fig 702.2 below). Zone 1 is extended when equipment around the pool (such as divingboards, chutes and springboards) is expected to be occupied by persons.

Zone 2 is limited by the edge of zone 1 on one side and then extends outwards from the pool basin. The exact dimensions are best understood by referring to Fig 702.1 of *BS 7671* (reproduced as Fig 702.2 below)

Note: There is no zone 2 for fountains

Exercise 702.1

Refer to Regulation 702.32 and Figs 702.1 to 702.4 of *BS 7671*. (1) Review the dimensions relating to diving boards, springboards etc. (2) Review Fig 702.3 to see how a fixed partition affects zones. (3) Which figure in Section 702 relates to dimensions for zones for a basin above ground? (4) What is the minimum height of a fixed partition where it changes zone dimensions?

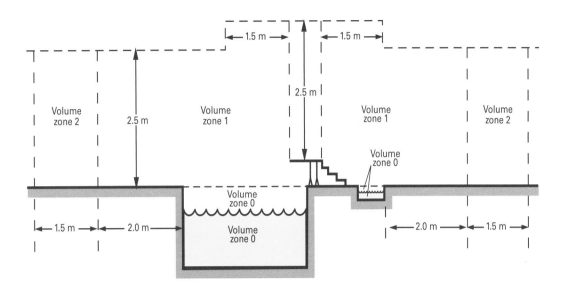

Fig 702.2 Zone dimensions for swimming pools and paddling pools

4. Protective measures against electric shock

a. Protective measures not permitted

See Section 700

b. Acceptable protective measures

Normally the protective measures used in a swimming pool or other basin would be automatic disconnection of supply, extra-low voltage provided by SELV or electrical separation. However, specific requirements may be required depending upon the type of equipment and the zone into which the equipment is being installed.

(i) Automatic disconnection of supply

Where the protective measure automatic disconnection of supply is being used, additional protection is required by the provision of supplementary equipotential bonding in all zones. Supplementary equipotential bonding is required in zones 0, 1 and 2 to connect all extraneous-conductive-parts to the protective conductors of exposed-conductive-parts of equipment situated within these zones.

Where the protective measure automatic disconnection of supply is being used in zones 1 or 2 there are several restrictions, and in all cases the circuit is required to be protected by an RCD in accordance with regulation 415.2.

notes

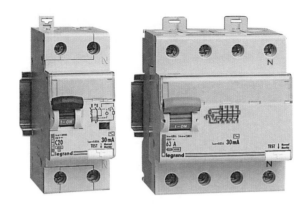

Fig 702.3 Where the protective measure is automatic disconnection of supply
RCDs are required for all circuits in zones 1 & 2.

(ii) SELV and PELV circuits *(for further information relating to protection by SELV and PELV refer to Section 414 of this Learning Guide)*

Normally, no further devices are required for basic protection where the protective measure is SELV, provided specified conditions are met. However, in locations containing a swimming pool or other basin, basic protection is required in addition to the SELV system by either:

• Barriers or enclosures affording a degree of protection of at least IPXXB or IP2X
• Basic insulation (complying with Regulation 416.1)

Further to the above requirements there are also upper voltage limits for SELV supplies in zone 0 and zone 1 as well as specific requirements relating to the location of SELV sources.

Exercise 702.2

You should now refer to Regulation Group 702.410 to review the requirements for protective measures and zones.

6. Selection and erection of electrical equipment

a. External influences

The types of electrical equipment to be installed must be selected to ensure that water or moisture is not detrimental to the safe working of the installed systems. The IP rating system (previously discussed in Part 2 and Section 522 of this Learning Guide) needs to be considered generally. However, there are specific requirements for locations containing swimming pools and other basins:

• Zone 0	**IPX8**
• Zone 1	**IPX4** or
	IPX5 where water jets are likely to occur for cleaning purposes
• Zone 2	**IPX2** for indoor locations
	IPX4 for outdoor locations or
	IPX5 where water jets are likely to occur for cleaning purposes

b. Wiring systems

The following requirements relate to wiring systems which are either on the surface or embedded in walls, ceilings and floors less than 50 mm below the surface.

Wiring systems in zones 0, 1 and 2 should preferably be installed in conduits made of insulating material. Where wiring systems are installed with metallic sheaths or metallic covering these must be connected to the supplementary equipotential bonding.

In zones 0 and 1 the only cables that should be installed are those supplying equipment within these zones. Also, in zones 0 and 1 junction boxes must not be installed except in the case of SELV which can have a junction box within zone 1.

For the wiring to fountains there are additional requirements in Regulation 702.522.23 in relation to cable routes and protection.

c. Switchgear and controlgear

Strict restrictions apply to the type of switchgear, controlgear and accessories that can be used in the zones associated with swimming pools and other basins as indicated below:

Zone 0 and 1 no socket-outlets, switchgear or controlgear to be installed

Zone 2 switches and sockets-outlets are allowed if the supply circuit is protected by one of the protective measures required by items (i), (ii) or (iii) of Regulation 702.53.

Note: For a swimming pool where it is not possible to locate a socket-outlet or switch outside zone 1, the regulations provide an alternative to the above for socket-outlets and switches, providing specific conditions relating to circuit protection and the position of these accessories are met. For further information see Fig 702.4 below.

(For further information relating to lighting equipment in a swimming pool where there is no zone 2 see item 6d below).

Key Facts
Review IP codes in Section 522 (external Influences) before carrying out work in swimming pools. Check the requirements relating to zones, protective measures and acceptable electrical equipment.

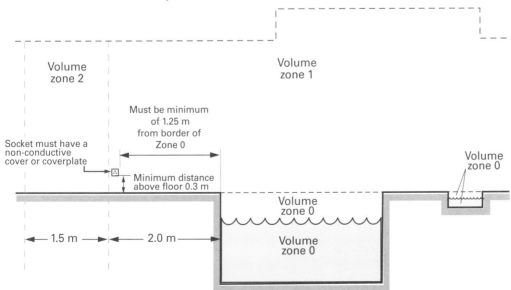

NOTE: Socket-outlet or switch must also be protected by SELV, or by the use of an RCD or by separation.

Fig 702.4 Swimming pool where it is not possible to locate a socket-outlet or switch outside zone 1

notes

d. Current-using equipment

In zone 0 or 1 it is only permitted to install fixed current-using equipment specifically designed for use in a swimming pool in accordance with regulations 702.55.2 and 702.55.4.

For swimming pools where there is no zone 2, lighting equipment supplied by other than a SELV source at 12 V a.c. rms or 30 V ripple free d.c. may be installed in zone 1 on a wall or on a ceiling provided:

• the circuit is protected by automatic disconnection of supply and additional protection by an RCD (having the characteristics specified in Regulation 415.1.1) *and*
• the height from the floor is at least 2 m above the lower limit of zone 1.

In addition the light fittings must have class II enclosure or equivalent and provide protection against mechanical impact of AG2.

Electric heating units embedded in the floor are permitted providing specific requirements relating to the source, supply circuit protection and supplementary equipotential bonding are complied with.

For more general information relating to floor heating systems see Section 753 of *BS 7671*. When these systems are being installed in locations containing swimming pools or other basins the requirements of Regulation 702.55.1 should be followed.

e. Underwater luminaires in swimming pools

Luminaires for use in the water or in contact with the water must be fixed and comply with *BS EN 60598-2-18*.

Where underwater luminaires are installed behind watertight portholes that are serviced from behind, they should be installed to ensure that there is no conductive connection between the exposed-conductive-part of the underwater luminaire and any conductive part of the porthole.

Fig 702.5 Underwater luminaires in swimming pool

g. Special requirements for the installation of electrical equipment in zone 1

The regulations related to fixed electrical equipment designed for swimming pools and other basins (such as filtration systems or jet stream pumps) need to be consulted when this type of work is in the design stage (see Regulation 702.55.4 of *BS 7671*)

7. Protective measures, wiring systems and equipment for fountains

Section 702 contains specific requirements for supplies to and electrical equipment in fountains. For further information see Regulations 702.32 (zones), 702.410.3.4.2 (protective measures against electric shock), 702.522.23 (wiring systems), 702.55.3 (equipment). Fig 702.4 of *BS 7671* provides an example of how to determine the zones of a fountain.

> Further information relating to Section 702 Swimming pools and other basins can be found in:
> * *BS 7671* Section 702
> * Electrical Safety Council Technical Manual articles S205-53
> * IEE Guidance Note 7

SECTION 702 FINAL REVISION EXERCISE

702.1 The interior of the basin of a swimming pool would by described as which of the following?
- ☐ a. Zone 0
- ☐ b. Zone 1
- ☐ c. Zone 2
- ☐ d. Outside the zones

702.2 For installed electrical equipment in Zone 0, the degree of protection must be which of the following?
- ☐ a. IPX4
- ☐ b. IPX5
- ☐ c. IPX7
- ☐ d. IPX8

702.3 Which of the following protective measures is allowed in a location containing a swimming pool or other basin?
- ☐ a. non-conducting location
- ☐ b. placing out of reach
- ☐ c. automatic disconnection of supply
- ☐ d. earth-free local equipotential bonding

702.4 In a swimming pool where it is not possible to locate a socket-outlet or switch outside zone 1 and the protective measure automatic disconnection of supply is being used, an RCD must be used having a maximum rated residual operating current of?
- ☐ a. 15 mA
- ☐ b. 30 mA
- ☐ c. 100 mA
- ☐ d. 300 mA

notes

702.5 Which zone does the description 'vertical plane 2 m from the rim of the basin' relate to?
- ☐ a. Zone 0
- ☐ b. Zone 1
- ☐ c. Zone 2
- ☐ d. Outside the zones

702.6 In zone 0 of a swimming pool, SELV switches supplied at which of the following voltages may be installed?
- ☐ a. 12 V a.c. rms
- ☐ b. 25 V a.c. rms
- ☐ c. 60 V ripple-free d.c.
- ☐ d. 120 V ripple-free d.c.

Things to do and find

1. What does the reference to IPX5 in Section 702 refer to? - Electrical equipment where .... are likely to occur for .... purposes.

2. What vertical height does Zone 1 extend to above a diving board?

3. What is the furthest distance along the floor from the rim of the swimming pool basin to the far end of zone 2?

4. For a swimming pool, where it is not possible to locate a socket-outlet or switch outside zone 1, they can be fitted in zone 1. What distance from the border of zone 0 must it be fitted and at what height above the floor? If the protective measure is automatic disconnection of supply, what additional protection is required?

5. What precaution or checks need to be taken when installing underwater lighting behind watertight portholes?

6. Can a junction box be used in zone 1? If so what are the restrictions?

7. When using metallic sheathed cables or metallic covered wiring systems in zones 0, 1 or 2 what additional requirements should be met?

8. What is the IP rating required for equipment in a zone 2 indoor location where water jets are unlikely?

9. Cables installed in zones 0 and 1 must be limited to supply equipment that is...

10. Review the requirements for supplementary equipotential bonding in locations containing swimming pools and basins.

11. What is the minimum external influence category specified in Section 702 to provide mechanical protection and submersion in water for a cable used in Zone 1 of a fountain.

Section 703
Rooms and cabins containing sauna heaters

1. Introduction

Rooms and cabins containing sauna heaters are considered by *BS 7671* to be a location of increased electric shock risk, as large areas of the human body are exposed and are wet due to perspiration and occasional high humidity

Consequently, such locations are covered by Part 7 (Special installations or locations) of *BS 7671*, the applicable section being Section 703 (Section 703 Rooms and cabins containing sauna heaters). However, it must be remembered that in addition to the requirements given in Section 703, all other relevant sections of *BS 7671* apply to such locations, albeit supplemented and modified by Section 703.

Fig 703.1 Sauna

2. Scope

The requirements of Section 703, covered in this topic, apply to sauna cabins erected on site (in a location or in a room) or a room where a sauna heater is fitted or the sauna heating appliances are installed.

The requirements of Section 703 do not apply to prefabricated sauna cabins complying with a relevant equipment standard.

3. Zonal concept

The zonal concept in relation to saunas relates to heat (rather than water as in swimming pools), although consideration must also be given to the effects of water on equipment. The interior of a hot air sauna is classified into three temperature zones (1, 2 and 3) for the purposes of selecting suitable equipment and safety measures. The zones, illustrated in Fig 703 of *BS 7671*, are reproduced in Fig 703.2 below for ease of reference.

Section 703
Rooms and cabins containing sauna heaters

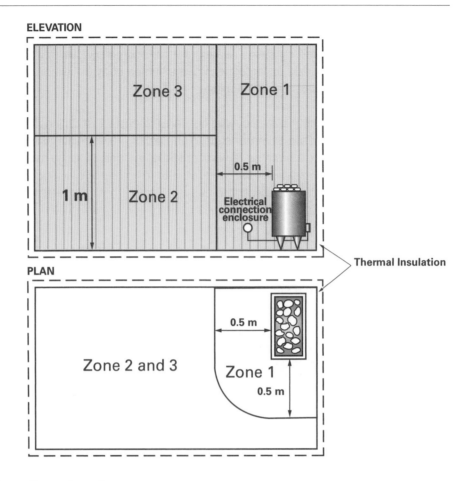

Fig 703.2 Zone dimensions for a sauna

Table 703A (*Learning Guide Table*) Acceptable equipment within zones

Zone 1	Only the sauna heater and equipment associated directly with it.
Zone 2	There is no special requirement concerning heat resistance of equipment
Zone 3	The **equipment** must withstand a minimum temperature of **125 °C** and the **insulation and sheaths of cables** must withstand a minimum temperature of **170 °C**

Exercise 703.1

(1) What is the minimum degree of protection for electrical equipment in a sauna? (2) What is the minimum degree of protection if cleaning is by use of water jets?

4. Protection against electric shock

a. Protective measures not permitted

See Section 700.

b. Acceptable protective measures

Normally the protective measures used in rooms and cabins containing sauna heaters would be automatic disconnection of supply or extra-low voltage provided by SELV or PELV.

c. Automatic disconnection of supply

Where the protective measure automatic disconnection of supply is being used, additional protection is required for all circuits by the provision of one or more RCDs having the characteristics specified in Regulation 415.1.1.

d. SELV and PELV (for further information relating to protection by SELV and PELV see the section covering 414 of this Learning Guide)

Normally, no further measures are required for basic protection where the protective measure is SELV or PELV, provided specified conditions are met. However, where a room or cabin containing sauna heaters is being considered, basic protection is required in addition to the SELV or PELV system by either:

• barriers or enclosures affording a degree of protection of at least IPXXB or IP2X (for further information relating to IP codes see Part 2 and/or Section 410 of this Learning Guide)

• Basic insulation (complying with 416.1 of *BS 7671*)

5. Selection and erection of electrical equipment

a. External influences

As mentioned above, the main criteria for selection and erection of equipment is in relation to heat. However, there is a general requirement for all equipment in a room or cabin containing sauna heaters to have a minimum degree of protection of IPX4 and if cleaning is to take place using water jets the degree of protection should be IPX5.

b. Wiring systems

If at all possible wiring systems should be installed outside the zones (on the cold side of the thermal insulation). If the wiring system is installed on the warm side of the thermal insulation in zones 1 & 3 it must be heat resistant in line with the requirements of the related zone. Metallic sheaths and metallic conduits must not be accessible in normal use.

Fig 703.3 Inside of a sauna showing lighting

notes

Key Facts
'Check out the minimum temperatures for equipment and insulation and sheaths of cables in saunas'

notes

c. Switchgear and controlgear

Switchgear and controlgear which form part of the sauna heater equipment (or other fixed equipment) installed in zone 2, may be installed within the sauna room or cabin in accordance with manufacturers' instructions. Other switchgear and controlgear, e.g. for lighting, must be placed outside the sauna room or cabin.

Socket-outlets must not be installed within the location containing the sauna heater.

d. Current-using equipment

Sauna heating appliances should comply with *BS EN 60335-2-53* and be installed in line with the manufacturers' instructions.

> Further information relating to Section 703 Rooms and cabins containing sauna heaters can be found in:
> - *BS 7671* Section 703
> - Electrical Safety Council Technical Manual articles S205-49
> - IEE Guidance Note 7

SECTION 703 FINAL REVISION EXERCISE

703.1 The immediate area next to a sauna heater is classed as which of the following?
- ☐ a. Zone 0
- ☐ b. Zone 1
- ☐ c. Zone 2
- ☐ d. Zone 3

703.2 For installed electrical equipment in a room or cabin containing sauna heaters, where the use of water jets may not reasonably be expected, the degree of protection should be at least which of the following?
- ☐ a. IPX2
- ☐ b. IPX4
- ☐ c. IP4X
- ☐ d. IPX5

703.3 Which of the following protective measures is allowed in a room or cabin containing sauna heaters?
- ☐ a. non-conducting location
- ☐ b. placing out of reach
- ☐ c. automatic disconnection of supply
- ☐ d. earth-free local equipotential bonding

703.4 Zone 1 extends to which of the following distances from the sauna heater?
- ☐ a. 0.25 m
- ☐ b. 0.5 m
- ☐ c. 1.0 m
- ☐ d. 1.5 m

703.5 **Which of the following describes the heat requirements for equipment to be installed in Zone 2 of a sauna?**
☐ a. There are no special requirements
☐ b. Only the sauna heater
☐ c. Equipment belonging to the sauna heater
☐ d. Equipment that can withstand a minimum temperature of 125 °C

Things to do and find

1. What does the reference to IPX5 in Section 703 refer to?

2. What vertical height does Zone 2 extend to from the floor of a sauna?

3. Where can socket-outlets be fitted in a sauna?

4. In relation to wiring systems, what types of wiring system components should not be accessible in normal use?

5. Where, preferably, should wiring be installed?

1. Introduction

Section 704 of *BS 7671* provides information relating to the additional requirements in relation to construction and demolition sites. It should be noted that further information can also be found in the references located at the end of this article.

Construction and demolition sites are specified as a special location due to the additional risks of danger. Danger, in relation to the increasing risk of electric shock, may arise due to the adverse conditions including:

- Trailing cables
- The use of portable electric tools
- Many extraneous-conductive-parts that cannot, practically, be bonded
- Adverse weather conditions and incomplete structures
- Difficult working conditions.

As can be seen from the above points, careful consideration needs to be given to the design, construction and verification of electrical installations on construction and demolition site installations.

Fig 704.1 Typical construction site

2. Scope

The requirements of Section 704, covered in this topic, apply to temporary installations for construction and demolition sites during the period of construction or demolition.

Typical of the building and installations that are covered by Section 704 are:

- Construction work on new buildings
- Repair, alteration, extension, demolition of existing buildings or parts of buildings
- Engineering works
- Earthworks
- Work of similar nature

The requirements relate to all such work from small home improvements to large construction sites and whether the installations are fixed or movable.

The requirements of Section 704 do not relate to:

Section 704
Construction and demolition installations

- Open cast mines and quarries
- Site offices
- Cloakrooms
- Meeting rooms
- Canteens
- Dormitories
- Restaurant and toilets

The general requirements of Parts 1 to 6 of *BS 7671* apply in these cases.

3. Supplies and equipment

Section 704 includes requirements relating to the protective measures that should be used. In some cases restricted voltages are the preferred option for certain types of equipment used on construction and demolition site installations. Wiring systems and equipment also have specific external influence requirements due to the adverse conditions likely to be encountered.

4. Protective measures against electric shock

a. General requirements

The protective measures of obstacles and placing out of reach are not permitted.

Circuits supplying a socket-outlet with a rated current up to and including 32 A and any other circuit supplying hand-held electrical equipment with a rated current up to and including 32 A must be protected by one of the protective measures outlined in Table 704A below.

Table 704A (*Learning Guide Table*) Protective measures for construction site supplies (socket-outlets and hand-held equipment up to and including 32 A)

Protective measure	Additional condition
Reduced low voltage	Source and fault protection as required by Regulation Group 411.8
Automatic disconnection of supply	With additional protection provided by an RCD having the characteristics specified in Regulation 415.1.1
Electrical separation	Each socket-outlet and hand-held electrical equipment being supplied by an individual transformer or by a separate winding of a transformer
SELV or PELV	With basic protection provision by: • barriers or enclosures affording a degree of protection of at least IPXXB or IP2X or • Basic insulation (complying with 416.1 of *BS 7671*)

b. Protective measure: Automatic disconnection of supply

TN-C-S systems must not be used for construction site supplies, except for supplies to fixed buildings of the construction site. *BS 7671* does not prohibit the use of TN-S supplies to construction and demolition site installations.

notes

Where distributors do not provide an earthed supply (TN-C-S or TN-S) to a construction or demolition site installation, a TT system should be installed. On larger sites, TN-S systems are sometimes installed for parts of the installation in conjunction with TT earthing systems.

Any circuit supplying one or more socket-outlets with a rated current exceeding 32 A must be provided with protection by an RCD having a rated residual operating current not exceeding 500 mA.

The disconnection time for the RCD should be in line with Regulations 411.3.2.2 to 411.3.2.4. The alternative disconnection conditions provided in Regulations 411.3.2.5 (disconnection not required for electric shock) and 411.3.2.6 (supplementary equipotential bonding) are not applicable for construction and demolition site installations.

Reduced low voltage systems are often referred to as 110 volt systems. Because of the supply transformer configuration these systems limit the voltage to earth to 55 V for single-phase circuits and 63.5 V for three-phase circuits (for further information in relation to reduced low voltage systems see Section 411 (3j) of this Learning Guide).

Exercise 704.1

(1) Are construction site offices covered by the requirements of Section 704? (2) What is the voltage to earth of a single-phase reduced low voltage system?

---

5. Selection and erection of electrical equipment

a. Assemblies for distribution

Assemblies for the moveable electrical distribution system on construction and demolition site installations must comply with *BS EN 60439-4*. The term assemblies includes transforming or switching devices with associated control, measuring, signalling, protective and regulating equipment designed and built for use on construction sites.

Fig 704.2 Typical distribution unit for construction and demolition sites
(*BS EN 60439-4*)

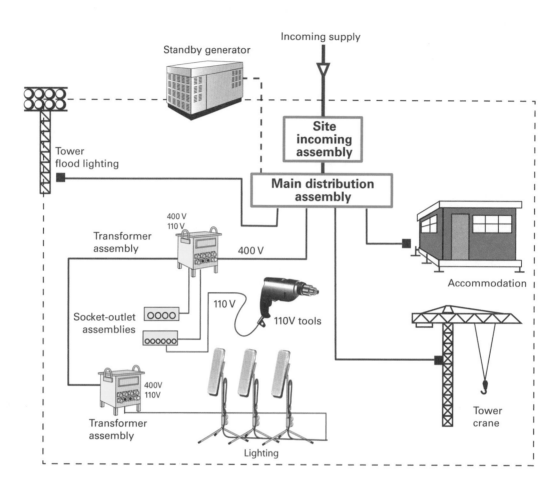

Fig 704.3 Typical electrical distribution on a large construction site

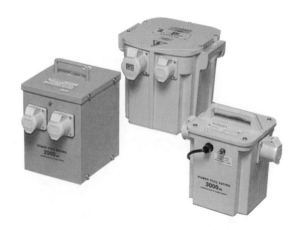

Fig 704.4 110 V output construction site transformers

For compliance, all cable couplers (a cable coupler consists of a connector (socket-outlet) and a plug) which are part of the moveable site electrical distribution system must be to *BS EN 60309-2.*

This standard specifies different plug and socket-outlet configurations relating to different voltages and the number of phases or required conductors. This is to help maintain compatibility between systems at the same time ensuring different systems are not interconnected.

Identification of the different supply voltages that could exist on the same site is also a requirement of *BS 7671* (Regulation 704.313.3). Different colour coded accessories relating to different voltages have been adopted in the UK as outlined in the following table.

Fig 704.5 Plugs, socket-outlets and cable couplers to *BS EN 60309-2*

Key Facts
'Mechanical protection of wiring systems and protection against a range of adverse conditions is essential on construction sites'

Table 704A (*Learning Guide Table*) Colour codes for supply voltages for plugs, socket-outlets and cable couplers to BS EN 60309-2 (within the UK)

Supply system voltage	Accessory colour
25 V	Violet
50 V	White
110 V	Yellow
230 V	Blue
400 V	Red

b. Wiring systems

Particular care should be taken when installing wiring systems and cables on construction and demolition site installations to ensure that adequate mechanical protection has been provided. Careful consideration also needs to be made in relation to external influences (See Part 2 and Section 522 of this Learning Guide). Regulation 704.522.8.11 prescribes specific requirements for flexible cables.

In line with colour co-ordination adopted for plugs and socket-outlets, cables supplying reduced low voltage circuitry are normally coloured yellow, although this is not a requirement of *BS 7671*.

c. Devices for isolation

Each Assembly for Construction Sites (ACS) must incorporate suitable devices for the switching and isolation of the incoming mains. For further information relating to ACSs see Regulation 704.537.2.2.

Exercise 704.2

(1) You should now refer to Regulation Group 704.52 to review the requirements in relation to cable selection and installation practices. (2) What is required in relation to securing of the incoming isolation device? (3) What three devices/accessories might you expect to see supplied by an ACS?

notes

Further information relating to Section 704 Construction and demolition site installations can be found in:

- *BS 7671* Section 704
- *BS 7375* Code of practice for distribution on construction and building sites
- Health & Safety Executive document HS (G) 141 Electrical Safety on Construction sites
- Electrical Safety Council 'Electrical safety in construction' download
- Electrical Safety Council Technical Manual articles S205-9, S205-13, S205-17, S205-21 and S205-25

SECTION 704 FINAL REVISION EXERCISE

704.1 Which of the following sites is not covered by Section 704?
- ☐ a. Construction work on new buildings
- ☐ b. Repair, alteration, extension, demolition of existing buildings or parts of buildings
- ☐ c. Surface mining
- ☐ d. Earthworks

704.2 Which of the following is the preferred electrical system for portable hand lamps in confined or damp locations?
- ☐ a. SELV
- ☐ b. 110 V centre point earthed reduced low voltage
- ☐ c. 110 V 3-phase, star point earthed
- ☐ d. 230 V, 1 phase

704.3 To which of the following should assemblies for the distribution of electricity on construction sites conform to?
- ☐ a. *BS EN 60309-2*
- ☐ b. *BS EN 60439-4*
- ☐ c. *BS EN 60947-3*
- ☐ d. *BS EN 60898*

704.4 To which of the following should plugs and socket-outlets used as part of the movable electrical installation on construction sites conform to?
- ☐ a. *BS EN 60309-2*
- ☐ b. *BS EN 60439-4*
- ☐ c. *BS EN 60947-3*
- ☐ d. *BS EN 60898*

704.5 Which of the following colours should be used for 110 V supplies on a construction site?
- ☐ a. yellow
- ☐ b. red
- ☐ c. blue
- ☐ d. violet

704.6 Where the protective measure, automatic disconnection of supply, is being provided, any circuit supplying one or more socket-outlets exceeding 32 A must be protected by an RCD with a rating not exceeding which of the following?

☐ 10 mA
☐ 30 mA
☐ 300 mA
☐ 500 mA

Things to do and find

1. Make a list of typical locations that are covered by Section 704.

2. What is the preferred voltage and related supply source for portable hand-held tools?

3. What type of earthing system might a distributor not provide on a construction site?

4. If the distributor does not provide an earth with the supply, what sort of earthing system would be employed?

5. What type of cable should be used for reduced low voltage systems

6. What type of wiring would you expect to see for fixed distribution cables on a construction site? (not specified in Section 704, but consider the requirements of *BS 7671* generally).

1. Introduction

Section 705 of *BS 7671* provides information relating to the additional requirements in relation to fixed electrical installations indoors and outdoors in agricultural and horticultural premises.

Agricultural and horticultural premises are specified as a special location due to the increased risk of electric shock because of the lower contact resistance of the body that is associated with, for example, wet hands, wet clothing and wet footwear, and because of the increased likelihood of contact with the general mass of Earth (i.e., the ground). Electric shocks in such conditions are more likely to cause serious injury or death than those where the conditions are dry and no contact is made directly with the general mass of Earth.

The risk of electric shock to livestock can often be greater than for people, because some livestock have a large exposed body area for contact with exposed-conductive-parts and/or extraneous-conductive-parts. Also the feet of livestock are likely to be in contact directly with the general mass of Earth, often in wet conditions.

Fig 705.1 Milking parlour

In addition to the particular risks in relation to electric shock, special precautions may also be required in relation to protection against fire due to the storage of flammable materials such a straw, hay and grain.

Finally, consideration should also be given to the risks of mechanical damage to electrical equipment by machinery, livestock and rodents.

Fig 705.2 Cable damage by mice

Section 705
Agricultural and horticultural premises

2. Scope

The requirements of Section 705, covered in this topic, apply to agricultural and horticultural premises.

Typical of the building and installations that are covered by Section 705 in relation to agricultural premises are:

- Stables
- Cattle sheds
- Milking parlours
- Barns
- Chicken-houses
- Piggeries
- Feed-processing locations
- Storage areas for hay, straw and fertilizers

And for horticultural premises:

- garden centres
- nurseries
- greenhouses

The requirements of Section 705 do not apply to:

- Rooms, locations and areas for household applications and similar. For example, dwellings intended solely for human habitation.
- Electric fence installations

Key Facts

'Special considerations need to be taken when livestock are being considered in relation to electrical installations'

3. Protective measures against electric shock

a. General

The selection of an earthing system for use in horticultural and agricultural premises should be considered carefully. *BS 7671* prohibits the use of TN-C supplies to horticultural and agricultural premises, although TN-C-S supplies may be installed. However, many Distributors may be reluctant to provide a protective multiple earthed (PME)* supply due to the difficulties in ensuring that the requirements for main equipotential bonding have been met within these types of premises. In locations intended for livestock, special considerations in relation to the earthing will be required due to the sensitivity of livestock to small voltages (potential differences) that can exist between conductive-parts (extraneous-conductive-parts or exposed-conductive-parts).

* Note: PME relates to the supply side of a TN-C-S earthing system (the TN-C part of the TN-C-S system).

Where Distributors do not provide an earthed supply (TN-C-S or TN-S) a TT system should be installed. Special attention will then be necessary in relation to the selection of RCDs to ensure discrimination in the event of an earth fault.

b. Protective measures not permitted

See Section 700 of this Learning Guide.

c. Acceptable protective measures

(i) Automatic disconnection of supply.

Where automatic disconnection of supply is the protective measure, all circuits will require residual current protection (RCD) as indicated in Table 705A. The requirements for RCD protection are required for protection against fire as well as helping to reduce the risk of serious injury from electric shock.

Table 705A (*Learning Guide Table*) RCD requirements for agricultural and horticultural installations

Type of circuit	Rated residual current IΔn
Final circuits supplying socket-outlets with rated current not exceeding 32 A	Not exceeding 30 mA
Final circuits supplying socket-outlets with rated current more than 32 A	Not exceeding 100 mA
All other circuits	Not exceeding 300 mA

(ii) SELV and PELV

SELV and PELV can be used with additional basic protection measures (see Section 700). In locations where a fire risk exists, more stringent requirements for barriers or enclosures are stipulated (see Regulation 705.422.8)

d. Supplementary equipotential bonding

In addition to RCD protection, supplementary equipotential bonding is required in locations intended for livestock. The supplementary bonding is required to connect all exposed-conductive-parts and extraneous-conductive-parts that can be touched by livestock. Where a metallic grid is laid in the floor, this should be included within the supplementary bonding system. Where a metal grid is not laid in the floor a TN-C-S supply is not recommended.

Protective bonding conductors must be protected against mechanical damage and corrosion as well as being selected to avoid electrolytic effects. Regulation 705.544.2 provides three suitable alternatives for use as protective bonding conductors.

Exercise 705.1

Refer to Regulations 705.415.3.2.1 and 705.544.2 to review the requirements in relation to supplementary equipotential bonding (including metallic grids). List the three options that may be used as protective bonding conductors.

Fig 705.3 shows typical requirements for supplementary bonding, including connections to the metal grid.

notes

1   Feedboxes and silos
2   Watering places, doors
3   Parts of steel construction
4   Foundation of earth electrode or main earth electrode
5   Animal boxes
6   Metallic grid
7   Trellised partitions made of steel
8   Protective conductors (PE/PEN)

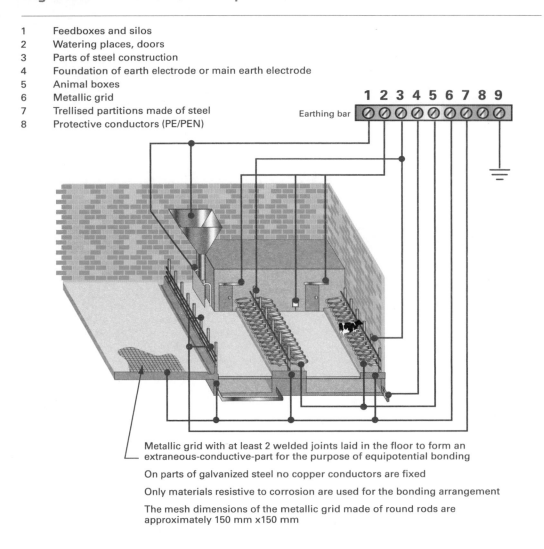

Earthing bar

Metallic grid with at least 2 welded joints laid in the floor to form an extraneous-conductive-part for the purpose of equipotential bonding

On parts of galvanized steel no copper conductors are fixed

Only materials resistive to corrosion are used for the bonding arrangement

The mesh dimensions of the metallic grid made of round rods are approximately 150 mm x150 mm

Fig 705.3 Example of supplementary bonding within a cattle shed

4. Protection against thermal effects

Care should be taking where heating appliances are used for breeding and rearing of livestock. An appropriate distance should be maintained between radiant heaters and livestock and/or combustible materials; a minimum distance of 0.5 m is required or such other clearance as recommended by the manufacturer.

For fire protection purposes, RCDs must be installed to:

• Have a maximum rated residual operating current of 300 mA,
• Disconnect all live conductors,
• Be of an S type or incorporate a time delay, where improved continuity of services is required (and not protecting socket-outlets).

5. Selection and erection of electrical equipment

Careful consideration needs to be given to all electrical equipment to be installed in agricultural and horticultural premises. Regulation Group 705.5 covers the selection and erection of electrical equipment and it provides extensive information. The following is a summary of some of the requirements:

• Equipment to have a minimum degree of protection of IP44 or if not available be placed in an enclosure with that protection
• Socket-outlets must be positioned so that they are unlikely to come in contact with combustible materials and must have appropriate mechanical protection.

- The effects of corrosion may need to be considered in some locations (cattle-sheds, dairies etc).
- Electrical equipment should be inaccessible to livestock or be adequately constructed and installed to avoid damage by livestock and to minimize the risk of injury.
- Detailed as-fitted plans and diagrams are required.
- Where overhead or underground cables are to be installed Regulation 705.522 should be consulted.
- Specific isolation and switching positioning and labelling is necessary.
- Standby supplies may be required.
- Luminaires should comply with *BS EN 60598* and selected in relation to the appropriate degree of protection.

Exercise 705.2

You should now refer to Regulation Group 705.5 to review the special requirements in relation to electrical equipment in agricultural and horticultural premises. What are the specific requirements relating to: (1) conduits and trunking and (2) types of socket-outlets (3) buried cables

5. Safety services

In installations where high density livestock rearing takes place it is often essential that supplies are maintained. Failure of supplies can result in serious loss of life when the provision of food, water, lighting, air or heating is not sustained. The initial design of these types of installation should carefully consider all operational factors that could affect the health of livestock. Standby electrical systems are normally required as well as separate circuitry for essential services. Temperature and voltage monitoring may also be required along with audible or visual warning systems.

Further information relating to agricultural and horticultural premises can be found in:
- *BS 7671* Section 705
- Electrical Safety Council Technical Manual articles S205-1, S205-2, S205-3 and S205-4
- IEE Guidance Note 7

SECTION 705 FINAL REVISION EXERCISE

705.1 **Which of the following locations is not covered by Section 705?**
- ☐ a. Stables
- ☐ b. Barns
- ☐ c. Farm houses
- ☐ d. Greenhouses

705.2 **When used under normal conditions, electrical equipment in agricultural or horticultural premises should have a minimum degree of protection of which of the following?**
- ☐ a. IPX2
- ☐ b. IP42
- ☐ c. IP44
- ☐ d. IPX4

notes

notes

705.3 For the protection of socket-outlets with a rated current of more than 32 A, an RCD is required with a rated residual operating current not exceeding which of the following?
- ☐ a. 30 mA
- ☐ b. 100 mA
- ☐ c. 300 mA
- ☐ d. 500 mA

705.4 The minimum recommended clearance distance for radiant heaters for use in locations for breeding and rearing of livestock, when manufacturers' information is not available is which of the following?
- ☐ a. 0.3 m
- ☐ b. 0.5 m
- ☐ c. 1.0 m
- ☐ d. 5.0 m

Things to do and find

1. Make a list of typical locations that are covered by Section 705

2. Outline the reasons why agricultural or horticultural premises are considered to be a special location

3. What are the additional requirements to protection against fire in agricultural or horticultural premises?

4. Why might a standby source be required in high density livestock rearing premises?

5. What are the requirements relating to electrical equipment and wiring systems in relation to their accessibility to livestock?

1. Introduction

A Restrictive conductive location is defined in *BS 7671* as *'A location comprised mainly of metallic or conductive surrounding parts, within which it is likely that a person will come into contact through a substantial portion of their body with the conductive surrounding parts and where the possibility of preventing this contact is limited.'*

Examples of what may constitute a restrictive conductive location are the interior of a large boiler, a metal storage tank or large diameter metal pipe, into which a person may have to enter to carry out inspection or maintenance.

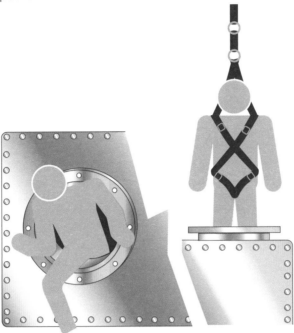

Fig 706.1 Examples of typical conductive locations with restricted movement

The risks associated with conductive locations with restricted movement are that people working in these locations may find it difficult to avoid coming into contact with the metal surroundings or to escape from such contact, due to the confined space.

2. Protection against electric shock

As can be imagined, the use of electrical equipment in restricted conducting locations should be limited to essential equipment. Normally, this will include handlamps and hand-held tools, although there may also be fixed equipment.

The protective measures that can be used are strictly limited as indicated below:

• For supplies to handlamps only SELV supplies are permissible. Additional requirements also apply for the provision of basic protection (irrespective of voltage) and restrictions may apply to the SELV source location

• For hand-held tools or an item of portable equipment, SELV or electrical separation are permissible, providing only one item of electrical equipment is connected to a secondary winding of the transformer

• For permitted protective measures for supplies to fixed equipment Regulation 706.410.3.10, item (iii) should be consulted.

notes

Exercise 706.1

You should now refer to Regulation 706.410.3.10 (iii) for further information relating to fixed supplies in conducting locations with restricted movement.

Further information relating to Conducting locations with restricted movement can be found in:
- *BS 7671* Section 706
- Electrical Safety Council Technical Manual articles S205-41
- IEE Guidance Note 7

SECTION 706 FINAL REVISION EXERCISE

706.1 **Which of the following protective measures are permitted for the supply to a handlamp in a conducting location with restricted movement?**
- ☐ a. SELV
- ☐ b. PELV
- ☐ c. Automatic Disconnection of Supply
- ☐ d. Electrical separation

706.2 **How many items of electrical equipment are allowed to be connected to the secondary winding of a transformer when the protection measure electrical separation is being used in a conducting location with restricted movement?**
- ☐ a. 1
- ☐ b. 2
- ☐ c. 4
- ☐ d. An unlimited number

Things to do and find

1. What are the requirements for basic protection in relation to SELV supplies in a conducting location with restricted movement?

2. What protective measure requires supplementary equipotential bonding when used in a conducting location with restricted movement?

3. Where should the source for SELV or PELV be situated where it is not part of the fixed installation within the conducting location with restricted movement?

4. Where Class II equipment is being used to supply fixed equipment within a conducting location with restricted movement, what additional protection is required?

1. Introduction

Section 708 outlines the requirements for caravan/camping parks and similar locations. These locations are designated as a special location due to the increasing risk of electric shock because of the lower contact resistance of the body that is associated with, for example, wet hands, wet clothing and wet footwear, and because of the increased likelihood of contact with the general mass of Earth (i.e., the ground). Electric shocks in such conditions are more likely to cause serious injury or death than those where the conditions are dry and no contact is made directly with the general mass of Earth. The selection of an appropriate earthing system is, therefore, imperative (see Item 3 below). There may also be issues relating to the frequent connection and disconnection of supplies by site visitors. Mechanical protection of cables is, therefore, a serious consideration (see Wiring systems (4b) below).

Fig 708.1 Caravan site

Key Facts
"Special considerations need to be given to earthing systems, protective measures and wiring systems on caravan sites'

2. Scope

Section 708 covers the electrical installations of caravan parks intended to provide supplies for caravans, motor caravans and certain other leisure accommodation vehicles or tents. The term *leisure accommodation vehicle* is defined in *BS 7671* as a: *'unit of living accommodation for temporary or seasonal occupation which may meet the requirements for construction and use of road vehicles'.*

This section does not cover the requirements for the internal electrical installation of caravans (see Section 721 of *BS 7671* and this Learning Guide) or to transportable units (see Section 717 of *BS 7671* and this Learning Guide) or to mobile homes and residential park homes to which the general requirements of *BS 7671* apply.

The electrical installations of permanent buildings on a caravan park, such as administrative buildings, shops and cafeterias, are not required to comply with the requirements of Section 708.

3. Protective measures against electric shock

a. General

The maximum nominal voltage for the supply of leisure accommodation vehicles is 230 V a.c. single-phase or 400 V a.c. three-phase.

The selection of an earthing system for use in caravan/camping parks and similar locations should be considered carefully. The Electricity Safety, Quality and Continuity Regulations 2002 prohibit distributors from connecting a PME* network to any metalwork in a caravan (or boat). *BS 7671* also prohibits any connection between a PME earthing terminal and caravan pitch socket-outlet protective conductors.

* Note: PME relates to the supply side of a TN-C-S earthing system (the TN-C part of the TN-C-S system).

Section 708
Electrical installations in caravan/camping parks and similar locations

Normally, caravan site distribution circuits should utilize a TT earthing system for caravan supplies. A TN-S earthing system, however, is not precluded. Both TN-C-S and TN-S earthing systems can be used for fixed installations on the site, although TN-C-S systems are not recommended for bath or shower blocks, unless there is a metal grid cast into the floor and connected to the equipotential bonding. Normally, a caravan site will be either TT in its entirety or there will be a separation between the TN-C-S or TN-S system and the caravan supply TT system.

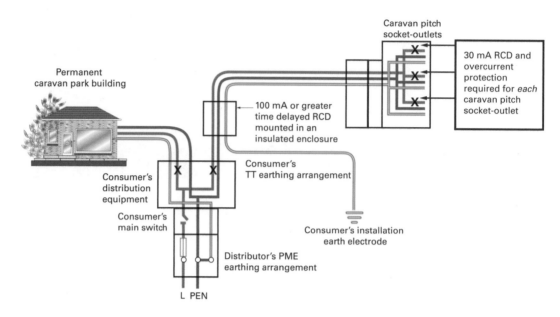

Fig 708.2 Separation of caravan pitch TT earthing arrangement from distributor's PME earthing facility at consumer's distribution position (typical arrangement)

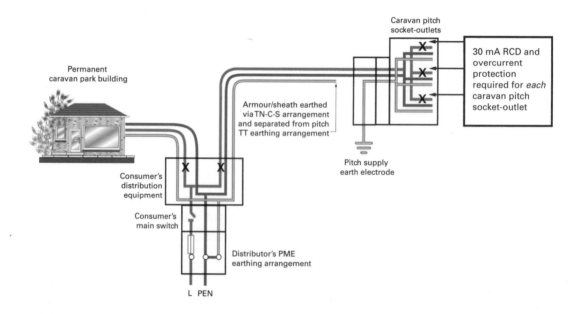

Fig 708.3 Separation of caravan pitch TT earthing arrangement from distributor's PME earthing facility at pitch supply position (typical arrangement)

b. Protective measures not permitted

See Section 700.

c. Acceptable protective measures

Automatic disconnection of supply would be the normal protection measure. Other protection methods are not precluded, but would be unlikely.

Every caravan pitch should have its own socket-outlet protected individually by an RCD with a rated residual operating current not exceeding 30 mA. The RCD should disconnect both line and neutral (i.e. double pole for single-phase or four pole for three-phase).

> **Exercise 708.1**
>
> (1) What type of supply is prohibited for supplies to caravans? (2) Can a TN-C-S supply be used for fixed installations on a caravan site? (3) If a TN-C-S supply is used for shower blocks what additional precautions should be taken?

4. Selection and erection of equipment

a. External influences

Electrical equipment installed outside in caravan parks should comply with the following minimum external influences requirements outlined in Table 704A below.

Table 704A (*Learning Guide Table*) Minimum external influence requirements for electrical equipment outside in caravan parks

External influence category		Minimum IP/IK rating
Presence of water	AD4 (Splashes)	IPX4
Presence of foreign solid bodies	AE2	IP3X
Mechanical stress	AG3	IK08

Note: Caravan pitch socket-outlets and enclosures require a minimum degree of protection of IP44.

b. Wiring systems in caravan parks

Cables supplying caravan pitches should preferably be underground.

Underground cables should be at least 0.6 m deep, and, unless additional mechanical protection is provided, be placed outside of caravan pitches, away from any surface where tent pegs or ground anchors are expected to be present.

Overhead conductors must be insulated and at a height above ground of not less than 6 m in all areas subject to vehicular movement (3.5 m in all other areas).

c. Caravan pitch electrical supply equipment

Caravan pitch supply equipment should be located adjacent to the pitch and not more than 20 m from the connection facility on the leisure accommodation vehicle or tent when on its pitch. To avoid supply cables crossing a pitch other than the one intended to be supplied it is recommended that not more than four socket-outlets are grouped in one supply/board.

d. Socket-outlets

The following table outlines the requirements for socket-outlets and enclosures forming part of caravan pitch electrical supply equipment.

Table 708A (*Learning Guide Table*)

1. Must comply with *BS EN 60309-2* with a degree of protection of at least IP44
2. Be mounted between 0.5 m and 1.5 m from the ground to the lowest part of the socket-outlet (where there are risks of flooding or heavy snowfall the maximum height may be exceeded)
3. Minimum current rating of socket-outlets to be 16 A
4. At least one socket-outlet for each caravan pitch
5. Each socket-outlet to be provided with individual overcurrent protection
6. Each socket-outlet to be protected individually by an RCD (rated residual operating current not exceeding 30 mA). The RCD must disconnect all poles (including the neutral).
7. Socket-outlet protective conductors must not be connected to any PEN conductor of the electricity supply. For a supply with a PEN conductor each socket-outlet must be connected to an earth electrode and meet the requirements of a TT system.

Fig 708.4 Pitch supply equipment

Fig 708.5 Pitch supply isolation and Circuit protective device equipment

Exercise 708.2

(1) You should now refer to Fig 708 in BS 7671 to review the special requirements in relation to a typical cord extension set. (2) How many caravan pitchs can be supplied from a socket-outlet? (3) For caravan pitch supplies how many socket-outlets can be supplied from a single overcurrent protective device? (4) For caravan pitch supplies how many socket-outlets can be supplied from a single RCD?

Further information relating to Electrical installations in caravan/camping parks and similar locations can be found in:
- *BS7671* Section 708
- Electrical Safety Council Technical Manual articles C5-77, E5-1, E5-5, E5-9, O61-5, R101-5, R101-19, S205-5, S205-6,
- IEE Guidance Note 7

SECTION 708 FINAL REVISION EXERCISE

708.1 Electrical equipment installed outside in caravan parks should comply with at least which of the following external influences?
- ☐ a. IP2X
- ☐ b. IP4X
- ☐ c. IP34
- ☐ d. IP43

708.2 Generally, the minimum and maximum heights for socket-outlets supplying caravan pitches is which of the following?
- ☐ a. 0.3 m and 1.0 m
- ☐ b. 0.5 m and 1.0 m
- ☐ c. 0.5 m and 1.5 m
- ☐ d. 0.6 m and 1.4 m

708.3 The minimum depth for burying an underground cable for a caravan distribution supply is which of the following?
- ☐ a. 0.3 m
- ☐ b. 0.45 m
- ☐ c. 0.5 m
- ☐ d. 0.6 m

708.4 The minimum height for an overhead line in an area where vehicle movement is expected is which of the following?
- ☐ a. 3.5 m
- ☐ b. 5.0 m
- ☐ c. 6.0 m
- ☐ d. 8.0 m

notes

708.5 The number of socket-outlets used to supply caravan pitches supplied from a single RCD is which of the following?
- ☐ a. 1
- ☐ b. 2
- ☐ c. 4
- ☐ d. 6

708.6 Which of the following is the maximum distance between caravan pitch supply equipment and the connection facility on the leisure accommodation vehicle or tent when on its pitch?
- ☐ a. 3.5 m
- ☐ b. 6 m
- ☐ c. 16 m
- ☐ d. 20 m

Things to do and find

1. What type of plugs and connectors should be used for a caravan cord extension set?

2. What is the maximum recommended length of a cord extension set for a caravan?

3. What type of earthing system would you normally expect to find connected to a caravan pitch socket-outlet?

4. What type of earthing system cannot be connected to caravan pitch socket-outlets?

5. What is the preferred method of wiring system for distribution circuits feeding caravan pitch electrical supply equipment?

1. Introduction

Section 709 of *BS 7671* provides information relating to the additional requirements in relation to circuits intended to supply pleasure craft or houseboats in marinas and similar locations.

Marinas and similar locations are specified as a special location due to the increased risk of electric shock because of the lower contact resistance of the body that is associated with, for example, wet hands, wet clothing and wet footwear, and because of the increased likelihood of contact with the general mass of Earth (i.e., the ground). Electric shocks in such conditions are more likely to cause serious injury or death than those where the conditions are dry and no contact is made directly with the general mass of Earth.

It should also be noted that the environmental conditions likely to be encountered in marinas will be very harsh. Mechanical protection of electrical equipment will be necessary due to the movement of jetties, pontoons and boats. Salt water can also seriously corrode equipment and consideration must be given to the effects of water splashes, water jets and waves. Consideration may also need to be given to the presence of flammable fuels and vapours. Electrolytic corrosion can also be a problem due to stray electric currents that can pass from the shore-side earthing systems to pleasure craft and house boats when they connect to the marina supply.

Finally, because of the mobile nature of the electrical installations being supplied, standardisation of power facilities is essential.

Fig 709.1 Marina

2. Scope

The requirements of Section 709, covered in this topic, apply to the electrical installations of marinas providing facilities for the supply of electricity to pleasure craft and houseboats.

> **Exercise 709.1**
>
> (1) You should now refer to Part 2 Definition and review the definition for a 'marina'

The requirements of Section 709 do not relate to:

- Offices, workshops and leisure accommodation which forms part of the marina complex
- Supplies to houseboats that are directly connected to the public network
- The internal electrical installations of pleasure craft or houseboats.

notes

3. Protective measures against electric shock

a. General

The maximum nominal voltage for the supply of a pleasure craft or a houseboat is 230 V a.c. single-phase or 400 V a.c. three-phase.

The selection of an earthing system used as part of a supply to pleasure craft or houseboats should be considered carefully. The Electricity Safety, Quality and Continuity Regulations 2002 prohibit distributors from connecting PME* networks to any metalwork in a boat.

* Note: PME (protective multiple earthing) relates to the supply side of a TN-C-S earthing system (the TN-C part of the TN-C-S system).

Normally, the supplies to pleasure craft and houseboats in marinas and similar locations should utilise a TT earthing system. A TN-S earthing system is, however, not precluded.

Both TN-C-S and TN-S earthing systems could also be used to supply an isolating transformer (complying with *BS EN 61558*). Where this system is employed, only one craft should be connected to each secondary winding. It is also important to note that the shore supply protective conductor must not be connected to the earthing and bonding arrangements of the pleasure craft. However, the earthing and bonding conductors of the pleasure craft must be connected to one of the isolating transformer's secondary winding terminals. This method has the advantage of reducing the possibility of electrolytic corrosion.

It is also worth noting that both TN-C-S and TN-S earthing systems can be used for fixed installations on the site, although TN-C-S systems are not recommended for bath or shower blocks, unless there is a metal grid cast into the floor and connected to the equipotential bonding.

To summarise, the main options for earthing systems are:

- a TT earthing system throughout the site *or*
- a TN-C-S or TN-S incoming earthing system to the site and a separated TT earthing system to supply the pleasure craft and/or houseboats *or*
- A TN-S earthing system throughout the site *or*
- A TN-C-S or TN-S earthing system and isolating transformers feeding the pleasure craft and/or house boats

Where Distributors do not provide an earthed supply (TN-C-S or TN-S), a TT system should be installed. Special attention will then be necessary in relation to the selection of RCDs to ensure discrimination in the event of an earth fault.

b. Protective measures not permitted

See Section 700.

c. Acceptable protective measures

(i) Automatic disconnection of supply.

Where automatic disconnection of supply is the protective measure, socket-outlets supplying pleasure craft and houseboats and all final circuits intended for fixed supplies to houseboats require an RCD having the characteristics specified in Regulation 415.1.1. RCDs must also be of a type that disconnects all poles (including the neutral).

Key Facts

'There are many external influences to be considered when designing, installing or inspecting electrical installations at marinas'

4. Selection and erection of electrical equipment

Careful consideration needs to be given to all electrical equipment to be installed on or above a jetty, wharf, pier or pontoon. Because of the extremely arduous conditions Section 709 outlines several requirements to be considered when choosing electrical equipment as indicated in the table below:

Table 709A (*Learning Guide Table*) Selection of equipment for use in marinas

External influence		Minimum IP Rating
Water splashes	AD4	IPX4
Water jets	AD5	IPX5
Water waves	AD6	IPX6
Ingress of small objects	AE2	IP3X
Corrosive or polluting substances, if hydrocarbons are present	AF2 AF3	
Impact (medium severity)	AG2	IK08

5. Wiring systems of marinas

Careful consideration should be given to the type of wiring system to be used for supplies to pleasure craft and houseboats. Apart from providing protection against mechanical damage they may also have to deal with constant flexing, corrosion and the presence of water. The effects of tidal and other movement must also be considered.

The following table (709B) outlines the wiring systems that are suitable for distribution circuits of marinas.

Table 709B (*Learning Guide Table*) Acceptable wiring systems for distribution circuits of marinas

1. Underground cables
2. Overhead cables or overhead insulated conductors
3. Cables with copper conductors and thermoplastic or elastomeric insulation and sheath installed within an appropriate management system
4. Mineral-insulated cables with a PVC protective covering
5. Cables with armouring and serving of thermoplastic or elastomeric material
6. Other cables and materials that are no less suitable than those listed above (1 to 5)

Onshore cables feeding boat distribution outlets should preferably be routed underground at a sufficient depth to avoid damage.

Overhead conductors must be insulated and at a height above ground of 6 m in all areas subject to vehicular movement (3.5 m in all other areas).

Cable management systems should incorporate drainage where relevant.

Section 709
Marinas and similar locations

Where the cable armouring is susceptible to corrosion a separate circuit protective conductor should be used.

The following table outlines the wiring systems that cannot be used on or above a jetty, wharf, pier or pontoon.

Table 709C (*Learning Guide Table*) Prohibited wiring systems

1. Cables in free air suspended from or incorporating a support wire
2. Non-sheathed cables in conduits, trunking etc
3. Cables with aluminium conductors
4. Mineral-insulated cables (without a PVC protective covering)

6. Distribution boards, feeder pillars and socket-outlets supplying pleasure craft and houseboats

Fig 709.2 Marina showing distribution equipment

a. Devices for protection against overcurrent

Each socket-outlet and fixed connection for a supply to a houseboat requires an individual overcurrent protective device.

b. Isolating and switching

At least one means of isolation is required in each distribution cabinet. The means of isolation must disconnect all live conductors (including the neutral) and be limited to isolating a maximum of four socket-outlets.

c. Socket-outlets

There are many requirements relating to the socket-outlets used to supply pleasure craft and houseboats. The table below (709D) outlines the requirements.

Table 709D (*Learning Guide Table*) Requirements for marina socket-outlets

1. One socket-outlet to supply only one pleasure craft or houseboat.

2. Socket-outlets to be mounted at least 1 m above the highest water level (300 mm on floating pontoons, providing additional measures are taken to protect against the effects of splashing).

3. Socket-outlets to comply with *BS EN 60309-1* (above 63 A) or *BS EN 60309-2* (below 63 A). – Colour coded and non-interchangeable for each rating and voltage. In general, single-phase socket-outlets with rated voltage 200 V – 250 V and rated current 16 A should be provided.

4. Socket-outlets to be at least IP44 (see table 709A above where higher codes may be applicable).

5. Every socket-outlet should be located as close as practicable to the berth to be supplied.

6. Socket-outlets to be installed in a distribution board (cabinet) or separate enclosure.

7. To avoid hazards due to long connection cords, the maximum number of socket-outlets grouped together in one enclosure should be limited to four.

8. It is recommended that an instruction label is placed adjacent to each group of socket-outlets.

Fig 709.3 Marina distribution cabinet

Exercise 709.2

(1) You should now refer to Section 709 (Fig 709.3) to review the special requirements in relation to instructions for electricity supply for pleasure craft operators.

Further information relating to marinas and similar locations can be found in:
- Section 709 of *BS 7671*
- IEE Guidance Note 7

SECTION 709 FINAL REVISION EXERCISE

709.1 Electrical equipment installed on or above a jetty, wharf, pier or pontoon must comply with a minimum degree of protection for external mechanical impact of which of the following?
- ☐ a. IK 02
- ☐ b. IK 04
- ☐ c. IK 06
- ☐ d. IK 08

709.2 Electrical equipment installed on or above a jetty, wharf, pier or pontoon must comply with a minimum degree of protection for water·jets to which of the following?
- ☐ a. IPX2
- ☐ b. IPX4
- ☐ c. IPX5
- ☐ d. IPX6

709.3 Which of the following earthing systems is not allowed to be used as part of the supply to a pleasure craft or houseboat?
- ☐ a. TT
- ☐ b. TN-S
- ☐ c. TN-C-S
- ☐ d. TN-C-S or TN-S with the supply to the boat via an isolating transformer

709.4 Which of the following are the correct standards for socket-outlets for use on marinas?
- ☐ a. *BS EN 60309-1* and *BS EN 60309-2*
- ☐ b. *BS EN 60742-1* and *BS EN 60742-2*
- ☐ c. *BS EN 60309-2* and *BS EN 60309-3*
- ☐ d. *BS EN 60898* and *BS EN 61009*

709.5 When not erected on a floating pontoon or walkway, a marina socket-outlet must be placed at a height of not less than which of the following?
- ☐ a. 300 mm above the highest water level
- ☐ b. 500 mm above the highest water level
- ☐ c. 600 mm above the highest water level
- ☐ d. 1.0 m above the highest water level

Things to do and find

1. Outline the reasons why a marina is considered to be a special location.

2. Which set of Regulations prohibit distributors from offering connections to earthing terminals from PME networks for consumers' installations in caravans and boats?

3. What type of earthing system does a PME network form a part of?

4. What are the four categories of external influence listed in Section 709?

5. What type of mineral-insulated cable can be used for distribution circuits on marinas?

6. What type of conductor material cannot be used for wiring systems on or above a jetty, wharf, pier or pontoon?

7. What are the two methods suggested in Section 709 to allow the drainage of water from cable management systems?

8. What is the maximum rated residual operating current required for protection of socket-outlets on marinas?

9. What is the maximum rated residual operating current required for protection of final circuits intended for the fixed connection of a houseboat?

10. How many poles of an RCD, required for protection of socket-outlets on marinas, should be disconnected when it operates?

11. What is the maximum number of socket-outlets that can be grouped in an enclosure used to supply pleasure craft and houseboats?

1. Introduction

Section 711 of *BS 7671* provides information relating to the additional requirements in relation to temporary electrical installations in exhibitions, shows and stands.

Temporary electrical installations in exhibitions, shows and stands are specified as a special location due to the temporary nature of the installation, the lack of permanent structures, severe mechanical stresses, increased risk of electric shock, fire and burns and access to these installations by the general public.

2. Scope

Typical of the types of installations that are covered by Section 711 are:

• Exhibitions
• Trade fairs
• Outdoor shows
• Temporary entertainment venues
• Kiosks
• Outdoor fast food outlets.

The requirements of Section 711 do not apply to:

• The fixed electrical installation of the buildings where exhibitions, shows or stands may take place
• Electrical systems as defined in *BS 7909* used in structures, sets, mobile units etc as used for public or private events, touring show, theatrical, radio, TV or film productions and similar activities of the entertainment industry
• Unless specifically stated, exhibits for which requirements are given in the relevant standards.

3. Protective measures against electric shock

a. General

The maximum nominal voltage of a temporary electrical installation in an exhibition, show or stand is 230 V a.c. single-phase, 400 V a.c. three-phase or 500 V d.c.

Because of the practical difficulties ensuring protective equipotential bonding of all extraneous-conductive-parts, TN-C and TN-C-S systems are prohibited in installations covered by Section 711. That leaves two main alternative earthing systems, TT and TN-S. TT supplies are most likely to be used for outdoor exhibitions, shows and stands and a TT system is perfectly acceptable for inside supplies. A TN-S system can also be used outside or inside. The earthing system available within buildings housing exhibitions and stands will depend on the distributor's provision and could well be TN-S or TN-C-S. If it is TN-C-S this could create additional work trying to segregate the fixed installation earthing system from the exhibition/stand wiring supplies.

RCD protection is required for earth fault protection at the origin of the supply cable feeding a temporary structure, irrespective of the protective measure used. For automatic disconnection of supply, 30 mA protection is also required, as indicated in Table 711A below.

Section 711
Exhibitions, shows and stands

Table 711 A (*Learning Guide Table*)RCD requirements for exhibitions, shows and stands

Type of circuit	Maximum rated residual current IΔn
At the origin of a cable intended to supply a temporary structure	300 mA incorporating time delay to provide discrimination with final circuit RCDs (*BS EN 60947-2* or S-type to *BS EN 61008-1* or *BS EN 61009-1*)
Where the protective measure is automatic disconnection of supply	
Each socket-outlet circuit rated current up to 32 A	30 mA
All final circuits (other than those supplying emergency lighting)	30 mA

b. Protective measures not permitted

See Section 700 of this Learning Guide.

c. Acceptable protective measures

(i) Automatic disconnection of supply

Where automatic disconnection of supply is the protective measure, circuits will require residual current protection (RCD) as indicated in Table 711.A above. RCD protection is required to help prevent electrical fires as well as reduce the risk of serious electric shocks.

In addition to RCD protection, protective equipotential bonding is required between structural metallic parts that are accessible from within a stand, vehicle, wagon, caravan or container and the earthing terminal within the unit.

(ii) SELV and PELV can be used with additional basic protection measures (see Section 700 of this Learning Guide).

4. Protection against thermal effects

Consideration must be given to the increased risk of fire and burns and Chapter 42 of *BS 7671* or this Learning Guide should be referred to for further guidance.

Exercise 711.1

(1) You should now refer to Chapter 42 Protection against thermal effects including Section 422 to review the precautions that are required where particular risks of fire exist.

Particular attention should be given to the choice of lighting equipment and locations for installation. The construction material of showcases and signs should have adequate heat resistance, mechanical strength and electrical insulation. Because of the concentration of heat that may be present adequate ventilation will also be required.

Regulation Group 711.559 provides more specific information relating to luminaires and lighting installations.

5. Selection and erection of electrical equipment

a. General

Switchgear and controlgear should be placed in closed cabinets only accessible by the use of a key or a tool unless designed and intended to be operated by ordinary persons.

Every separate temporary structure intended to be occupied by one specific user and each distribution circuit supplying outdoor installations must be provided with its own readily accessible and identifiable means of isolation.

Fig 711.3 Isolator with label indicating location of separate temporary structure

b. Wiring systems

Cables used to supply exhibitions, shows and stands should be armoured or protected against mechanical damage where required. Only copper conductors are acceptable and the minimum cross-sectional area should be 1.5 mm^2.

Flexible cords must not be laid in areas accessible to the public unless they are protected against mechanical damage.

Special conditions apply to the selection of wiring systems in buildings where there is no fire alarm.

Joints should only be made when necessary as a connection into a circuit, and where joints are made, a degree of protection of at least IP4X or IPXXD is required.

Where strain can be transmitted to terminals, the connection must incorporate a suitable cable anchorage.

Section 711
Exhibitions, shows and stands

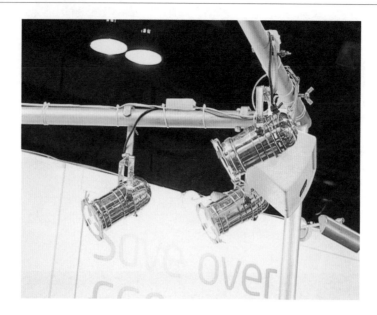

Fig 711.4 Stand wiring

c. Other equipment

Specific requirements are provided in Regulation Group 711.55 in relation to electric motors and ELV transformers and electronic converters.

An adequate number of socket-outlets should be installed, and where they are floor-mounted they require adequate protection from accidental ingress of water and sufficient strength to be able to withstand the expected traffic load.

6. Inspection and testing

All temporary electrical installations of exhibitions, shows and stands are required to be inspected, tested and certified in line with Chapter 61 of *BS 7671* after each assembly on site.

Further information relating to Exhibitions, shows and stands can be found in:
- *BS 7671* Section 711
- IEE Guidance Note 7

SECTION 711 FINAL REVISION EXERCISE

711.1 Which of the following is the maximum rated residual operating current of an RCD required at the origin of a cable intended to supply temporary structures in exhibitions, shows or stands?
- ☐ a. 30 mA
- ☐ b. 100 mA
- ☐ c. 300 mA
- ☐ d. 500 mA

711.2 Which of the following is the minimum cross-sectional area of a conductor used as part of a wiring system in an exhibition, show or stand?
- ☐ a. 1.0 mm²
- ☐ b. 1.5 mm²
- ☐ c. 2.5 mm²
- ☐ d. 4.0 mm²

Things to do and find

1. Make a list of typical locations that are covered by Section 711.

2. Outline the reasons why temporary electrical installation in exhibitions, shows and stands are considered to be a special location.

3. What are the additional requirements when installing a floor mounted socket-outlet in accordance with Section 711?

4. What are the conditions for use in relation to insulation *piercing* lampholders?

5. Why might adequate ventilation be a requirement for stand installations?

Section 712
Solar photovoltaic (PV) power supply systems

1. Introduction

Section 712 of *BS 7671* covers the requirements relating to solar photovoltaic (PV) power supply systems including systems with a.c. modules. The requirements relate to systems that are intended to operate in parallel with public low voltage distribution networks.

Persons intending to design or install a PV power supply system should consult the manufacturers' guidance in the first instance.

In addition to the requirements of Section 712 of *BS 7671*, installers should also consult the Electricity Safety, Quality and Continuity Regulations 2002 (ESQCR), as PV power supplies are classed within the definition 'embedded generators'.

However, if the output of the PV power supply and any other microgeneration systems connected to the same electrical installation does not exceed 16 A per phase at 230 V a.c., and the conditions listed below are also met, these systems are exempt from the requirements of the ESQCR:

- The system has protection which will disconnect it from the distributor's network automatically in the event of a local fault on that network
- The consumer's installation complies with the current edition of *BS 7671*
- The installer notifies the distributor before or at the time of commissioning the microgenerator. Otherwise, reverse power transfer may occur through the distributor's energy meter, which may damage it or lead the distributor to believe energy is being stolen from the network.

Nevertheless, installations will need to meet the requirements of the Energy Networks Association's Engineering Recommendation G83/1 Recommendations for the connection of small scale embedded generators (up to 16 A per phase) in parallel with public low-voltage distribution networks.

For installations generating a total of over 16 A per phase, Engineering Recommendation G59/1 Recommendations for the connection of embedded generating plant to the regional electricity companies' distribution systems should be followed and approval from the Distributor will be required prior to works commencing.

Fig 712.1 Photovoltaic (PV) cells on dwelling roof

Section 712
Solar photovoltaic (PV) power supply systems

Because of the specialist nature of this subject the following text is not intended to cover the subject fully, but to identify the relevant sections in *BS 7671* and outline some key issues.

2. Scope

The requirements of Section 712, covered in this topic, apply to solar photovoltaic (PV) power supply systems operating in parallel with public low voltage distribution networks. The requirements of Section 712 do not relate to PV systems that are intended for stand-alone operation.

Key Facts
'Unless you are experienced further reading is recommended prior to installing PV systems'

3. Special risks associated with solar photovoltaic (PV) power supply systems

Solar photovoltaic (PV) power supply systems are specified as a special installation in *BS 7671* because:

- Electrical installations fitted with PV power supplies have two sources of supply and both sources need to be considered when any work on related circuitry is being carried out (Isolation procedures in particular need to be considered carefully)
- Additional labeling is required to warn occupiers and operatives working on the system that two sources may be supplying the electrical installation
- Photovoltaic cells will produce an output whenever they are exposed to light and additional precautions may be required to prevent danger such as electric shock and burns. Photovoltaic cells should be considered to have an output at all times.
- All installed electrical equipment must be fit for purpose and manufacturer's instructions strictly adhered to.
- Compliance with the relevant requirements of ESQCR must be met.

4. General arrangements for PV systems

The following illustration shows the basic layout of a PV system. Electricity is generated by the PV cells, normally mounted on the roof. The PV array or cells produce direct current, so this needs to be fed via a convertor so that the PV source can be connected in parallel with the alternating current mains supply. As well as the conversion from d.c. to a.c. the two sources need to be synchronized to ensure the two a.c. supplies are in phase, prior to the two supplies being paralleled. Any synchronizing system should be automatic and of a type that considers frequency, phase and voltage magnitude. The electrical equipment that ensures synchronization conditions are met is usually provided within the convertor equipment.

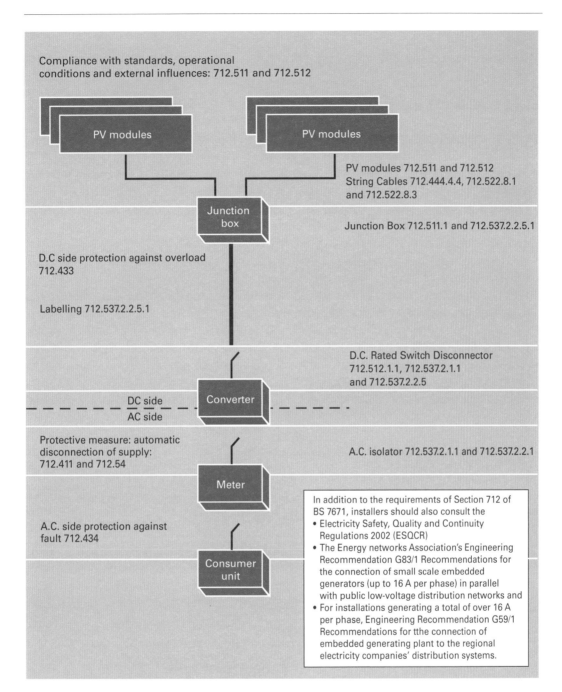

Fig 712.2 Basic layout of a PV system

5. Protection for safety

a. Protective measures not permitted

See Section 700 of this Learning Guide.

b. Acceptable protective measures

(i) Automatic disconnection of supply.

Where automatic disconnection of supply is the protective measure, the required protection on the a.c. side will depend upon the type of device (convertor) used between the d.c. side and a.c. side of the system. RCD protection (Type B to IEC 60755 or Type A to *BS EN 61008* or *BS 61009*) may be required.

Section 712
Solar photovoltaic (PV) power supply systems

(ii) Double or reinforced insulation

Protection by use of Class II or equivalent insulation is the preferred option on the d.c. side.

6. PV module and d.c. side supply requirements

The following are some of the requirements relating to the PV module and d.c. supply side:

- PV modules and PV array junction boxes must comply with the relevant equipment standard (See Regulation 712.511).
- Overload protection may be omitted to PV string and PV array cables on the d.c. side, providing certain conditions relating to cable current-carrying capacity and short-circuit current levels are met.
- PV string cables, PV array cables and PV d.c. main cables must be selected and erected to minimize the risk of earth faults and short-circuits.
- Wiring systems should be selected with consideration being given to any expected external influences, for example wind, ice and solar radiation.
- Consideration needs to be made in relation to segregation between d.c. and a.c. wiring systems, for example where cables in different voltage bands run through roof spaces.
- A switch disconnector must be fitted on the d.c. side of the converter. This device must be designed for d.c. switching operations.
- All junction boxes must be fitted with warning notices to indicate that the parts inside may remain live after isolation of the PV convertor

7. PV convertor requirements

Means of isolating the PV convertor from both a.c. and d.c. sides of the system must be provided to allow maintenance to be carried out safely.

Convertors must carry a Type Test certificate to the requirements of Engineering Recommendation G83/1 or comply with all other parts of that document unless specifically agreed by the Distributor in writing. A key element of the requirements of G83/1 is that the converter must disconnect the PV system supply from the distributor's network automatically in the event of a local fault on that network.

Fig 712.3 Converter with a.c. and d.c. isolation

8. A.C supply side requirements

An isolator will be required on the mains side (a.c.) of the convertor.

The a.c. circuitry from the convertor has to feed onto the existing mains and careful consideration needs to be given as to where this connection is made. There are two options, either connection by means of a dedicated circuit or connection into an existing final circuit. A dedicated circuit is preferable, but in either case there are several issues to be considered and further investigation in each case will be required.

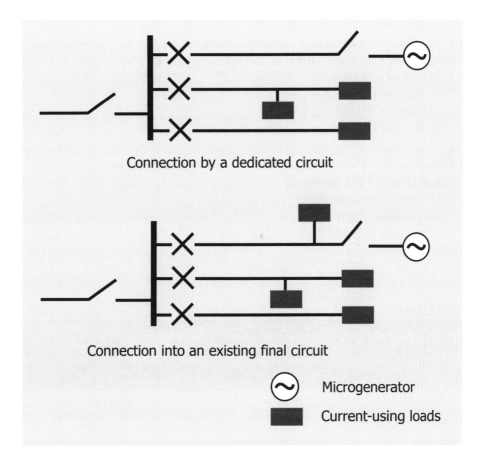

Connection by a dedicated circuit

Connection into an existing final circuit

Microgenerator

Current-using loads

Fig 712.4 Connection arrangements

Further information relating to Solar photovoltaic (PV) power supply systems can be found in:
- *BS 7671* Section 712
- IEE Guidance Note 7
- Electrical Safety Council Best Practice Guide, Connecting a microgeneration system to a domestic or similar electrical installation
- DTI Guide, Photovoltaics in Buildings. Guide to the installation of PV systems

Section 712
Solar photovoltaic (PV) power supply systems

SECTION 712 FINAL REVISION EXERCISE

712.1 Where an electrical installation includes a PV power supply system, without at least simple separation between the a.c. side and d.c. side, which of the following types of RCD is required? (by Regulation 712.411.3.2.1.2)
- ☐ a. Type A
- ☐ b. Type AC
- ☐ c. Type B
- ☐ d. Type S

712.2 In relation to isolation at a convertor, installed as part of a photovoltaic power supply system, which of the following is true? An isolation device is:
- ☐ a. Not required at all
- ☐ b. Required on the d.c. side
- ☐ c. Required on the a.c. side
- ☐ d. Required on both the a.c. and d.c. side

712.3 Wiring loops in PV systems should be kept as short as possible to reduce the risk of which of the following?
- ☐ a. Excessive overcurrent
- ☐ b. Excessive earth faults
- ☐ c. Induced voltages
- ☐ d. Induced currents

Things to do and find

1. Make a list of typical external influences that may need to be considered in relation to PV systems on the d.c. side.

2. Overload protection on the d.c. side may be omitted to PV string and PV array cables providing the continuous current carrying capacity of the cable is how much greater than $I_{sc\ STC}$ (the short-circuit current under standard test conditions)?

3. What consideration must be given to the isolating device on the d.c. side of the converter?

4. In a PV system, where should warning labels be fitted to indicate that live parts may be present?

1. Introduction

Section 717 of *BS 7671* provides information relating to the additional requirements in relation to mobile or transportable units. In Section 717 the term *unit* is intended to mean a vehicle and/or mobile or transportable structure in which all or part of an electrical installation is contained, which is provided with a temporary supply by means of a plug and socket. These units will be typically of two types:

• Mobile (vehicles, self-propelled or towed)
• Transportable (containers or cabins)

Temporary electrical installations providing supplies to mobile or transportable units are specified as a special location due to:

• the temporary nature of the installation
• the risks associated with repeated connection of the units and the possible affect on connections and cables
• the risks associated with different connection facilities and earthing arrangements
• difficulties establishing an equipotential zone
• vibration problems due to trailer or vehicular movement.

2. Scope

Typical of the industries that may employ mobile or transportable units (covered by Section 717) are:

• Entertainments
• Medical
• Advertising
• Fire fighting
• Industry (workshops)
• Commerce (offices)
• Catering

The requirements of Section 717 do not apply to special installations or locations covered by other sections within Part 7 of *BS 7671* or where the installations are outside the remit of *BS 7671*. Section 717, therefore, does not apply to generator sets, marinas and pleasure craft, caravans, Mobile machinery in accordance with *IEC 60204-1 Safety of machinery. Electrical equipment of machines. General requirements, traction equipment of electric vehicles* or electrical equipment required by a vehicle to allow it to be driven safely or used on the highway.

notes

Fig 717.1 Typical mobile unit

3. Protective measures against electric shock

a. General

Because of the practical difficulties ensuring protective bonding of all extraneous-conductive-parts, TN-C-S systems are prohibited unless the installation is continuously under the supervision of a skilled or instructed person and the suitability and effectiveness of the means of earthing has been confirmed prior to connection of the unit.

RCD protection is required for every socket-outlet intended to supply current-using equipment outside the unit, unless the socket-outlets are protected by SELV, PELV or electrical separation.

b. Protective measures not permitted

See Section 700 of this Learning Guide.

c. Acceptable protective measures

(i) Automatic disconnection of supply.

Where automatic disconnection of supply is the protective measure, circuits will require protection by means of an RCD.

In addition to RCD protection, protective equipotential bonding is required between accessible conductive parts of the unit, such as the chassis, to the main earthing terminal within the unit. The main protective bonding conductors should be finely stranded.

(ii) IT systems

IT systems are earthing systems where the earth is connected through either a source impedance, there is no source earth at all or the source earth is not used.

Protection is effected by monitoring and automatic disconnection and these functions are facilitated within the units. Different options are provided in *BS 7671*, all with strict requirements. These systems will normally be installed by the person responsible for the internal wiring within the unit (see 4a 'Identification' below). It is important that electrical operatives employed to connect up mobile and transportable units are aware of typical requirements in relation to temporary site supplies to these units.

> **Exercise 717.1**
>
> (1) You should now refer to regulation 717.411.6.2 to review the requirements for IT earthing systems in mobile or transportable units. What are the three sources of supply that are allowed for an IT system?

4. Selection and erection of electrical equipment

a. Identification

It is important that operatives on site are aware of the internal wiring systems and protective measures of units to be connected. A permanent notice of durable material must be fixed in each unit in a prominent position, preferably adjacent to the supply inlet connector (see Fig 717.2 for a typical notice). The notice should clearly indicate:

- The type of supply that may be connected to the unit
- The voltage rating
- The number of phases and their configuration
- The on-board earthing arrangement
- The maximum power requirement

MEDICAM-STAT MOBILE UNIT 8

The type of supply suitable for connection to this unit is: TN-S or TT.
(Note: An earth electrode must be fitted for a TT earthing system).
The voltage rating is 230 V single-phase (50 Hz).
The on-board earthing arrangement is protective earthing and protective bonding with automatic disconnection being provided by a 30 mA RCD
(in compliance with Regulation 415.1.1).
The maximum power requirement is 7 kW (32 A at 230 V).

Fig 717.2 Typical label outlining the connection requirements for mobile and transportable units.

b. Wiring systems

The cables connecting the unit to the supply must be flexible, made of copper, have a minimum cross-sectional area of 2.5 mm^2 and enter the unit by an insulating inlet.

The cables to be used for the internal wiring of the unit should be thermoplastic or thermosetting insulated only cables installed in conduits. Thermoplastic or thermosetting insulated and sheathed cables can be installed provided precautionary measures are taken to avoid mechanical damage likely to occur due to any sharp-edged parts or abrasion.

Section 717
Mobile or transportable units

c. Connectors

Connectors (plugs and socket-outlets) used to connect to units must be in compliance with *BS EN 60309-2 Plugs, socket-outlets and couplers for industrial purposes – Dimensional interchangeability requirements for pin and contact-tube accessories.*

Plugs must be made of insulating material and the plug part situated on the unit. Appliance inlets with their enclosures and plugs and socket-outlets (if located outside) must afford a degree of protection of IP44.

Fig 711.3 Connection of mobile/transportable unit

Further information relating to mobile and transportable units can be found in:
- Section 717 of *BS 7671*
- IEE Guidance Note 7

SECTION 717 FINAL REVISION EXERCISE

717.1 A permanent durable label is required on every mobile or transportable unit to provide information for the electrical operative connecting up the unit on site. Which of the following items is not required on the label?
- ☐ a. voltage rating
- ☐ b. number of phases
- ☐ c. earth loop impedance
- ☐ d. on-board earthing arrangement

717.2 The minimum cross-sectional area of a conductor used for connecting a mobile or transportable unit to the supply is which of the following?
- ☐ a. 1.0 mm²
- ☐ b. 1.5 mm²
- ☐ c. 2.5 mm²
- ☐ d. 4.0 mm²

717.3 In relation to supplies to mobile or transportable units, which of the following protection measures requires additional protection by an RCD with a rated residual operating current not exceeding 30 mA?
- ☐ a. Automatic disconnection of supply
- ☐ b. Electrical separation
- ☐ c. SELV
- ☐ d. PELV

717.4 Which of the following IP ratings is the minimum for a socket-outlet located outside a mobile or transportable unit?
- ☐ a. IP2X
- ☐ b. IP34
- ☐ c. IP44
- ☐ d. IP56

Things to do and find

1. Make a list of typical examples of mobile or transportable units.

2. What is the major difference between a mobile and a transportable unit?

3. What are the requirements in relation to plugs and socket-outlets used to connect mobile or transportable units?

4. What are the specific requirements relating to wiring systems in gas cylinder storage compartments in mobile or transportable units?

1. Introduction

Section 721 of *BS 7671* provides information relating to the electrical installations of caravans and motor caravans. Caravans are regarded by *BS 7671* as being locations of increased electric shock risk. This is because their electrical installations are exposed to arduous conditions, and persons using them are liable to be minimally clothed and/or exposed to wetness from, for example, wet weather or perspiration, and when outside the caravan may be in contact directly with the general mass of Earth. Additional considerations are also necessary due to the likelihood of frequent road movement and the associated risk of vibration, as well as potential problems relating to frequent connection and disconnection of supplies.

Photograph Courtesy of J Bradley

Fig 721.1 Touring caravan

2. Scope

The requirements of this section relate to the electrical circuits and equipment intended for the use of the caravan for habitation purposes.

Exercise 721.1

(1) You should now refer to Part 2 Definition and review the definitions for a caravan and motor caravan.

The requirements of Section 721 do not relate to:

• Electrical installations in caravan/camping parks and similar locations (covered by Section 708 of *BS 7671* and this Learning Guide)
• Electrical circuits and equipment for automotive purposes
• Mobile homes, residential park homes or transportable units
• Extra-low voltage installations (12 V d.c.) in caravans or motor caravans (covered by *BS EN 1648-1* and *BS EN 1648-2*)

Note: Annex A of Section 721 of *BS 7671* gives guidance on extra-low voltage d.c installations, but this is not covered in this section of this Learning Guide.

3. Protective measures against electric shock

a. General

The maximum nominal voltage for the supply to a caravan or motor caravan is 230 V a.c. single-phase, 400 V a.c. three-phase and/or 48 V d.c.

Section 721
Electrical installations in caravans and motor caravans

The selection of an earthing system used as part of a supply to a caravan or motor caravan should be considered carefully. The Electricity Safety, Quality and Continuity Regulations 2002 prohibit distributors from connecting a PME network to any metalwork in a caravan. *BS 7671* also prohibits any connection between a PME earthing terminal and caravan pitch socket-outlet protective conductors.

Key Facts
Don't get confused between caravan internal wiring (Section 721) and caravan site wiring (Section 708)

Note: PME (protective multiple earthing) relates to the supply side of a TN-C-S earthing system (the TN-C part of the TN-C-S system).

Normally, the caravan site distribution circuits will utilise a TT earthing system for caravan supplies. However, a TN-S earthing system is not precluded.

Within the caravan, circuit protective conductors must be either incorporated in a multicore cable with the live conductors or in a conduit together with the live conductors.

b. Protective measures not permitted

See Section 700 of this Learning Guide.

c. Acceptable protective measures

(i) Automatic disconnection of supply.

Where automatic disconnection of supply is the protective measure, caravan and motor caravan electrical installations require an RCD having a rated residual current not exceeding 30 mA. RCDs must be of a type that disconnects all live conductors (including the neutral). The RCD will normally also be the consumer unit main switch.

Main equipotential bonding (minimum CSA of 6 mm^2) is required from the main earthing terminal to structural metallic parts (such as the chassis) which are accessible from within the caravan.

(ii) Electrical separation

This protective measure can only be used for shaver socket-outlets.

(iii) SELV or PELV

Extra-low voltage systems must be SELV or PELV. The following nominal voltages are applicable: for d.c. : 12 V, 24 V and 48 V. and for a.c.: 12 V, 24 V, 42 V and 48 V.

4. Protection against overcurrent

Each final circuit requires an overcurrent protective device that disconnects all live conductors (double-pole for single-phase circuits).

5. Selection and erection of electrical equipment

a. General

Regulation Group 721.5 of *BS 7671* includes numerous regulations relating to the selection and installation of wiring, accessories and instructions for the user. Normally, caravans are wired in factories and delivered to site.

Therefore, it is unusual for electricians to become involved in the wiring of caravans, apart from alterations and additions and periodic inspection and testing. The following, therefore is only a brief summary of the requirements for the internal electrical installation.

b. Caravan internal wiring systems

Table 721A (*Learning Guide Table*) Main points to note in relation to caravan wiring systems

1. Where the caravan has more than one electrically independent installation, each requires a separate connecting device. Segregation (in accordance with Section 528) and separation (in accordance with Section 414) should be followed, where relevant.

2. Only flexible and/or stranded conductors are permitted.

3. Special precautions are required to ensure that mechanical damage does not occur because of vibration (road movement)

4. Cables must have a csa not less than 1.5 mm^2.

5. Cables to be supported at a maximum distance of 0.4 m for vertical runs and 0.25 m for horizontal runs.

6. Cables to comply with *BS EN 60332-1-2* or better (required for structures constructed mainly of combustible material – see Section 422 of *BS 7671*)

c. Proximity to non-electrical services

Electrical equipment including wiring systems (except ELV equipment for gas-supply equipment) should not be installed in any gas cylinder storage compartment. Where they have to be run through such a compartment they must be run at a height of at least 500 mm above the base of the cylinders and protected against mechanical damage by installation within a continuous gas tight conduit or duct passing through the compartment. The conduit or duct must be able to withstand an impact equivalent to AG3 without visible physical damage.

d. Connection to the caravan pitch socket-outlet

The means of connection to the caravan pitch socket-outlet must be in accordance with sub-section 721.55. Fig 721.2 below shows a typical connection unit.

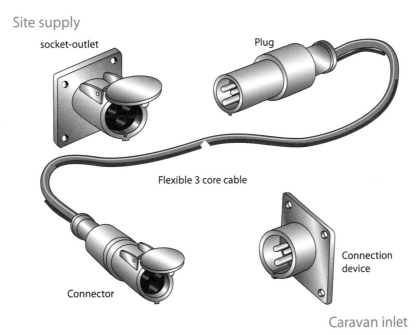

Fig 721.2 Connection method to caravan pitch socket-outlet

notes

c. Accessories

Accessories located in a position where they may be exposed to moisture should be constructed or enclosed to provide a degree of protection of at least IP44. Every socket-outlet supplied at extra-low voltage must have its voltage visibly marked. Luminaires should, preferably, be fixed directly to the lining of the caravan. Where pendant luminaires are fitted, provision must be made for securing the luminaire when the caravan is moved.

> **Exercise 721.2**
>
> You should now refer to Regulation Group 721.55. and Table 721. (1) What is the minimum length of a flexible cord for a caravan connection lead? (2) What would be the minimum CSA for a 16 A supply? (3) What is the maximum height to the inlet on a caravan? (4) What is the minimum degree of protection for a caravan inlet connection device?

b. Instructions for electricity supply

Instructions, providing a description of the installation, function of the RCD operation, function of the main isolating switch and instructions for connection and disconnection of the caravan are required so that caravan users can connect, disconnect and operate the caravan electrical system safely. Fig 721 of *BS 7671* provides an example instruction.

> **Exercise 712.3**
>
> You should now refer to Fig 721 of *BS 7671* for details of the Instructions for electricity supply.

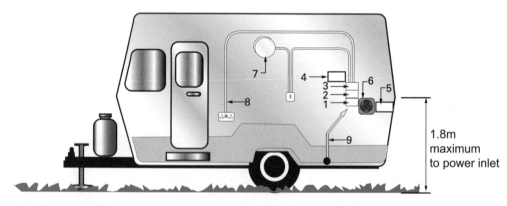

1	DP isolating switch	6	Power inlet
2	RCD (30 mA)	7	Luminaire fixed to caravan wall
3	DP overcurrent protective devices	8	Wiring system which must include a cpc
4	Periodic inspection and test notice	9	Main protective bonding conductor connecting structural
5	Power inlet notice		metallic parts which are accessible from within the

9 Main protective bonding conductor connecting structural metallic parts which are accessible from within the caravan to the main earthing terminal within the caravan. (e.g. at consumer unit earth bar)

Fig 721.3 Some of the main features of a caravan electrical installation

notes

Further information relating to Electrical installations in caravans and motor caravans can be found in:

- Section 721 of *BS 7671*
- IEE Guidance Note 7
- Electrical Safety Council Technical Manual articles S205-5 & S205-6

SECTION 721 FINAL REVISION EXERCISE

721.1 The electrical appliance inlet to a caravan must have a minimum degree of protection to which of the following?
- ☐ a. IPX2
- ☐ b. IPX4
- ☐ c. IP34
- ☐ d. IP44

721.2 The electrical inlet to a caravan should be not more than which of the following?
- ☐ a. 0.4 m above ground level
- ☐ b. 0.5 m above ground level
- ☐ c. 0.8 m above ground level
- ☐ d. 1.8 m above ground level

721.3 A flexible cord supplying a caravan with a rated supply current of 16 A requires a minimum cross-sectional area of which of the following?
- ☐ a. 1.5 mm^2
- ☐ b. 2.5 mm^2
- ☐ c. 4.00 mm^2
- ☐ d. 6.00 mm^2

721.4 A flexible cord supplying a caravan with a rated supply current of 32 A requires a minimum cross-sectional area of which of the following?
- ☐ a. 2.5 mm^2
- ☐ b. 4.0 mm^2
- ☐ c. 6.00 mm^2
- ☐ d. 16.00 mm^2

721.5 The recommended length of a flexible cord unit (within plus or minus 2 m) used to supply a caravan is:
- ☐ a. 10 m
- ☐ b. 15 m
- ☐ c. 25 m
- ☐ d. 50 m

721.6 Where cables are installed in a caravan and unless they are enclosed in rigid conduit they should be supported:
- ☐ a. 0.25 m for vertical and horizontal runs
- ☐ b. 0.4 m for vertical and horizontal runs
- ☐ c. 0.25 m for vertical runs and 0.4 m for horizontal runs
- ☐ d. 0.25 m for horizontal runs and 0.4 m for vertical runs

notes

Things to do and find

1. Outline the reasons why a caravan is considered to be a special installation.

2. What type of conductors are permitted for caravan wiring and what is the minimum csa?

3. What type of cables are required in caravans and why?

4. What are the maximum voltages for a.c. and d.c. supplies to caravans?

5. What type of earthing system is prohibited by the ESQC Regulations from being connected to a caravan?

6. What is the maximum rated residual operating current required for an RCD for protection of circuits in a caravan?

7. What are the special requirements for luminaires in caravans?

Section 740
Temporary electrical installations for structures, amusement devices and booths at fairgrounds, amusement parks and circuses

1. Introduction

Section 740 of *BS 7671* provides information relating to the additional requirements in relation to temporary electrical installations for structures, amusement devices and booths at fairgrounds, amusement parks and circuses.

Temporary electrical installations for structures, amusement devices and booths at fairgrounds, amusement parks and circuses are specified as a special location due to:

- the temporary nature of the installation,
- the risks associated with repeated connection of the units and the possible effect on connections and cables
- the risks associated with different connection provision at different sites
- difficulties establishing an equipotential zone
- vibration problems due to trailer or vehicular movement
- the effects of vibration and movement of structures during operation.

These installations may also include the potential risks outlined in relation to similar special locations such as caravans, mobile or transportable units and agricultural and horticultural installations.

Due to the specialist nature of these installations, the following text is only intended to provide a brief overview of Section 740.

2. Scope

Section 740 relates to the safe design, installation and operation of temporary erected mobile or transportable electrical machines and structures which incorporate electrical equipment relating to amusement devices and booths at fairgrounds, amusement parks and circuses.

The requirements of Section 740 do not apply to:

- Internal electrical wiring of machines (see *BS EN 60204-1*)
- Permanent electrical installations

Fig 740.1 and 740.2 Typical circus and fairground scenes

3. Protective measures against electric shock

a. General

The maximum nominal voltage for temporary electrical installations for booths, stands and amusement devices is 230 V a.c. single phase, 400 V a.c. three phase or 440 V d.c.

Section 740
Temporary electrical installations for structures, amusement devices and booths at fairgrounds, amusement parks and circuses

Because of the practical difficulties ensuring main equipotential bonding of all extraneous-conductive-parts, the use of a TN-C-S system should be carefully considered. TN-C-S supplies to caravans are prohibited and the electrical installations at fairgrounds, amusement parks and circuses should be assessed to see if they constitute similar risks.

Irrespective of the number of sources of supply, the phase and neutral conductors from different sources must not be interconnected downstream of the origin of the temporary electrical installation and the instructions of the operator for the supply of the system to the public must be followed.

b. Protective measures not permitted

See Section 700 of this Learning Guide. It should be noted that whilst the basic provision placing out of reach is normally not permitted in special installations or locations it is acceptable for electric dodgems. However, they should only be operated at voltages not exceeding 50 V a.c. or 120 V d.c. and have an electrical separation from the supply mains by means of a transformer in accordance with *BS EN 61558-2-4* or a motor-generator set.

Fig 740.3 Dodgems fed by overhead trailing supply

c. Acceptable protective measures

(i) Automatic disconnection of supply

One or more RCDs (rated residual operating current not exceeding 300 mA) are required at the origin of the electrical installation. The RCD must incorporate a time delay in accordance with *BS EN 60947-2* or be of the S-type to *BS EN 61008-1* or *BS EN 61009-1*, to provide discrimination, where necessary, with RCDs protecting final circuits.

RCD protection (having the characteristics specified in Regulation 415.1.1) is also required for all final circuits supplying lighting, socket-outlets rated up to 32 A and portable equipment connected by means of a flexible cable or cord with a current-carrying capacity up to 32 A.

In addition to RCD protection, supplementary equipotential bonding may be required in locations intended for livestock (see Section 705 of *BS 7671* and this Learning Guide for further details).

Exercise 740.1

You should now refer to Regulation Sub-Group 740.415 to review the requirements for additional protection.

4. Protection against thermal effects

Automatically or remotely controlled motors which are not continuously supervised must be fitted with a manually reset protective device against excessive temperature.

5. Selection and erection of electrical equipment

The requirements relating to selection and erection of equipment are too numerous to outline in this Learning Guide. The following are some of the general requirements or categories that need to be considered:

- Switchgear and controlgear security
- Electrical equipment to have a minimum degree of protection of IP44
- Accessibility to connections is required for operation, inspection and maintenance as well as special requirements for joints and terminations
- Restricted types of wiring systems
- Every electrical installation (booth, stand etc) to have its own isolation and isolation devices must isolate all live conductors
- Detailed requirements are outlined relating to luminaires, safety isolating transformers, electronic convertors, socket-outlets, plugs and low voltage generating sets (see Regulation Group 740.55)
- Connection points at each amusement device must be marked to indicate rated voltage, rated current and rated frequency.

> **Exercise 740.2**
>
> (1) What are the recommendations relating to the number of socket-outlets in booths, stands and for fixed installations? (2) What are the requirements relating to the types of socket-outlet for use outdoors?

Luminaires and decorative lighting chains mounted less than 2.5 m (arm's reach) above floor level or otherwise accessible to accidental contact should be firmly fixed and so sited or guarded as to prevent risk of injury to persons or ignition of materials.

Fig 740.4 Fun fair Side stall lighting

403

Section 740
Temporary electrical installations for structures, amusement devices and booths
at fairgrounds, amusement parks and circuses

notes

6. Inspection and testing

The electrical installation, between its origin and any equipment is required to be inspected, tested and certified, in line with Part 6 of *BS 7671*, **after each assembly on site**.

> Further information relating to mobile and transportable units can be found in:
> • Sections 740 and 717 of *BS 7671*

SECTION 740 FINAL REVISION EXERCISE

740.1 Which of the following characteristics is not required to be permanently marked at each amusement device?
- ☐ a. rated voltage
- ☐ b. rated frequency
- ☐ c. rated power
- ☐ d. rated current

740.2 The protective provision placing out of reach is not permitted on a fairground apart from where it relates to which of the following?
- ☐ a. Roller coasters
- ☐ b. Dodgems
- ☐ c. Shooting galleries
- ☐ d. Food stalls

740.3 Electrical equipment used for electrical installations for structures, amusement devices and booths at fairgrounds, amusement parks and circuses should have a minimum degree of protection of which of the following?
- ☐ a. IPX2
- ☐ b. IP42
- ☐ c. IP44
- ☐ d. IPX4

Things to do and find

1. Why are temporary installations for structures, amusement devices and booths at fairgrounds, amusement parks and circuses considered to be special locations?

2. What are the restrictions in relation to insulation-piercing lampholders?

3. What additional protection is required in a location intended for livestock?

4. In relation to a generator used as part of an installation complying with Section 740 of *BS 7671* where should the neutral conductor of the star-point of the generator be connected?

5. What are the specific requirements where luminaires and decorative lighting chains are mounted less than 2.5 m?

1. Introduction

Section 753 of *BS 7671* covers the requirements relating to the installation of electric floor and ceiling heating systems. The requirements relate to systems that are erected as either thermal storage heating systems or direct heating systems.

When installing electric floor and ceiling heating systems Regulation Group 554.4 should also be referred to for further information relating to heating conductors and cables.

Persons intending to design or install a floor or ceiling heating system should consult the manufacturer's guidance in the first instance. Heating systems should comply with the relevant product standard.

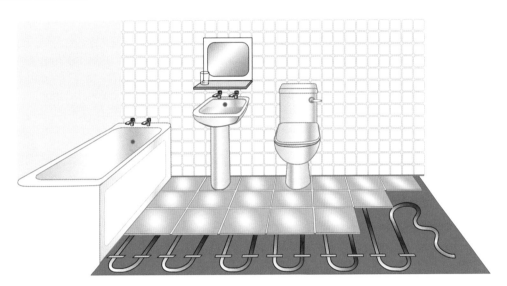

Key Facts
'Further reading is recommended prior to installing floor or ceiling heating systems'

Fig 753.1 Floor heating system

Because of the specialist nature of this subject the following text is not intended to cover the subject fully, but to identify the relevant sections in *BS 7671* and outline some key issues.

2. Scope

The requirements of Section 753, covered in this topic, apply to floor and ceiling heating systems (both thermal storage and direct heating).

The requirements of Section 753 do not relate to:

• The installation of wall heating systems
• Heating systems for use outdoors

3. Special risks associated with floor and ceiling heating systems

Floor and ceiling heating systems are specified as a special installation in BS 7671 because:

• There is a risk that floor and ceiling heating systems may be penetrated by nails or similar devices
• Special precautions are required to protect against the potential additional risk of fire.

notes

4. Protection against electric shock

a. Protective measures not permitted

In addition to the prohibited measures outlined in Section 700 of this Learning Guide, the protective measure electrical separation is also prohibited.

b. Acceptable protective measures

(i) Automatic disconnection of supply

All systems require protection by an RCD with a rated residual operating current not exceeding 30 mA.

For heating units that are manufactured without exposed-conductive-parts, a suitable conductive covering, for example, a grid with spacing of not more than 30 mm must be provided above floor heating elements and below ceiling heating elements. The conductive covering must be connected to the protective conductor of the electrical installation.

(ii) Class II construction or equivalent

All systems require protection by an RCD with a rated residual operating current not exceeding 30 mA. (having the characteristics specified in Regulation 415.1.1)

5. Protection against thermal effects

Care should be taken to ensure the surface temperature of floors cannot cause burns (normally limited to 35 °C).

Measures also need to be taken to limit the maximum temperature of floor or ceiling heating systems in buildings.

Exercise 753.1

(1) You should now refer to Regulation Group 753.424. What are the three measures that should be followed to ensure heating unit maximum temperatures are limited to 80 °C?

Special consideration needs to be given to the connection between the heating elements and fixed wiring supplying the heating system. It is important that connections within the floor are secure and that heat is not transmitted to the fixed wiring. The section of cable that connects the heating element to the fixed wiring is referred to as the cold tail (also known as a cold lead). The connection point where the cold tail joins the heating element (heating unit) must be inseparable (for example by a crimped connection).

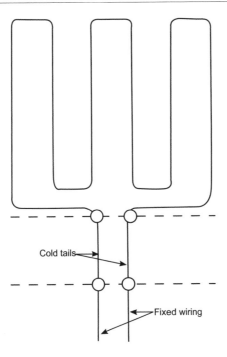

Fig 753.3 Connection of cold tails (cold leads)

Heating-free areas must be provided as necessary for the attachment of room fittings (for example sanitary ware) and information relating to heating zones and heating-free zones must be given to other contractors.

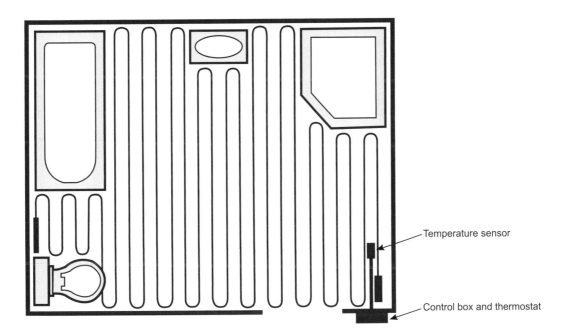

Fig 753.4 Heating-free zones

6. Operational conditions and external influences

Heating units must not cross expansion joints of the building or structure.

Heating units in ceilings must have a degree of protection of at least IPX1. Heating units in a floor of concrete or similar must have a degree of protection of at least IPX7 and must have the appropriate mechanical properties.

Section 753
floor and ceiling heating systems

The designer of the installation/heating system or installer must provide a very detailed plan of each heating system. Regulation 753.514 provides the details for the plan and includes sixteen items. The plan should be fixed adjacent to the distribution board supplying the heating system.

In addition to the above plan, information must be provided for the user of the installation. Details of this requirement are provided in Fig 753 of *BS 7671*.

Further information relating to floor and ceiling heating systems can be found in:
- *BS 7671* Section 753
- IEE Guidance Note 7

SECTION 753 FINAL REVISION EXERCISE

753.1 In floor areas where contact with skin or footwear is possible, the maximum surface temperature of the floor should not exceed which of the following?
- ☐ a. 25 °C
- ☐ b. 30 °C
- ☐ c. 35 °C
- ☐ d. 40 °C

753.2 Where a heating unit is installed, without exposed-conductive-parts, a grid should be fitted with spacing not exceeding which of the following?
- ☐ a. 15 mm
- ☐ b. 25 mm
- ☐ c. 30 mm
- ☐ d. 40 mm

753.3 The maximum temperature (in °C) for the zone where heating units are installed should be limited to which of the following?
- ☐ a. 35 °C
- ☐ b. 50 °C
- ☐ c. 70 °C
- ☐ d. 80 °C

753.4 For a heating unit installed in a floor of concrete or similar material, the minimum degree of protection should be which of the following?
- ☐ a. IPX4
- ☐ b. IPX5
- ☐ c. IPX6
- ☐ d. IPX7

Things to do and find

1. What are the three measures that could be applied to ensure a heating system does not exceed the maximum temperature?

2. What is the maximum rated residual operating current for an RCD required for a floor or ceiling heating system?

3. What is the name of the cable that connects the heating unit to the installation wiring?

4. What is the name of the areas provided to allow fixings into the floor or ceiling to avoid heating systems?

5. Where should the plan (giving details of the heating system) be located?

Appendices, answers and index

Appendices to *BS 7671*

1. Introduction

Whilst the appendices are not part of the main body of the Regulations and do not have the same status as the Regulations, they are important in that they either provide information for designers, installers and inspectors to ensure the requirements of *BS 7671* have been met or provide useful reference information.

In this section of the Learning Guide each appendix will be covered by a short overview. In most cases the information in the appendices will have already been covered within another section of the Learning Guide and therefore only a short reference to these appendices is made. Some appendices, which haven't been covered within the Learning Guide previously cover specialised areas and, therefore, these topics only receive a short outline.

Table App 1 (*Learning Guide Table*) List of appendices contained within *BS 7671*

Appendix No	Title
Appendix 1	British Standards to which reference is made in the Regulations
Appendix 2	Statutory Regulations and associated memoranda
Appendix 3	Time/current characteristics of overcurrent protective devices and RCDs
Appendix 4	Current-carrying capacity and voltage drop for cables and flexible cords
Appendix 5	Classification of external influences
Appendix 6	Model forms for certification and reporting
Appendix 7	Harmonized cable core colours
Appendix 8	Current-carrying capacity and voltage drop for busbar trunking and powertrack systems
Appendix 9	Definitions – Multiple source, d.c. and other systems
Appendix 10	Protection of conductors in parallel against overcurrent
Appendix 11	Effect of harmonic currents on balanced three-phase systems
Appendix 12	Voltage drop in consumers' installations
Appendix 13	Methods for measuring the insulation resistance/impedance of floors and walls to earth or to the protective conductor system
Appendix 14	Measurement of earth fault loop impedance: consideration of the increase of the resistance of conductors with increase in temperature
Appendix 15	Ring and radial final circuit arrangements (Regulation 433.1)

2. Appendix 1 British Standards to which reference is made in the Regulations

Appendix 1 provides a list of all the British Standards, Harmonized European Standards and Harmonized International Standards referred to in *BS 7671*. The standards covered in Appendix 1 relate to wiring systems, installation codes of practice or equipment standards. Where further information is required on a specific subject in *BS 7671*, reference to one of the standards listed in Appendix 1 may well provide the required information.

3. Appendix 2 Statutory Regulations and associated memoranda

Many of the relevant Statutory Regulations and their associated Memoranda are listed in Appendix 2 of *BS 7671*. The regulations listed represent the principal legal requirements relating to electrical installations.

notes

4. Appendix 3 Time/current characteristics of overcurrent protective devices and RCDs

Appendix 3 provides the time/current characteristics relating to common overcurrent protective devices and RCDs. The characteristics are provided in the form of graphs or charts plotting time in seconds against prospective current, r.m.s. in amperes. By referencing the graphs, the disconnection times of a range of overcurrent devices can be ascertained, if the current passing through the device is known. Conversely, the current required to disconnect a device in a given time can also be determined. The charts provide information for a wide range of current flow (for each type of overcurrent device) from the devices normal rating, through relatively low overloads to high fault currents. To provide a chart with such a wide range of current they are produced using a logarithmic scale and care needs to be taken when values are being determined.

To save designers and installers having to read the graphs directly, a table accompanies each graph giving the current required for common disconnection times. It should be noted that for circuit-breakers there is only one current/time as this relates to the instantaneous operating current which relates to an operating time of 100 mS.

Appendix 3, therefore, can be used to identify the current required for a required disconnection time. This current can then be used to calculate the maximum earth fault loop impedance. Many of these figures are already provided in the tables in Section 411 of *BS 7671* (Tables 41.2 to 41.6) but Appendix 3 provides the information for a wider range of times and currents.

Table 3A in Appendix 3 provides information relating to time/current performance criteria for RCDs to *BS EN 61008* and *BS EN 61009*. This table provides the required tripping times, along with the required residual current test current for a range of RCDs and residual operating currents.

> **Exercise App. 1**
>
> (1). What is the current that will operate a 30 A BS 1361 fuse in 5 seconds? (2) What is the time of operation for a *BS EN 60269-2* 63 A fuse when a fault of 500 A occurs?

5. Appendix 4 Current-carrying capacity and voltage drop for cables and flexible cords

Appendix 4 was covered in detail in Sections 523/525 of this Learning Guide. It should be noted that Appendix 4 contains a lot of information and may well need careful scrutiny when more unusual wiring systems or installation methods are employed.

6. Appendix 5 Classification of external influences

Appendix 5 was covered in detail in Part 2 (Definitions) and Section 522 of this Learning Guide. Designers and installers need to become familiar with Appendix 5 as the classifications referred to are used throughout *BS 7671*.

7. Appendix 6 Model forms for certification and reporting

Model forms for certification and reporting were partly covered in Part 6 of this Learning Guide. It is recommended that anyone carrying out inspection, testing, certification and/or reporting and requiring further information should attend one of the inspection and testing courses referred to in the introduction of this Learning Guide.

Another recommendation for anyone requiring further knowledge on this subject is to refer to IEE Guidance Note 3 or to the NICEIC Inspection, testing and certification including periodic reporting (Practical advice and guidance) book as well as reviewing the information in Appendix 6 of *BS 7671*.

8. Appendix 7 Harmonized cable core colours

The requirements of *BS 7671* relating to cable colour identification were covered in Chapter 51 of this Learning Guide. Appendix 7 provides further information relating to the harmonization process and how colour identification should be applied on existing installations, where new and old cable colours interface. This subject is also covered in depth in NICEIC Snags and Solutions Part 2 Wiring systems.

9. Appendix 8 Current-carrying capacity and voltage drop for busbar trunking and powertrack systems

Busbar and powertrack systems are covered in Section 521 of this Learning Guide. Appendix 8 and Section 521 of *BS 7671* inform installers that installation of these systems must be in accordance with manufacturers' instructions.

10. Appendix 9 Definitions – Multiple source, d.c. and other systems

Appendix 9 provides recommendations for the connection of conductors relating to multiple source, d.c and other systems. These systems will normally require specialised knowledge and/or adherence to manufacturers' guidance. It is not intended to provide guidance on Appendix 9 in this Learning Guide.

11. Appendix 10 Protection of conductors in parallel against overcurrent

As the introduction to Appendix 10 points out, where conductors are installed in parallel and the conductors have the same cross-sectional area, conductor material length and disposition (same method of installation and route) the requirements for overcurrent protection are straightforward. Where more complex conductor arrangements are required, considerations need to be given to the effects on conductors and protective devices of unequal current sharing. Appendix 10 gives further information in these cases. This subject can be quite complicated and normally only relates to larger installations where higher current carrying requirements have to be met. This subject, therefore, is not covered in this Learning Guide. It is recommended that where parallel conductors are being designed or installed and particularly where the design or installation is considered to be outside standard circuit practices, further guidance is sought including reference to Appendix 10.

12. Appendix 11 Effect of harmonic currents on balanced three-phase systems

There are many references in *BS 7671* to the effects of harmonics and Appendix 11 gives further guidance to the values of harmonic currents that need to be given specific consideration.

Harmonic currents can have an effect on the neutral conductor in an electrical system. Particular attention is required in relation to the effects of triple-N (triplen) harmonic currents. Triplen harmonics are odd multiples of the third harmonic, having a frequency of three times or multiples of three times the fundamental frequency (typically 50 Hz), including the 3rd, 9th, 15th harmonic.

Triplen harmonic currents can, amongst other things, cause problems such as overheating in the neutral conductor and its connections or terminations.

The problems associated with harmonic currents and their effects on the neutral conductor are referred to in several places in *BS 7671* including Section 132, Section 331, Regulation 431.2.3, Regulation Group 523.6, Section 524 and Part 5 External influences. For example, discharge lighting circuits or polyphase circuits (such as a three-phase circuit) having a harmonic content in excess of 10 % of the fundamental are required to have a neutral conductor with a cross-sectional-area (csa) not less than that of the line conductor(s) (Regulation 523.6.3 refers).

Additionally, Regulation 431.2.3 requires the provision of overload detection for the neutral conductor in a polyphase circuit in a TT or TN system where the harmonic content in the line currents is such that the current in the neutral conductor is likely to exceed that in the line conductors. The detection must disconnect the line conductors but not necessarily the neutral conductor. (The Regulation assumes that the csa of the neutral conductor is at least equal to or equivalent to that of the line conductors).

Effects of triple-N (triplen) harmonics

In a perfectly balanced three-phase system where the load current is harmonic free, the resulting current in the neutral conductor is zero Amperes. However, in practice, electrical and electronic equipment will inherently produce a certain amount of harmonic current. In such cases, irrespective of whether the load is perfectly balanced, there will be a resultant current in the neutral conductor.

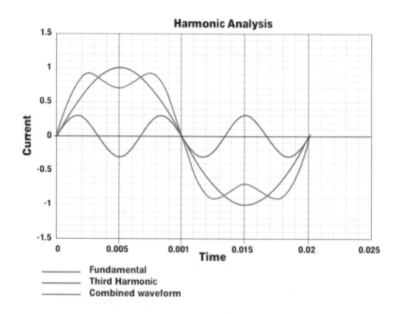

Fig App 1 Fundamental and third harmonic with their combined value

Appendix 11 provides example calculations relating to the percentage of third harmonic content and how this factor should be applied to conductor current carrying capacity.

---

13. Appendix 12 Voltage drop in consumers' installations

The subject of voltage drop is covered in Section 523/525 of this Learning Guide (particularly Section 525). The information provided in *BS 7671* in Section 525 and Appendix 11 addresses the subject of voltage drop in a simplistic way. By analysing the current distribution in an installation, more accurate calculations can be produced.

14. Appendix 13 Methods for measuring the insulation resistance/impedance of floors and walls to earth or to the protective conductor system

The requirement to measure the insulation resistance/impedance of floors and walls to earth or to the protective conductor system only relates to very specialised electrical installations and, therefore, is not covered in this Learning Guide

15. Appendix 14 Measurement of earth fault loop impedance: consideration of the increase of the resistance of conductors with increase in temperature

Appendix 14 provides information in relation to the effects of temperature on conductors. Normally, impedance measurements are made at ambient temperature and, therefore, adjustments are often required to compensate for the increase in temperature due to circuit loading.

Where the measured impedance of the fault current loop has been measured and the circuit is considered to be at ambient temperature, the measurement must be increased by a factor described in Appendix 14, and the adjusted measurement then compared against the maximum values of earth fault loop impedance prescribed in Chapter 41 or Appendix 3.

16. Appendix 15 (Informative) Ring and radial final circuit arrangements Regulation 433.1

Appendix 15 provides further information to help designers and installers comply with the requirements of Regulation Group 433.1 and in the specific case of ring final circuits Regulation 433.1.5.

It is important for designers and installers to understand that every circuit needs to be designed. When using 'standard' circuit arrangements, such as those outlined in Appendix 15 it is essential that all conditions are understood and complied with. Where the specified criteria are not met, individual calculations relating to the specific situation will be necessary. An example of this is where cables are covered or partially covered by thermal insulation. This may well result in an increase in conductor cross-sectional area compared to the ones in Appendix 15.

There are many factors to be considered when the cables and overcurrent protective devices are being selected. Appendix 15 provides the criteria for domestic ring and radial circuits using socket-outlets and fused connection units. Considerations have been given to overcurrent protective devices, automatic disconnection requirements, cable type, conductor cross-sectional area, voltage drop, load distribution, types of loads, maximum circuit length, circuit configuration and where spurs (fused and non-fused) can be located. The following table outlines the three types of final circuit.

Table App 2 (Learning Guide Table) Ring and radial final circuit arrangements

Final circuit type	Overcurrent protective device rating	Minimum live conductor cross-sectional area (copper)	Maximum floor area served
Ring final circuit	30 A or 32 A	2.5 mm^2	100 m^2
20 A radial final circuit	20 A	2.5 mm^2	50 m^2
30/32 A radial final circuit	30 A or 32 A	4.0 mm^2	75 m^2

Note: for mineral insulated cable cross-sectional areas see Regulation Group 433.1

Exercise App. 2

Refer to Appendix 15 of *BS 7671*. The following questions relate to the conditions specified in Appendix 15 or Regulation. (1) What is the recommended maximum area covered by a radial final circuit protected by a 20 A device? (2) What is the maximum number of double socket-outlets that can be spurred from a ring circuit where a fused connection unit is used to protect the spur? (3) List the types of loads that shouldn't be supplied on a ring circuit with standard conditions provided in Appendix 15. (4) What does Regulation 433.1.5 require in relation to the type of accessory used in a ring final circuit?

Further information relating to Appendices can be found in:
- *BS 7671* Appendices 1 to 14
- Electrical Safety Council Technical Manual articles (Numerous references – search by topic)
- NICEIC Inspection, testing and certification (including periodic reporting). Practical advice and guidance
- NICEIC Snags and Solutions Part 2 Wiring systems
- IEE Guidance Notes

APPENDICES FINAL REVISION EXERCISE

APP1 Which of the following Appendices would you refer to for information relating to current-carrying capacity and voltage drop for cables and flexible cords?
- ☐ a. Appendix 3
- ☐ b. Appendix 4
- ☐ c. Appendix 6
- ☐ d. Appendix 10

APP2 Which of the following appendices would you refer to for information relating to model forms for certification and reporting?
- ☐ a. Appendix 3
- ☐ b. Appendix 4
- ☐ c. Appendix 6
- ☐ d. Appendix 10

APP3 Appendix 5 relates to which of the following?
- ☐ a. current-carrying capacity and voltage drop for cables and flexible cords
- ☐ b. model forms for certification and reporting
- ☐ c. classification of external influences
- ☐ d. voltage drop in consumers' installations

APP4 Appendix 12 relates to which of the following?
- ☐ a. current-carrying capacity and voltage drop for cables and flexible cords
- ☐ b. model forms for certification and reporting
- ☐ c. classification of external influences
- ☐ d. voltage drop in consumers' installations

APP5 Which of the following is the current that would cause disconnection in a *BS 3036* semi-enclosed fuse rated at 20 A in 0.4 seconds?
- ☐ a. 92 A
- ☐ b. 260 A
- ☐ c. 900 A
- ☐ d. 130 A

Answers to phase and final section tests

Introduction

ExSTR1. (1). 7. (2) Special installations and locations. (3) Part 5. **ExSTR2.** (1) Initial verification. (2) Part 6, Chapter61, Section 610, Regulation 610.1. (3) A Competent Person. **ExSTR3.** (1) 542.2.1 (2) Part 5, Chapter54, Section 542, Regulation group 542.2.

Final revision exercise. Str1 (a), Str2 (c), Str3 (c), Str4 (c), Str5 (b), Str6 (c).

Things to do and find. (1) 41. (2) Sources for SELV and PELV systems. (3) 527.2, Sealing of wiring system penetrations. (4) Chapter 56, Chapter 35 (5) (i) 543.7, (ii) 415.1, (iii) 522.8.

Part 1, Chapter 11 and 12

Ex 11.1 (i) included- marinas, public premises, (ii) excluded-equipment on ships lightning protection system, (iii) supplementary document may be required-fire detection and alarm systems, electric heating systems

Ex 12.1 (i) on the first page in the Sections to be signed 'for design', 'for construction', and for' inspection and testing'.

Final revision exercise 11.1(a), 11.2(a), 11.3(d), 11.4(a).

Things to do and find. (1) 1000 V a.c. and 1500 V d.c. (2) Yes. (3) No (4) ESQC Regulations 2002, and Electricity at Work Regulations 1989. (5) Petrol filling stations, caravan parks, Houses of multiple occupancy (HMO's), places of entertainment. (6) On the first page in the Sections to be signed 'for design', 'for construction', and for' inspection and testing'.

Part 1, Chapter 13

Ex 13.1 (1) Ignition of potentially explosive atmosphere, undervoltages, overvoltages, electromagnetic influence, power supply interruptions of safety services **Ex 13.3** (1) Shock, excessive temperature likely to cause burns, fires, arcing, burning plus items in answer to **Ex 13.1** (2) Basic and fault protection **Ex 13.4** (1) Line, neutral, protective and PEN (2) nominal voltage frequency, maximum current, prospective short-circuit current, earth fault loop impedance, protective measures inherent in the supply, particular requirements of the distributor **Ex 13.5** (1) The nature of the location, the nature of the supporting structure of wiring, accessibility of wiring to persons or livestock, voltage, electromagnetic stresses or interference, other external influences **Ex 13.7** (1) overcurrent, earth fault current, overvoltage, undervoltage and no-voltage (2) linked

Final revision exercise. 13.1 (d), 13.2 (b)

Things to do and find. 1. Calculation, measurement, enquiry or inspection (2) on the first page below the inspection and testing signature

Part 2

Ex 2.1 (1) Ambient temperature. (2) A flexible cable in which the csa of each conductor does not exceed 4 mm2. **Ex 2.2** A Distributor. (2) yes. **Ex 2.3** Fault. (2) Residual current device. **Ex 2.4**. (1) PVC cable in conduit. (2) A fire alarm system. (3) Inspection, testing, and certification. (4) Class I - brass light fitting; Class II - a power tool. **Ex 2.5** Circuit protective conductor, protective bonding conductor, earthing conductor, functional earthing conductor, supplementary equipotential bonding conductor – extraneous-conductive-part, exposed-conductive-part. **Ex 2.6** (1) T – denotes that one or more points of the source of energy are directly connected to earth ('T' stands for earth), N – denotes that the exposed-conductive-parts of the installation are directly connected to the earthed point of the source of energy ('N' represents neutral), C – denotes that the neutral and protective functions are both performed by a single conductor, called a combined protective and neutral (PEN) conductor. ('C' stands for combined). S – denotes that separate neutral and protective conductors are provided ('S' stands for separate). (2) IT. (3) TN-C-S. **Ex 2.8** (1) AD5- environment, water jets. (2) BA4- utilisation, instructed people only allowed. (3) CA2- Buildings, combustible materials. **Ex 2.9** (1) IPXXB or IP2X. (2) IP4X or IPXXD. (3) IP2X or IPXXB. (4) IPX8. (5) IP44.

Final revision exercise. 2.1 (a), 2.2 (b), 2.3 (b), 2.4 (a), 2.5 (a), 2.6 (c)

Things to do and find. (1) Gas, water, other services, structural steelwork, central heating and air conditioning (if entering an installation from outside). (2) Fuse element. (3) Overload current is an overcurrent occurring in a circuit which is electrically sound. An overcurrent is a current exceeding the rated value. For conductors the rated value is the current carrying capacity. (4) Band I. (5) Class I- equipment in which protection against electric shock does not rely upon basic insulation only, but which includes means for the connection of exposed conductive parts to a protective conductor in the fixed wiring of the installation. Class II- equipment in which protection against electric shock does not rely on basic installation only, but which additional safety precautions such as supplementary insulation are provided, there being no provision for connection of exposed metal work of the equipment to a protective conductor, and no reliance upon precautions to be taken in the fixed wiring of the installation. (6) TN-C-S. (7) Extra-low voltage does not exceed 50 v a.c or 120 V d.c.

Part 3

Ex3.1 To reduce the possibility of unwanted tripping, mitigate the effects of EMI and prevent the indirect energizing of a circuit **Ex3.2** The neutral supplies more than 1 circuit which may cause indirect energising of a circuit. **Ex3.3** (i) rapidly fluctuating loads, (ii) d.c. feedback, (iii) high frequency oscillations, (iv) earth leakage currents, (v) necessity for additional connection to earth, (vi) earth leakage currents in computer installations.

Final revision exercise. 3.1 (a), 3.2 (d), 3.3 (b), 3.4 (c).

Things to do and find. (1) selection of earthing system, selection of the protective device in order to achieve discrimination, number of circuits, multiple power supplies, use of monitoring devices. (2) A motor. (3) Conductors should be connected at corresponding terminals so that each final circuit is separate from another to avoid indirect energising. (4) An RCD should be installed at the origin with a minimum value of 100mA with time delay to provide discrimination, a 30mA RCD without time delay should be fitted at each relevant final circuit as required by Regulation 415.1. (5) Indirect energising of another circuit. (6) Ze, nominal voltage, nature of current and frequency, prospective short circuit current. Maximum demand.

Section 410

EX 41.1 (1) A warning label (2) IP XXD or IP 4X **EX 41.2** (1) Metal supports of overhead line insulators (2) Steel reinforced concrete poles (3) small (below 50 mm x 50 mm) exposed-conductive-parts or (4) inaccessible street furniture.

Final revision exercise 41.1 (d), 41.2 (a), 41.3 (c), 41.4 (d), 41.5 (a), 41.6 (c)

Things to do and find. (1) Basic and fault protection (2) Insulation of conductor or other electrical equipment (3) as the lid or cover of a distribution board (4) ADS, Double or reinforced insulation, Electrical separation, SELV/PELV (5) They can only be used where the installation is controlled or supervised by skilled or instructed persons (6) Paint, varnish or lacquer.

Section 411

EX 411.2 (1) Earthing and bonding arrangements should be checked to see they are adequate before the addition or alteration takes place. **EX 411.3** (1) 0.3 secs (2) 0.2 secs **EX411.4** (1) 1.7 Ω (2) 1.04 Ω **EX411.5** (1) 1.44 Ω (2) 0.72 Ω (3) 0.18 Ω **EX411.6** (1) 2.8 Ω (2) 1.84 Ω (3) this is because more energy is required to rupture the element for a faster disconnection time. **EX411.7** (1) 0.17 Ω (2) 0.8 Ω

Final revision exercise 411.1(a), 411.2(a), 411.3(b), 411.4(c), 411.5(b), 411.6(c)

Things to do and find. (1) water installation pipes, gas installation pipes, central heating & air conditioning systems, exposed metallic structural parts of a building (2) insulation of live parts, barriers and enclosures. (3) Chapter54,(4) cpc, MET, metallic return path, path through the earthed neutral point of the transformer, transformer winding, line conductor from transformer to fault. (5) fig 3.5 (6) construction site, demolition site. (7) exposed conductive parts of an FELV system are connected to the protective conductor of the primary circuit of its source (8) 0.09 Ω (9) 0.2 seconds.

Section 412

EX 412.2 (1) ▢ (2) terminate at earthing terminal within box using propriety screw.

Final revision exercises 412.1(b), 412.2(a), 412.3(c)

Things to do and find. (1) Verify that the installation or circuit comprises entirely of double or reinforced insulation. The circuit or installation is under effective supervision. Not applied to any circuit that includes a socket outlet. (2) cpc, (3) so no change can be made to impair the effectiveness of the protective measure.

Section 413

Final revision exercise 413.1 (d), 413.2 (a)

Things to do and find. (1) The upper limit of the voltage of an SELV system is 50 V a.c. where as up to 500 V a.c. may be used for electrical separation. (2) Basic insulation is provided by insulation of live parts and barriers and enclosures, fault protection is provided by simple separation. (3) exposed-conductive-parts of a separated circuit must not be connected to earth or exposed-conductive-parts of other circuits

Section 414

Final revision exercise 414.1 (c), 414.2 (a), 414.3 (a)

Things to do and find. (1) separated extra-low voltage (SELV).Protective extra-low voltage(PELV) (2)a PELV system is not electrically separated from earth, but an SELV system is electrically separated from earth. (3) If voltage exceeds 25 V a.c. or 60 V d.c., or if equipment is immersed. (4) (i)SELV and PELV circuit conductors enclosed in non metallic sheath.

(ii) SELV and PELV circuit conductors separated from conductors of other circuits at voltages higher than band I by an earthed metallic sheath or earthed metallic screen.(iii)circuit conductors at voltages higher than band I may be contained in a multi-conductor cable or other grouping of conductors if SELV and PELV conductors are insulated for highest voltage present. (iv) the wiring system of other circuits are in compliance with 412.2.4.1, (5)(i) Safety isolating transformer complying with *BS EN 61558-2-6*. (ii) Motor- generator. (iii)Electromechanical source such as a battery. (iv) Certain electronic devices.

Section 415

Final revision exercise 415.1 (d), 415.2 (b), 415.3 (a), 415.4 (a).

Things to do and find. (1) All socket-outlets not exceeding 20 A used by ordinary persons, and where socket outlet is for general use. (ii) mobile equipment, (iii) All circuits of a location in Section 701. (2) (i) part of an installation, (ii) a location, (iii) an item of equipment, (3)167 Ω for a 230 V a.c. system. (4) 0.25 Ω (5) (i) 701 Room containing a bath or shower, (ii) Construction and demolition site, (iii) Electrical installation in a caravan park.

Section 417 and 418

Final revision exercise 417.1 (c), 417.2 (c), 417.3 (d).

Things to do and find. (1) Electrical separation where more than one current-using item is supplied. Earth-free local equipotential bonding. Non-conducting locations (also basic provisions, obstacles and placing out of reach). (2) Distances required by 417.3.1 and 417.3.2 should be increased to suit the long or bulky object. (3) 50 kΩ. (4) Dimensions for accessibility should be increased to take account of the long or bulky object. (5) Where more than 1 item of current using equipment is fed from the unearthed source.

Chapter 42

EX 42.3 (1)0.8 m. **EX42.4** (1) 0.5 m

Final revision exercise 42.1 (a), 42.2 (b), 42.3 (b), 42.4 (c).

Things to do and find. (1) 25 litres, (2) 526.5, (3) 90 deg C, (4) 0.8 m

Chapter 43

EX 43.1 (i) overload current – e.g. intended load replaced by another load requiring a current in excess of design current. (ii) overcurrent – a current exceeding the rated value of for example a cable, this could be a 30 amp load connected to a 20 amp rated cable. (iii) Short-circuit current – accidental simultaneous contact between two live conductors. (iv) Earth fault current – accidental simultaneous contact between a live conductor and an exposed or extraneous conductive part. **EX 43.4** (i) k is a factor taking into account the resistivity, temperature coefficient and heat capacity of the conductor material, and appropriate initial and final temperatures. (ii) k= 143, (iii) k= 103

Final revision exercise. 43.1 (d), 43.2 (c), 43.3 (c), 43.4 (a), 43.5 (b), 43.6 (b)

Things to do and find. (1) the protective device is not installed further than 3 m away from reduction in cable size, installed in a manner as to reduce the risk of fault to a minimum, and fire or danger to persons to a minimum. (2) A lifting magnet, the secondary circuit of a transformer, the exciter circuit of a rotating machine. (3) *BS 1361, BS 88, BS 3036, BS EN 60898, BS EN 61009- 1, BS EN 60269, BS EN 60947-2,* (4) Ring circuits shall be wired with copper conductors having line and neutral conductors min csa of 2.5 mm^2, or 1.5 mm^2 for micc cable. Such circuits must meet requirements of 433.1.1, (5) Appendix 10 of *BS 7671: 2008,* (6) t is the duration in seconds, s is the csa of the conductor in mm^2, I is the effective current in amperes, k is a factor taking into account the resistivity, temperature coefficient and heat capacity of the conductor material, and appropriate initial and final temperatures

Chapter 44

EX44.1 (i) overvoltage and faults between high voltage systems and earth, overvoltage due to atmospheric conditions, electromagnetic influence. (ii) 2.5 kV for 230/240 and 277/480 V, 4 kV for 400/690 V, 6 kV for 1000 V installations. **Ex 44.2** A circuit supplying rotating equipment or machinery.

Final revision exercise. 44.1 (b), 44.2(b), 44.3 (d), 44.4 (c), 44.5 (b), 44.6 (a)

Things to do and find. (1) (i) Loss of supply neutral in the low voltage system, (ii) short- circuit between a line conductor and neutral in the low voltage installation, (iii) accidental earthing of a line conductor of a low voltage IT system, (iv) a fault between the high voltage system and earth in the transformer substation that supplies the low voltage installation. (2) Table 44.3. (3) 6kV (4) Category IV.

Chapter 51

EX51.1 The resulting degree of safety should not be less than that obtained by compliance with *BS 7671* and the details should be provided on the EIC. **Ex 51.2** (1) At their terminations and preferably throughout their length (2) Orange

Final revision exercise. 51.1(a), 51.2 (c), 51.3 (a), 51.4 (d), 51.5 (d), 51.6 (b)

Things to do and find. (1) (i) Nominal voltage of the system, (ii) the design current allowing for capacitive and inductive effects, (iii) the current likely to flow in abnormal conditions (the characteristics of the protective device will affect the duration of the current), (iv) the frequency, (v) power characteristics, (vi) compatibility with other equipment. (2) Appendix 5. (3) (i) Voltage, (ii) isolation, (iii) earthing and bonding connections, (iv) non-standard colours. (4) Blue. (5) (i) The type, and composition of each circuit (number of points served, number and size of conductors, type of wiring), (ii) the method for providing shock protection (which protective measure (such as ADS) has been provided), (iii) the information necessary for the identification of each device performing the functions of protection, isolation and switching, and its location, (iv) any circuit or equipment vulnerable to a typical test. (6) Quarterly (3 monthly). (7) BS 951. (8) Earth free equipotential bonding.

Chapter 52 - Sections 520 and 521

Ex520.1 (1) No. **Ex520.2** (a) Reference method B. (b) Reference method 100. (c) Reference method E or F. **Ex520.3** (a) Water AD or high temperature from other services, (b) dust AE if it was a woodworking shop. **Ex520.4** (1) Non ferromagnetic entry plate, all cables passing through the same entry/exit hole. (2) Grouping factor, if circuits are of a different voltage band every cable or conductor is insulated to the highest voltage present. (3) Conduit, ducting, trunking. (4) Aluminium, wood.

Final revision exercise. 521.1 (d), 521.2 (a), 521.3 (b), 521.4 (c)

Things to do and find. (1) Flexible cables or flexible cords shall be used for fixed wiring only where the relevant provisions of *BS7671* are met, flexible cables and cords cannot be used for equipment supplied by contact rails. (2) mechanical protection, e.g. conduit ,trunking (3) (i) Nature of the location, (ii) the nature of the structure supporting the wiring system, (iii) accessibility of wiring to persons and livestock. (iv) voltage, (v) electromagnetic interference, (vi) external influences, (vii) electromechanical stresses likely to occur in the event of short circuits or earth faults. (4) The junction box shall comply with *BS EN 60670-22* or *BS EN 60947-7*. (5) *BS EN 60670-22* - particular requirements for connecting boxes and enclosures. *BS EN 60947-7* Specification for low-voltage switchgear and controlgear.

Section 522

Ex522.1 (1) AD7- immersion in water, AE4- light dust, BA4- instructed persons, BE- materials, CA2- combustible materials. **Ex55.2** (1) (a) Radiated heat from the sun, (b) conducted heat from a hot water pipe, (c) convected heat from a manufacturing process. (2) 90deg C. **Ex522.3** (1) A saw mill. A build up of saw dust on equipment can create over heating, and cause switches not to operate correctly. Solutions could be to ensure all electrical equipment and containment has a suitable IP rating, install electrical wiring system outwith dusty areas where possible, and provide regular maintenance. (2) Reduction of lumen output, tracking of contacts, build up of heat. Conductive dust can cause tracking of contacts and conductors causing a short circuits and fire. **Ex 522.4** (1) Cutting, drilling, and fixing. (ii) Re coat after work is complete. **Ex 522.5** (1) Impact from screwing and nailing. This could be prevented by routing cable in metal conduit. (2) (i) The mechanical characteristics of the wiring system, (ii) the location selected, (iii) the provision of additional local or general protection against mechanical damage. **Ex522.7** (1) grommet, cable gland. (2) Route cable in metal conduit or cover cable with channeling. (3) De-burr ends of conduit prior to screwing of gluing, provide access points for drawing cables, install suitable access points at bends, clean conduit from oil, grease, dirt, condensation.

Ex 522.8 (1) Armoured cable, galvanised conduit. PVC/ PVC flat cable should not be used due to degradation of the cable sheath and discolouring. If plastic conduits are to be used adequate shielding should be provided to protect conduit from solar ionising radiation and expansion couplings should be installed.

Final revision exercise. 522.1 (d), 522.2 (c), 522.3 (b) 522.4 (b), 522.5 (d), 522.6 (b)

Things to do and find. (1) Where cables are run less than 50 mm from the surface of a wall or partition the following requirements must be met: the cable must incorporate an earthed metallic covering or the cable must be enclosed in earthed conduit satisfying the requirements for a protective conductor or the cable must be enclosed in earthed trunking or ducting satisfying the requirements for a protective conductor or the cable must be mechanically protected against damage sufficient to provide protection against the penetration by nails, screws and the like *or* the cable must be installed in the specified zones as prescribed in Regulation 522.6.6 (v). Where Regulation 522.6.6 (v) applies and the installation is not intended to be under the supervision of a skilled or instructed person an RCD having the characteristics specified in Regulation 415.1.1 must be fitted. (2) Shielding, placing sufficiently far from the heat source, local reinforcement or substitution of insulating material. (3) A flexible wiring system shall be used. (4) The provision of additional local or general protection against mechanical damage, select a wiring system with suitable mechanical characteristics, select the location of wiring route

Sections 523 and 525

Ex 523/5.1 (1) Table 4D4A. (2) Table 4D1A is for single core cables, table 4D2A is for multi core cables. (3) Table 4D5. **Ex 523/5.2** (1) 90 °C **Ex 523/5.3** (1) Method 101, (2) Method 101 is used where the insulation exceeds 100 mm thickness, method 100 is used where the insulation does not exceed 100 mm thickness. (3) E or F. **Ex 523/5.4** (1) 0.96 (2) 0.85 (3) 34 A **Ex 523/5.5** (1) 0.63 **Ex 523/5.6** (1) 3% (2) Appendix 4 (Tables 4D1A to 4J4A)

Calculation revision exercises. (1) 1.5 mm^2. (2) 6 mm^2

Final revision exercise. Ex 523.1 (b), Ex 523.2 (d), Ex 523.3 (a), Ex 523.4 (a), Ex 523.5 (b), Ex 523.6 (c).

Things to do and find. (1) The reference methods are those methods of installation for which the current -carrying capacity has been determined by test or calculation. The installation method is how the cables are actually installed. (2) Below 30%. (3) A rating factor of 0.725 is applied reducing the current-carrying capacity by approximately 30%. (4) 3%. (5) C_a- ambient temperature rating factor, C_g- cable grouping factor, C_i- rating factor if cable is applied if cable is surrounded with thermal insulation, C_c is the rating factor depending upon the protective device (e.g. a *BS 3036* fuse). (6) 4.7 V. (7) Table 52.2. (8) 70°C. (9) Table 4D2.

Section 524

Ex 524.1 (1) 1 mm^2. (2) 0.75 mm^2. **Ex 524.2** (1) 16 mm^2 (2) Appendix 11 covers harmonic current in balanced 3 phase installations and will need to be consulted if the harmonic content of the installation is high and an increased neutral csa is required.

Final revision exercise. 524.1(c), 524.2 (c)

Section 526

EX 526.1 (1) copper, aluminium, steel. (2) Thermosetting, thermoplastic, mineral insulated. (3) Rigid, flexible, solid (4) A device to *BS EN 60947-7*, a device to *BS EN 60998* series.

Final revision exercise 526.1 (d), 526.2 (b), 526.3 (d), 526.4 (a)

Things to do and find. (1) material of conductor and its insulation, the number and shape of the wires forming the conductor, the cross Sectional area of the conductor, the number of the conductors to be connected together, the provision of adequate locking arrangements in situations subject to vibration or thermal cycling. (2) Mechanical protection. (3) A suitable accessory complying with the appropriate product standard, an equipment enclosure complying with the appropriate product standard, an enclosure partly formed or completed with building material which is non combustible. (4) A joint designed to be buried in the ground, a compound filled or encapsulated joint, a connection between a cold tail and a heating element as in a ceiling or floor heating system.

Section 527

Ex 527.2 (1) 32 mm^2

Final revision exercise. 527.1 (c). 527.2 (a)

Things to do and find. (1) (i)The sealing arrangement shall be resistant to the products of combustion to the same extent as the elements of building construction which have been penetrated, (ii) shall provide the same degree of protection from water penetration as that required for the building construction element in which it has been installed, (iii) shall be compatible with the material of the wiring system with which it is in contact, (iv) it shall permit thermal movement of the wiring system without reduction in the sealing quality, (v) it shall be of adequate mechanical stability to withstand the stresses which may arise through damage to the support of the wiring system due to fire, (vi) the seal of the wiring system shall be protected from dripping water which may travel along the wiring system, or which may collect around the seals (2) temporary sealing arrangements shall be provided. (3) Sealing which has been disturbed shall be reinstated as soon as possible.

Sections 528 and 529

Ex 528.2 Item i relates to separate cables or conductors, item ii relates to conductors within a multicore cable.

Final revision exercise. 528.1 (b). 528.2 (d), 528.3(a), 528.4(b).

Things to do and find. (1) Condensation, heat. (2) A circuit forming part of the lift installation as defined by **BS EN 81-1**. (3) Heat, smoke, fumes, condensation.

Chapter 53

Ex53.1 In a multi-phase circuit the neutral need not be switched. In a single phase circuit the neutral can be switched but not alone. The neutral must therefore be switched with a live conductor in a DP switch. **Ex53.2** Metal boxes and plaster-depth boxes for recessed accessories or metal or plastic boxes for surface mounted accessories. **Ex53.4** (1) 300 mA (2) at the origin (3) monitoring by insulation monitoring devices **Ex53.5** (1) 0.6 mm. (2) They must be installed in such a manner that they can be removed or replaced without unintentional contact of live parts

Final revision exercise 53.1 (d), 53.2 (c), 53.3 (d), 53.4 (a).

Things to do and find. (1) RCD to be placed at the origin of the installation unless the part of the installation between the origin and the device complies with the requirements for protection by the use of class II equipment or equivalent installation. (2) Incorporation of a time delay within the RCD upstream. (3) (i) RCD to comply with 531.2 for fault protection, (ii) RCD must be installed at the origin of the circuit to be protected, (iii) RCD to switch all live conductors, or (iv)related residual operating current should not exceed 300 mA. (4) (i) the device should have marked on or adjacent to it an indication of the fuselink intended to be used, (ii) Be of the type that cannot be inadvertently replaced by a fuselink having rated current but a higher fusing factor than intended. (5) 60 A. (6) Back-up protection is the provision of protective device upstream, having the necessary breaking capacity to protect a device down stream which has a lower breaking capacity than the prospective short-circuit or earth fault at its point of installation. In a domestic installation back-up protection may be afforded by the distributor's protective device on the supply side. (7) As close as practicable to the origin of the system to either (i) the neutral point of the supply (ii) an artificial neutral point (iii) a line conductor or two or more line conductors

Section 537

Ex537.1 (1) This would remove the earth from the installation. (2) A main switch is required for each source and a durable warning notice to be installed in a prominent position so that any person seeking to operate any of the main switches will be warned of the need to operate all such switches to achieve isolation. Alternatively a suitable interlocking system should be provided. **Ex537.2** Provision for disconnection of the neutral is required in an accessible position only to be disconnected by means of a tool. It must be mechanically strong and maintain electrical continuity **Ex537.4** (1) (i) In a supply main switch, (ii) at a shower switch. (2) Install a locking device on circuit breaker or isolator. **Ex 537.6** (1) Time switch for floodlighting. (2) Not for d.c. circuits, but it can for a.c. equipment rated up to 16 A. (3) No. **Ex 537.7** (2) External illuminated sign, interior discharge lighting installations operating at a voltage exceeding low voltage. **Ex 537.8** (1) Isolation- RCD's, fuses to *BS EN 60269-2*, mechanical maintenance-fuse to *BS EN 60269-2*, MCB's to *BS EN 60898*, emergency switching- switched fused connection unit to BS 1363-4, RCD's, functional switching- contactors to *BS EN 60947- 4-1*, RCD's. (2) (i) yes, (ii) no

Final revision exercise. 537.1 (d), 537.2 (b), 537.3 (b).

Things to do and find. (1) Fuses to *BS EN 6029-2* and 3 can be used for isolation, but not emergency or functional switching. (2) A semi conductor device to *BS EN 60669-2-1* can be used for functional switching, but not for emergency switching or isolation. (3) 2.75 m. (4) A function intended to cut off for reasons of safety the supply from all, or a discrete Section, of the installation by separating the installation or Section from every source of electrical energy.

Chapter 54

Ex 54.3 (1) 16 mm^2, **Ex 54.4** (1) 6 mm^2, (2) 16 mm^2, (3) 25 mm^2, (4) 95 mm^2. **Ex 54.5** (1) 16 mm^2. **Ex 54.6** A gas pipe, an oil pipe, flexible or pliable conduit, support wires **Ex 54.9** (1) 25 mm^2

Final revision exercise. 54.1 (b), 54.2 (c), 54.3 (d), 54.4 (c), 54.5 (b), 54.6 (a).

Things to do and find. (1) (i) water installation pipes, (ii) gas installation pipes, (iii) other installation pipe work or ducting, (iv) central heating or air conditioning systems, (iv) exposed metallic structural parts of a building, (vi) connection of a lightning protection system in accordance with *BS EN 62305* (2) (i) A single core cable, (ii) the core of a cable, (iii) a fixed bare or insulated conductor, (iv) a metal covering, for example, the sheath, screen or armouring of a cable, (iv) an extraneous- conductive- part complying with 543.2.6, (3) (i) its electrical continuity shall be assured, either by construction or by suitable connection, in such a way as to be protected against mechanical, chemical or electromechanical deterioration, and (ii) its csa shall be at least equal to that resulting from the application of 543.1, or verified by test in accordance with *BS EN 60439-1*, and (iii) it shall permit the connection of other protective conductors at every predetermined tap-off point. (4) If individual items of equipment have high protective conductors then the socket-outlet should comply with *BS EN 60309-2*. Where socket-outlets are used in circuits where there may be a collectively high protective conductor current there should be provision for two separate earth terminals. (5) Separate terminals at each socket-outlet, separate connections at the distribution board, information relating to the circuit at the distribution board (6) Rod, tape, wire, plate, underground structural metalwork, welded metal reinforcement of concrete lead sheaths (7) Buried pre-stressed concrete, gas or flammable liquid metal pipes, water utility pipework. (8) Table 54.7 Minimum csa of protective conductor in relation to the csa of associated line conductor. Table 54.8 Minimum csa of the main protective conductor in relation to the neutral of the supply. (9) 50 mm^2

Chapter 55

Ex55.1 (1) Yes. (2) Yes. (3) Yes. (4) Yes. **Ex55.2** Noxious gases, moving parts, high temperature, flammable fluids. **Ex55.3** Compensated windings, provision of filtering equipment. **Ex55.4** An electrical, mechanical or electromechanical interlock, a system of locks with a single transferable key, a three-position break-before-make changeover switch **Ex55.5** (1) (i) a system of locks with a single transferable key, (ii) a three position break-before-make changeover switch, (iii) an automatic change-over switching device with a suitable interlock. (2) The generating set shall be such that danger or damage to equipment does not arise after connection or disconnection of any intended load as a result of deviation of voltage or frequency from the intended operating range. Means shall be provided to automatically disconnect such parts of the installation as may be necessary if the capacity of the generating set is exceeded. (3) (i) Power factor, (ii) harmonic distortion, (iii) unbalance, (iv) voltage fluctuating effects of the main incoming supply cable **Ex55.6** (1) Battery connections shall have basic protection by insulation or enclosure, or shall be arranged so that two bare conductive parts having a potential difference between them exceeding 120 V cannot be inadvertently touched simultaneously. Batteries shall only be accessible by skilled people. **Ex55.7** (1) Rotating catering equipment, lathes, milling machines etc. **Ex55.8** (1) The coupler is fitted at the end of the cable remote from the supply. This is to ensure the protective conductor is connected, and live pins are not exposed. (2) *BS 1362* **Ex55.9** (1) A single-phase water boiler or heater having an uninsulated heating element immersed in water is deemed not to be an electrode water heater or electrode boiler. The difference in this case is that the resistive element between line and neutral is continuous and the current does not flow through the water. In an electrode boiler, the current carrying medium is the boiler water itself and the power supply contacts are the electrodes. Since the electrodes are always positioned nearer to each other than any other part of the boiler, the path of least resistance is a straight line from electrode to electrode so that most of the current will flow between electrodes. (2). A d.c. supply, as this would cause electrolysis to occur, causing the boiler water to break down into its elements of hydrogen and oxygen, thereby creating an explosion hazard. (3) The boiler shell must be connected to the neutral of the supply as well as to the circuit protective conductor (cpc) and/or metallic sheath or armour, if any, The purpose of this connection is to minimize the potential difference between the boiler electrode connected to the neutral conductor, and the boiler shell, which may otherwise result in stray leakage current from the boiler electrodes to the boiler shell.

Final revision exercise. 55.1(a), 55.2(a), 55.3 (b), 55.4 (c), 55.5 (a).

Things to do and find. (1) In a TN, TT, or IT system every circuit must be protected by a 30 mA RCD. (2) It should be mounted at a height above the floor or any working surface to minimise the risk of mechanical damage to the socket outlet or to an associated plug and its flex which might be caused during insertion or withdrawal of the plug. (3) Uninsulated electrode water heaters and boilers. (4) A linked switch for disconnecting the transformer from all live conductors of the supply.

Section 559

Ex559.1 (1) temporary festoon lighting. (2) low voltage. **Ex559.2** Ceiling rose to *BS 67*, LSC, batten lampholder or pendant set, luminaire to *BS EN 60598* or other items v to ix in Regulation 559.6.1.1 **Ex559.3** (1) (i) small bayonet cap, (ii) bayonet cap, (iii) small Edison screw, (iv) giant Edison screw (2) 250 V, (3) 5 kg. **Ex 559.4** (1) 2.5 m, (2) RCD, (3) ambient AA2 & AA4, climatic AB2 & AB4, (4) the csa must not be less than the copper equivalent of 6 mm^2 or that of the neutral supply conductor, whichever is smaller. **Ex559.6** (1) must be protected on the primary side by a protective device as per 559.11.4.2. (2) 1.5 mm^2

Final revision exercise. 559.1 (c), 559.2 (c), 559.3 (b), 559.4 (a), 559.5 (a), 559.6 (c).

Things to do and find. (1) (l) the maximum permissible power dissipated by the lamps, (ii) the fire resistance to the adjacent material at the point of installation, and in thermally affected areas, (iii) the minimum distance to the combustible materials, including materials in the path of the spotlight beam. (2) (i) Ambient temperature: AA 2 and AA 4 (from -40 deg C to +40 deg C), (ii) Climatic conditions: AB 2 and AB 4 (relative humidity between 5% and 100%. (3) No. Yes. (4) On the *outer* contact. (5) See Table 55.2 of *BS 7671*. (6) 6 mm^2.

Chapter 56

Ex 56.1 (i) storage batteries, (ii) primary cells, (iii) generator sets independent of the supply. (2) (i) short - 0.15s to 0.5s, (ii) medium - 5s to 15s

Final revision exercise. 56.1 (b), 56.2 (b), 56.3 (c), 56.4 (c), 56.5 (a).

Things to do and find. (1) Automatic and non-automatic. (2) A device which maintains a continuous supply to connected equipment by supplying power following the failure of the primary source. (3) Wiring for the service lift. (4) Electrical control equipment, distribution boards, safety equipment details, switching and monitoring equipment details.

Part 6

Ex6.3 (1) Fuse, single pole control and protective devices, Edison screw lamps except for E14 and E27 to *BS EN 60238*, socket- outlets and similar accessories.   **Ex6.4** (1) (i) Continuity of protective conductors, (ii) continuity of ring circuit final conductors, (iii) Insulation resistance, (iv) polarity.   (2) (i) Polarity, (ii) earth loop impedance, (iii) prospective fault current, (iv) functional testing.   (3) 1 MΩ

Final revision exercise. 6.1 (d), 6.2 (d), 6.3 (b), 6.4 (d), 6.5(a).

Things to do and find. (1) (i) Initial verification, (ii) periodic inspection and testing, (iii) certification and reporting. (2) (i) Shock currents, (ii) arcing or burning likely to cause blinding effects, excessive pressure or toxic gases, (iii) excessive temperatures likely to cause burns, fires etc. (3) (i) Nominal voltage, (ii) the nature of the current and frequency, (iii) the prospective short-circuit current at the origin of the installation. (4) (i) The type and composition of each circuit, (ii) method used for compliance with Regulation 410.3.2, (iii) any circuit vulnerable to a certain typical test. (5) Fuse, single pole control and protective devices, Edison screw lamps except for E14 and E27 to *BS EN 60238*, socket-outlets and similar accessories. (7) To ensure correct mechanical functioning of the RCD.

(8)

Circuit nominal voltage (V)	Test voltage d.c. (V)	Minimum insulation resistance (MΩ)
SEL and PELV	250	≥ 0.5
Up to and including 500 V with the exception of the above systems	500	≥ 1.0
Above 500 V	1000	≥ 1.0

Part 7

Final revision exercise. 700.1 (b), 700.2 (c), 700.3 (a), 700.4 (d).

Things to do and find. (1) Not greater than 50 V a.c. or 120 V d.c. (2) This is because they require special consideration in relation to the design and construction of the electrical installation. Part 7, therefore, contains additional Regulations that must be adhered to when installing electrical equipment in these locations. (3) Swimming pools, the basins of fountains, paddling pools and their surroundings are locations of increased electric shock risk due to: - a reduction in body resistance caused either by bodily immersion or by wet skin, and likely contact of substantial areas of the body with earth potential. (4) Construction and demolition sites are specified as a special location due to the additional risks of danger. Danger, in relation to the increasing risk of electric shock, may arise due to the adverse conditions including :(i) Trailing cables, (ii) the use of portable electric tools, (iii) many extraneous-conductive-parts that cannot, practically, be bonded, (iv) adverse weather conditions and incomplete structures, (v) difficult working conditions. (5) Section 709. (6) Construction and demolition site installations. (7) Section 708 is concerned with the electrical installations on the caravan/ camping parks and similar locations, but not in the caravans etc, whereas Section 721 is concerned with the electrical installations within the caravans and motor homes.

Section 701

Ex701.1 (1) 2.25 m. (2) 1.2 m. (3) 0.6 m

Final revision exercise. 701.1 (a), 701.2 (d), 701.3 (c), 701.4 (b), 701.5 (c), 701.6 (a).

Things to do and find. (1) whirlpool units, electric showers, shower pumps, equipment protected by SELV or PELV (maximum rated voltage 25 V a.c. or 60 V d.c.), ventilation equipment, towel rails, water heating appliances, luminaries. (2) Electrical equipment exposed to water jets (e.g. for cleaning purposes. (3) central heating pipework, hot water pipes, cold water pipes, any exposed-conductive-parts, any extraneous-conductive-parts(not mentioned above) (4) 2.25 m (5) 0.1 m

Section 702

Ex 702.1 (3) Fig 702.2 (4) 2.5 m **Ex 702.3** (1) Zone 2 (2) Zone 1 (3) insulating material (4) RCD protection as required by Regulation 415.1.1

Final revision exercise. 702.1 (a), 702.2 (d), 702.3 (c), 702.4 (b), 702.5 (b), 702.6 (a)

Things to do and find. (1) Electrical equipment where water jets are likely to occur for cleaning purposes. (2) 2.5 m. (3) 3.5 m. (4) (i) 1.25 m and 0.3 m above the floor (ii) An RCD having the characteristics specified in 415.1.1. (5) No intentional or unintentional conductive connection between any exposed conductive part of the underwater luminaire and any conductive parts of the portholes can occur. (6) Yes, but only with SELV circuits. (7) Connect to supplementary bonding system. (8) IPX2. (9) Situated in these zones. (11) AG2 and AD8.

Section 703

Ex703.1 (1) IPX4. (2) IPX5

Final revision exercise. 703.1 (b), 703.2 (b), 703.3 (c), 703.4 (b), 703.5 (a).

Things to do and find. (1) If cleaning by water jets is expected, electrical equipment shall have this degree of protection. (2) 1 m. (3) Socket-outlets cannot be fitted in the location containing the sauna heater. (4)Metallic sheaths and metallic conduits shall not be accessible in normal use. (5) Outside the zones.

Section 704

Ex 704.1 (1) Construction site offices are not covered by Section 704, (2) 55 V. **EX 704.2** (ii) The incoming isolation device must me capable of being secured in the 'off' position, e.g. by a padlock. (iii) overcurrent protective devices, devices affording fault protection, socket outlets.

Final revision exercise. 704.1 (c), 704.2 (a), 704.3 (b), 704.4 (a), 704.5 (a), 704.6 (d)

Things to do and find. (1)Engineering works, earthworks, construction work of new buildings, repair alterations or demolition of existing buildings. (2) The reduced low voltage system, (3) pme, (4) TT (5) 300/500 V thermoplastic or equivalent flexible cable, (6) Armoured cables or cables mechanically protected.

Section 705

Ex705.1 (i) Hot dip galvanised steel strip with a dimension at least 30 mm x 3 mm, (ii) hot-dip galvanised round steel with at least 8 mm diameter, (iii) copper conductors having a minimum csa of 4 mm^2. **Ex 705.2** (1) Conduits and trunking shall have protection against corrosion of at least class 2 for indoor and class 4 for outdoor.(2) Socket outlets up to 32 A shall be IP44 rated and be protected by a 30 mA RCD. They shall also be placed in a position where they are unlikely to come into contact with combustible materials. (3) Buried cables to be at least 0.6 m below surface and have additional mechanical protection.

Final revision exercise. 705.1 (c), 705.2 (c), 705.3 (b), 705.4 (b).

Things to do and find. (1) Stables, cattle sheds, milking parlours, greenhouses, nurseries. (2) Agricultural and horticultural premises are specified as a special location due to the increased risk of electric shock because of the lower contact resistance of the body that is associated with,for example, wet hands, wet clothing and wet footwear, and because of the increased likelihood of contact with the general mass of Earth (i.e., the ground). Electric shocks in such conditions are more likely to cause serious injury or death than those where the conditions are dry and no contact is made directly with the general mass of Earth. The risk of electric shock to livestock can often be greater than for people, because some livestock have a large exposed body area for contact with exposed-conductive-parts and/or extraneous-conductive-parts. Also the feet of livestock are likely to be in contact directly with the general mass of Earth, often in wet conditions. (3) 300 mA RCD. (4) In the event of a power failure to ensure light air and water supplies are maintained for the livestock. (5)Electrical equipment and wiring systems should not be accessible to livestock.

Section 706

Final revision exercise. 706.1(a), 706.2(a)

Things to do and find. (1) Basic protection must be provided irrespective of nominal voltage (416.2). (2) Automatic disconnection of the supply. (3) Outside the location. (4) An RCD having the characteristics specified in 415.1.1

Section 708

Ex708.1 (1) PME. (2) Yes. (3)Metal grid cast into the floor and connected to the equipotential bonding. **Ex708 2** (2) 1. (3) 1. (4) 1

Final revision exercise. 708.1 (c), 708.2(c), 708.3(d), 708.4 (c), 708.5 (a), 708.6 (d).

Things to do and find. (1) Plugs to BS EN 60309-2, connectors to BS EN 60309-2. (2) 25 m. (3) TT. (4) PME. (5) Underground distribution circuits.

Section 709

Final revision exercise. 709.1(d), 709.2 (c), 709.3 (c), 709.4 (a), 709.5 (d).
Things to do and find. (1) Marinas and similar locations are specified as a special location due to the increased risk of electric shock because of the lower contact resistance of the body that is associated with, for example, wet hands, wet clothing and wet footwear, and because of the increased likelihood of contact with the general mass of Earth (i.e., the ground). Electric shocks in such conditions are more likely to cause serious injury or death than those where the conditions are dry and no contact is made directly with the general mass of Earth. Also the added dangers due to potential mechanical damage and harsh environmental conditions. (2) ESQC Regulations 2002. (3) TN–C-S. (4) AD, AE, AF, AG. (5) micc with a pvc protective coating. (6) Aluminum conductors. (7) Drain holes or installation of equipment on an incline. (8) 30 mA. (9) 30 mA. (10) All poles including neutral. (11) 4.

Section 711

Final revision exercise. 711.1 (c), 711.2 (b).
Things to do and find. (1) Exhibitions, Trade fairs, Outdoor shows, Temporary entertainment venues, Kiosks, Outdoor fast food outlets. (2) Temporary electrical installations in exhibitions, shows and stands are specified as a special location due to the temporary nature of the installation, the lack of permanent structures, severe mechanical stresses, increased risk of electric shock, fire and burns and access to these installations by the general public. (3) Protection against accidental ingress of water, and have sufficient strength to withstand the traffic. The socket should also be protected by a 30 mA RCD. (4) They shall not be used unless the cable and lamp holders are compatible, and providing the lamp holders are non-removable once fitted to the cable. (5) To help reduce heat build-up from ELV transformers, concentration of electrical equipment and light fittings etc and so help protect against fire.

Section 712

Final revision exercise. 712.1 (c), 712.2 (d), 712.3 (c).
Things to do and find. (1) Wind, ice formation, temperature, solar radiation. (2) 1.25 times greater than Isc STC. (3) Public supply to be considered as source, and PV installation considered the load side. The switch must be a switch disconnector (Capable of closing and opening direct currents). (4) All junction boxes (PV generator and PV array boxes).

Section 717

Ex717.1 (1) Isolating transformer, transformer providing simple separation, LV generating set.
Final revision exercise. 17.1 (c), 17.2 (c), 17.3 (a), 17.4 (c).
Things to do and find. (1)Medical services, fire fighting, transportable catering unit, containers. (2) A mobile unit is wheeled and a transportable is not. (3) Connectors (plugs and socket-outlets) used to connect to units must be in compliance with *BS EN 60309-2* Plugs, socket-outlets and couplers for industrial purposes. Dimensional interchangeability requirements for pin and contact-tube accessories and meet the following requirements(i) Plugs enclosures to be made of insulating material, (ii)if located outside, provide a degree of protection not less than IP44, (iii) appliance inlets with their enclosures must provide a degree of protection not less than IP44, (iv)the plug part must be on the unit. (4) Only ELV equipment for gas supply control shall be installed in any gas cylinder storage compartment.

Section 721

Ex721.2 (1) 23 m. (2) 2.5 mm2. (3) Not more than 1.8 m. (4) IP44
Final revision exercise. 721.1 (d), 721.2 (d), 721.3 (b), 721.4 (c), 721.5 (c), 721.6 (d).
Things to do and find. (1) Caravans are regarded by *BS 7671* as being locations of increased electric shock risk. This is because their electrical installations are exposed to arduous conditions, and persons using them are liable to be minimally clothed and/or exposed to wetness from, for example, wet weather or perspiration, and when outside the caravan may be in contact directly with the general mass of Earth. (2) Only flexible/stranded conductors and a minimum csa of 1.5mm^2. (3) Cables complying with *BS EN 60332-1-2* as the structure of the caravan is mainly of combustible materials. (4) 230 V a.c. single phase, 400 V a.c. 3 phase, 48 V d.c. (5) PME (6) 30 mA. (7) Luminaires should be fixed directly to structure or lining of caravan, where a pendant luminaire is installed in a caravan provision shall be made for securing the luminaire to prevent damage when the caravan is moved. Dual voltage luminaries to comply with the appropriate standard.

Section 740

Ex740.2 (1) A socket outlet for each square metre or linear metre of wall. (2) Sockets are to be manufactured to *BS EN 60309-2, or 1* when interchangability is not required.
Final revision exercise. 740.1 (c), 740.2 (b), 740.3 (c).

Things to do and find. (1) Temporary electrical installations for structures, amusement devices and booths at fairgrounds, amusement parks and circuses are specified as a special location due to (i)the temporary nature of the installation, (ii) the risks associated with repeated connection of the units and the possible affect on connections and cables, (iii) the risks associated with different connection provision at different sites, (iv) difficulties establishing an equipotential zone, (v)vibration problems due to trailer or vehicular movement, (vi) the effects of vibration and movement of structures during operation. (2) They should not be used unless the cable and lamp holders are compatible, and lamp holders are non removable once fitted to the cable. (3) Supplementary bonding shall connect all exposed- conductive-parts and extraneous conductive parts that can be touched by the livestock. (4) The exposed –conductive–part of the generator. (5) Shall be firmly fixed and so sited or guarded as to prevent risk of injury to persons or ignition of materials.

Section 753

Ex 753.1 (1) (i) appropriate design of the heating system, (ii) use of protective devices, (iii) appropriate installation of the heating system in accordance with manufacturer's instructions
Final revision exercise. 753.1 (c), 753.2 (c), 753.3 (d), 753.4 (d).
Things to do and find. (1) (i) Appropriate design of the heating system, (ii) use of protective devices, (iii) appropriate installation of the heating system in accordance with manufacturers instructions. (2) 30 mA. (3) Cold lead or cold tail. (4) Heating-free areas. (5) Adjacent to the distribution board supplying the heating system.

Appendices to *BS 7671*

Ex App.1 (1) 125 A. (2) 0.4 secs **Ex App.2** (1) 50 m^2 (2) Depends upon the load characteristics, having taken diversity into account. (3) immersion heaters, comprehensive electric space heating cookers, ovens and hobs with a rated power exceeding 2 kW (4) Accessories to be BS 1363 supplied through a ring final circuit, with or without unfused spurs protected by a 30 A or 32 A protective device.
Final revision exercise. App 1 (b), App 2 (c), App 3 (c), App 4(d), App 5 (d)

An index of sections was included at the front of this Learning Guide.

For a full index of words and terms contained within *BS 7671* and their related Section, Regulation Group/ or Regulation refer to the comprehensive index in *BS 7671*. Information relating to the word or term can then be found in the same section within *BS 7671* or this Learning Guide.